OXFORD REVISION GUIDES

AS & A Level

GEOGRAPHY

for Edexcel Specification B

OXFORD
UNIVERSITY PRESS

Great Clarendon Street, Oxford OX2 6DP

Oxford University Press is a department of the University of Oxford.
It furthers the University's objective of excellence in research, scholarship,
and education by publishing worldwide in

Oxford New York

Auckland Bangkok Buenos Aires Cape Town Chennai
Dar es Salaam Delhi Hong Kong Istanbul Karachi Kolkata
Kuala Lumpur Madrid Melbourne Mexico City Mumbai Nairobi
São Paulo Shanghai Taipei Tokyo Toronto

Oxford is a registered trade mark of Oxford University Press
in the UK and in certain other countries

British Library Cataloguing in Publication Data

Data available

ISBN 0 19 914927 5

1 3 5 7 9 10 8 6 4 2

Typeset by Fakenham Photosetting Ltd, Norfolk

Printed in the UK

Dedicated to Angela, Rosie, Patrick and Bethany

Acknowledgements
The publisher and author would like to thank **Sue Warn** for her help and
advice throughout the preparation of this book, and for writing the book's
sample questions and answers.

Contents

Introduction to AS

The AS part of the syllabus encourages students to:

- acquire and apply knowledge and understanding of physical and human processes, their interactions over space and time, and relate this to particular events
- acquire and apply a range of skills
- develop an understanding of interrelationships between

people and environments, and of the opportunities, challenges, and constraints that people face in their environments
- appreciate the dynamic nature of Geography
- understand how decisions are made
- clarify and develop values and attitudes.

The specification framework

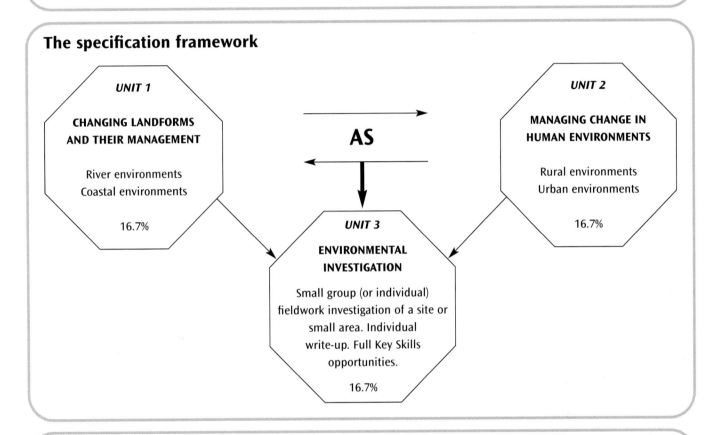

UNIT 1

CHANGING LANDFORMS AND THEIR MANAGEMENT

River environments
Coastal environments

16.7%

AS

UNIT 3

ENVIRONMENTAL INVESTIGATION

Small group (or individual) fieldwork investigation of a site or small area. Individual write-up. Full Key Skills opportunities.

16.7%

UNIT 2

MANAGING CHANGE IN HUMAN ENVIRONMENTS

Rural environments
Urban environments

16.7%

Scheme of assessment

	UNIT	STYLE OF ASSESSMENT	Duration and length	Advanced GCS (AS) weighting
AS	1. Changing landforms and their management	Each paper will consist of five short structured data-response questions. Each question will end with a short piece of extended writing worth 10 marks. Students will choose three questions, each worth 30 marks. The questions will be designed to ensure that students are tested across both sub-units. The total for each paper is 90 marks.	1 hr 30 mins	16.7% (33.3%)
	2. Managing change in human environments		1 hr 30 mins	16.7% (33.3%)
	3. Environmental investigation	A fieldwork investigation of a site or small-scale area linked to one of the environments studied for AS. Outline proposal to be approved by Edexcel. The primary data collection can be carried out in small groups (approx. 10–12) or individually, but the writing up of the investigation must be individuual. Each student will develop a research action plan which follows a route to enquiry on an issue or question, chosen by the student, arising out of the fieldwork. Secondary sources can be used to support the investigation. Students will be assessed on their ability to collect, represent, and analyse data using a range of techniques, and to evaluate their findings and draw conclusions. The total for the investigation will be 100 marks.	2500 words (penalty applies above this limit)	16.7% (33.3%)

The hydrological cycle

Pages 6 to 8 introduce fluvial systems.
* *How do fluvial systems operate within the global hydrological cycle?*
* *What impact does the hydrological cycle have on fluvial systems?*

Definitions

* **Hydrological cycle** This is the constant movement of water between air, land, and sea through a series of **flows** and **stores**. It varies from place to place and over time. On a global scale the hydrological cycle is a **closed system** (water is recycled around the earth's atmosphere without any significant loss from the system), whereas on a local scale the drainage basin component is an **open system**. Water is lost from the drainage basin through discharge, evapotranspiration, and so on, and water is carried into the system from the atmosphere.

* **Precipitation** – all forms of rainfall, snow, frost, hail, and dew. It is the conversion and transfer of moisture in the atmosphere to the land.

* **Interception** – precipitation that is collected and stored by vegetation.

* **Overland runoff** – water that runs over the land's surface. **Direct overland runoff** occurs, for example, when precipitation falls on an impermeable surface such as a road or a pavement. **Saturated overland runoff** occurs after the ground has become saturated with water, and any extra rain is forced to flow over the surface.

* **Transpiration** – water loss from vegetation to the atmosphere.

* **Evapotranspiration** (EVT) – the combined losses of evaporation and transpiration.

* **Percolation** – the process by which water moves downwards through rock.

* **Throughflow** – the movement of water downslope through the subsoil. It is especially important when the subsurface is underlain by an impermeable rock thereby preventing further infiltration.

* **Groundwater flow** or **baseflow** – the slow transfer of water through rocks.

The global hydrological cycle

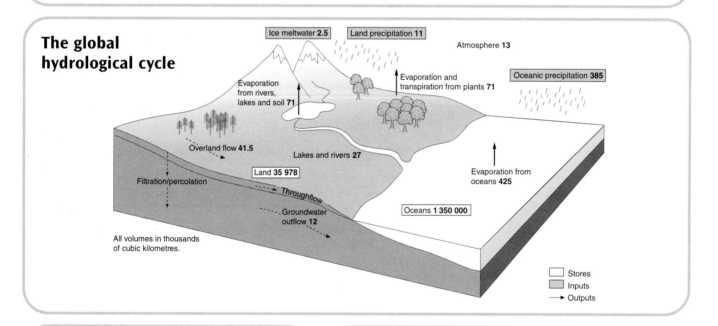

All volumes in thousands of cubic kilometres.

Evaporation

This is the physical process by which a liquid becomes a gas. It is a function of:

* vapour pressure
* air temperature
* wind
* rock surface, e.g. bare soils and rocks have high rates of evaporation compared with surfaces that have a protective tilth (cover) where rates are low.

High rates of evaporation are recorded in hot deserts, e.g. at Atbara (Sudan) the potential EVT is 6250 mm per year and at Helwan (Egypt) 2390 mm. Rates are much lower in tropical rainforests (500–750 mm) because of the high humidity, and in cooler climates, e.g. London 330 mm.

Infiltration

Infiltration is the process by which water sinks into the ground. **Infiltration capacity** is the amount of moisture that a soil can hold. The **infiltration rate** refers to the speed at which water can enter the soil. **Overland flow** occurs when precipitation intensity exceeds the infiltration rate, or when the infiltration capacity is reached and the soil is **saturated**. Vegetation increases infiltration as it reduces raindrop impact and increases the organic matter in the soil (which holds moisture).

Influence of ground cover on infiltration

Ground cover	Infiltration rates (mm/hr)
Old permanent pasture	57
Permanent pasture: moderately grazed	19
Permanent pasture: heavily grazed	13
Strip-cropped	10
Weeds or grain	9
Clean tilled	7
Bare, crusted ground	6

Storm hydrographs

Reading a storm hydrograph

A **storm** or **flood hydrograph** shows how a river channel responds to the key processes of the hydrological cycle. Usually they are drawn to show how a river reacts to a period of precipitation. Each storm hydrograph has a series of parts.

Rising limb

- indicates the amount of discharge and the speed at which it is increasing
- very steep in a flash flood or in small drainage basins where the response is rapid
- generally steep in urbanised catchments

Peak flow or discharge

- higher in larger basins
- steep catchments will have lower infiltration rates
- flat catchments will have high infiltration rates, so more throughflow and lower peaks

Hydrograph size (area under the graph line)

- the higher the rainfall, the greater the discharge
- the larger the basin size, the greater the discharge

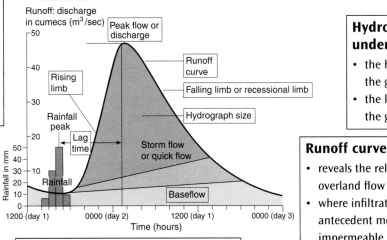

Lag time

- time interval between peak rainfall and peak discharge
- influenced by basin shape, steepness, stream order

Runoff curve

- reveals the relationship between overland flow and throughflow
- where infiltration is low, high antecedent moisture, impermeable surface and rainfall heavy, overland flow will dominate

Baseflow

- the seepage of groundwater into the channel – very important where rocks have large pore spaces
- a slow movement which is the main long-term supplier of the river's discharge

Recessional limb

- influenced by geological composition and behaviour of local aquifers
- larger catchments have less steep recessional limbs, likewise flatter areas

Variation in hydrographs

A number of factors affect flood hydrographs:

- climate (rainfall total, intensity, seasonality)
- soils (impermeable clay soils create more flooding)
- vegetation (vegetation intercepts rainfall and so flooding is less likely)
- infiltration capacity (soils with a low infiltration capacity cause much overland flow)
- rock type (permeable rocks will allow water to infiltrate, thereby reducing the flood peak)
- slope angle (on steeper slopes there is greater runoff)
- drainage density (the more stream channels there are the more water that gets into rivers)
- human impact (creating impermeable surfaces and additional drainage channels increases the risk of flooding; dams disrupt the flow of water; afforestation schemes increase interception)
- basin size, shape, and relief (small, steep basins reduce lag time, while basin shape influences where the bulk of the floodwaters arrive).

Urban hydrology and the storm hydrograph

Urban hydrographs are different from rural ones. They have:

- a shorter lag time
- a steeper rising limb
- a higher peak flow (discharge)
- a steeper recessional limb.

This is because there are more impermeable surfaces in urban areas (roofs, pavements, roads, buildings) as well as more drainage channels (gutters, drains, sewers).

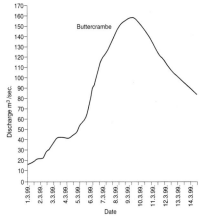

The hydrograph shows the increase in discharge for the Buttercrambe river in the Derwent river basin in North Yorkshire in 1999.

River regimes and soil moisture budgets

Impacts on river regimes

A **river regime** is the annual variation in the flow of a
river. River flows depend on a number of factors:

- temperatures experienced (role of evaporation, and
  also snow/glacier melt)
- amount and intensity of rain (governed by climate)
- infiltration capacity of soil and rock
- morphology of the basin and shape of the basin
  (high or low discharge)
- vegetation.

Simple regimes are where a simple distinction can be
made between one period of high water levels and
runoff, and one period of low water levels and runoff.

It is possible to have **complex regimes**. For example,
some rivers flow through several distinctive relief
regions and receive water from large tributaries which
themselves flow over varied terrain (e.g. River Rhône).

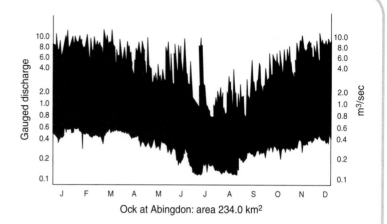

Ock at Abingdon: area 234.0 km²

Contrasting river regimes

The Rivers Ock and Kennet are tributaries of the River
Thames. The river regimes for the two rivers show a
similar pattern of peak water flow in winter and lower
flow in summer. Differences in the terrain the two rivers
pass over can, in part, account for the variation
between the two regimes.

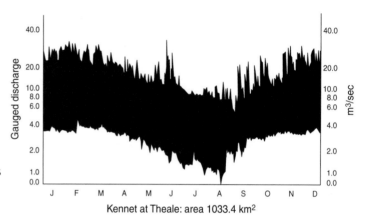

Kennet at Theale: area 1033.4 km²

River Ock: flows mainly over impermeable clays. Clay is impermeable and increases overland runoff.

River Kennet: flows mainly over Tertiary rocks, sands, and gravels. It drains an area over four times larger than the River Ock.
Some groundwater abstraction occurs (as well as use of water for agriculture and industry), but impacts are limited.

Variation in soil moisture budgets

- **Soil moisture deficit** is the degree to which soil
  moisture falls below **field capacity** (large pores in soil
  contain air, but micropores contain water that is
  available to plants). In Britain during late winter and
  early spring, soil moisture deficit is very low, due to high
  levels of precipitation and limited EVT.
- **Soil moisture recharge** occurs when precipitation
  exceeds potential EVT – there is some refilling of water
  in the dried-up pores of the soil.
- **Soil moisture surplus** is the period when soil is
  saturated and water cannot enter, and so flows over the
  surface.
- **Soil moisture utilisation** is the process by which water
  is drawn to the surface through capillary action and may
  be used by plants or evaporated.

In summer, Madrid has a major soil moisture deficit
because it is warmer (hence higher EVT) and has less
rainfall (therefore less moisture). Actual evaporation values
are higher in summer in Madrid. By contrast the winters in
London and Madrid are relatively similar.

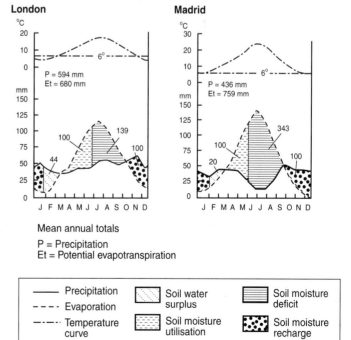

River profiles and geometry

Pages 9 to 14 cover process and change in riverine environments, landforms, and ecosystems.
- *What physical factors and processes influence channel characteristics and valley landforms?*
- *What ecosystems exist in a river environment?*

The long profile

A number of processes, such as weathering and mass movement, interact to create variations in **cross profiles** and **long profiles**. Irregularities, or **knick points**, may be due to:

- geological structure/lithology, for example hard rocks erode slowly, which can result in the formation of waterfalls and rapids
- variations in the load, for example when a tributary with a coarse load may lead to a steepening of the gradient of the main valley
- sea-level changes – a relative fall in sea-level (isostatic recovery, eustatic fall, etc.) will lead to renewed downcutting, which enables the river to erode former floodplains and form new terraces and knickpoints.

Rivers tend to achieve a condition of equilibrium, or grade, and erode the irregularities. There is a balance between erosion and deposition in which a river adjusts to its capacity and the amount of work being done. The main adjustments are in channel gradient leading to a smooth, concave profile.

The profile of the River Exe is typical of a graded river: concave and gradually decreasing towards the mouth of the river. In addition to changes in the profile there are also changes within the channel; these are shown in Bradshaw's model.

Changes in the River Exe as it travels downstream

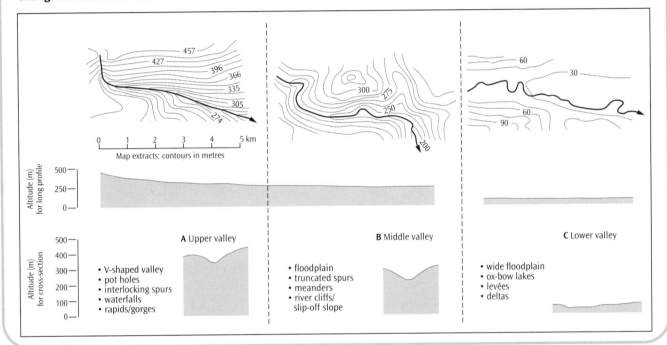

Changing channel characteristics

As a river travels downstream changes can occur to its width, depth, velocity, discharge, and efficiency. Efficiency is measured by the **hydraulic radius,** i.e. cross-sectional area (CSA)/wetted perimeter (WP).

River level

③ Flood – high friction
② Bankfull – maximum efficiency (low friction)
① Below bankfull – high friction

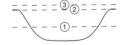

Shape

Stream **A**
4 m | Cross-section area = 24 m² | 4 m
6 m
Very efficient (low relative friction)

Stream **B**
2 m | Cross-section area = 24 m² | 2 m
12 m
Inefficient (high relative friction)

- - - wetted perimeter

Wetted perimeters	Hydraulic radius
Stream **A**: 4 + 4 + 6 = 14 m	Stream **A**: $\frac{24}{14}$ = 1.71 m
Stream **B**: 2 + 2 + 12 = 16 m	Stream **B**: $\frac{24}{16}$ = 1.5 m

Bradshaw model of channel variables

Bradshaw's model shows changes to channel characteristics over the course of a river. Water velocity and discharge increase downstream while channel bed roughness and load particle size decrease.

Upstream		Downstream
	Discharge	
	Occupied channel width	
	Water depth	
	Water velocity	
	Load quantity	
Load particle size		
Channel bed roughness		
Slope angle (gradient)		

The long profile

The change in gradient in a river with increasing distance from the source is known as the **long profile**. The long profile of the River Clarach in Dyfed, Wales is shown here. On a much larger scale, the Yellow River (Hwang He) in China illustrates the way in which geology influences the profile, as well as rates of erosion along the river.

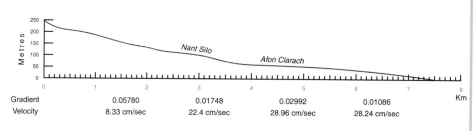

Gradient and velocity along the River Clarach

| Gradient | 0.05780 | 0.01748 | 0.02992 | 0.01086 |
| Velocity | 8.33 cm/sec | 22.4 cm/sec | 28.96 cm/sec | 28.24 cm/sec |

The Yellow River

The Yellow River is one of the world's great rivers. The river drains an area of over 750 000 km², in which a population of 84 million people live, farming 13 million ha of land. It is called the Yellow River because of the large amount of yellow wind-blown sediment (known as **loess**) that it erodes and deposits. The combination of this easily eroded material and the seasonal flow of the Yellow River causes great problems for the people who live in the lower parts of the catchment.

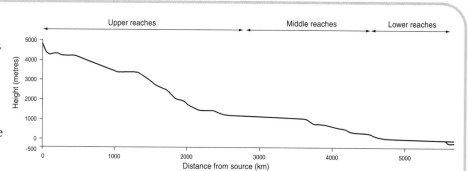

Long profile of the Yellow River

gives rise to extremely high rates of erosion and transport by the river. As it flows through the loess plateau rates of erosion increase dramatically.

Upper course

The Yellow River varies greatly on its course down from its source in Guzunglie Basin in Qinghai province. The area is a very cold plateau at an altitude of 5000 m. It produces a stream that is clear, and a valley that is narrow and shallow. As it flows over solid rock (bedrock) it carves a meandering channel, sometimes with deep gorges.

Middle course

In its middle stages the river flows across yellow loess deposits rather than solid rock. In some places the loess deposits are over 300 m thick. The combination of the seasonal flow of the Yellow River and the highly erodable nature of the loess

The influence of desert

The Yellow River then flows north through desert. As a result discharge and rates of erosion decrease. Here the river is said to be braided and consists of very wide channels separated by islands in the river.

The influence of loess

As the river flows south into a wetter region it flows across thick beds of loess again. Rates of erosion increase dramatically. In some parts, such as near Yulin close to the Great Wall of China, up to 25 000 tonnes of loess are eroded per km²!

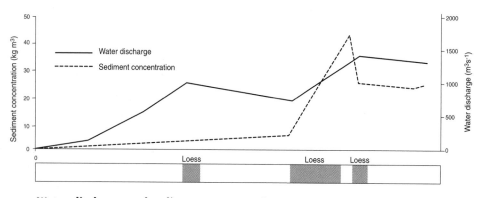

Water discharge and sediment concentration

Changes in channels

Causes of channel change

Erosion and deposition are natural features of a floodplain – hence we expect all rivers to change over time. Some important changes that occur in rivers include:

- cutoffs of meanders
- the gradual shifting of meanders
- **avulsion**, where a river in its lower course breaks through its levées, and finds an even steeper course; a good example of avulsion is the frequent change to the main channel of the Mississippi delta.

Rivers are **transport** systems carrying water and sediment. Each year 13 500 million tonnes of sediment are removed by rivers globally. Channel size and shape are related to the volume of water and sediment carried. Rivers can adjust their form in four main ways:

- cross-sectional form
- bed configuration
- channel pattern
- channel slope: local gradient and overall gradient.

Channel change can be:

- **autogenic** (internal change), such as migration of meanders, meander cutoff
- **allogenic** (external), e.g. discharge/load (human activity).

External changes and the effect on discharge and sediment load

	Discharge	Sediment load
Dam construction	0/–	–
Deforestation	+	+
Mining	0	+
Urbanisation	+	0/+
Key		
0 no change + increase – decrease		

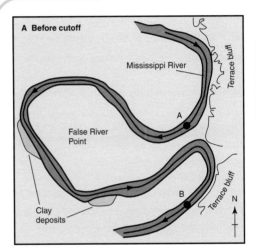 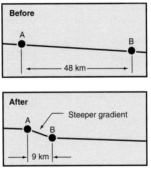 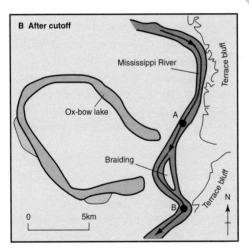

Cutoff of a meander loop of the Mississippi

Autogenic changes

Channel migration is a significant process, e.g. the River Axe in Devon has altered 40% of its course in 50 years. Rates of migration 10–15 m/yr are frequent and for large rivers, e.g. the Mississippi, it may reach up to 300 m/yr. The rate depends on

- power of the river
- resistance of the banks.

Channel migration may lead to erosion of floodplain features. During migration a cutoff may occur, e.g. on the River Irk in Lancashire, the neck is cut through in times of flood. A reduction in the length of the river course leads to increased channel slope, and an increased ability to carry sediment.

Allogenic changes

Channel straightening can be artificial, e.g. Mississippi 1932–42 decreased its length by 200 km (12%); consequently, the channel slope is now steeper and more unstable. **Floods** are a natural phenomenon, e.g. in the UK rivers overtop their banks for only a few days in most years.

In humid temperate areas floods do not generally produce large or lasting changes. Small floods (one or two a year) are thought to control the size and shape of the channel, and although large floods cause major changes, small floods will gradually adjust the channel back to its stable form.

Climatic change alters the discharge and sediment characteristics of a river. Former discharges in the UK were up to fifty times greater in the Pleistocene period (periglacial streams). However, reconstruction of past river histories is complex because only fragments remain.

Work of a river

The main types of erosion

- **Abrasion** (or **corrasion**) is the wearing away of the bed and bank by the load carried by a river.
- **Attrition** is the wearing away of the load carried by a river. It creates smaller, rounder particles.
- **Hydraulic action** is the force of air and water on the sides of rivers and in cracks.
- **Solution** (or **corrosion**) is the removal of chemical ions, especially calcium, which causes rocks to dissolve.

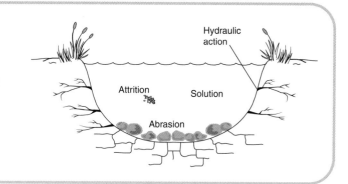

Factors affecting erosion

- **Load** – the heavier and sharper the load the greater the potential for erosion.
- **Velocity and discharge** – the greater the velocity and discharge the greater the potential for erosion.
- **Gradient** – increased gradient increases the rate of erosion.
- **Geology** – soft, unconsolidated rocks, such as sand and gravel, are easily eroded.
- **pH** – rates of solution are increased when the water is more acidic.
- **Human impact** – deforestation, dams, and bridges interfere with the natural flow of a river and frequently end up increasing the rate of erosion.

Theory of river channel load

The **capacity** of a stream refers to the largest amount of debris that a stream can carry; its **competence** refers to the diameter of the largest particle that can be carried. The **critical erosion velocity** is the lowest velocity at which grains of a given size can be moved. The relationship between these variables is shown by means of a **Hjulström curve**.

There are three important features on Hjulström curves:

- the smallest and largest particles require high velocities to lift them
- higher velocities are required for entrainment than for transport
- when velocity falls below a certain level (**settling** or **fall velocity**), particles are deposited (Stokes Law).

Features of erosion

Waterfalls frequently occur on horizontally bedded rocks. The soft rock is undercut by hydraulic action and abrasion. The weight of the water and the lack of support cause the waterfall to collapse and retreat. Over thousands of years the waterfall may retreat enough to form a **gorge of recession**.

Ox-bow lakes are the result of erosion and deposition. Lateral erosion, caused by helicoidal flow, is concentrated on the outer, deeper bank of a **meander**. During times of flooding, erosion increases. The river breaks through and creates a new, steeper channel. In time, the old meander is closed off by deposition to form an ox-bow lake. An excellent example is on the Evenlode River in the Cotswolds, close to the village of Combe.

Other features of erosion include pot holes, river cliffs, and V-shaped valleys.

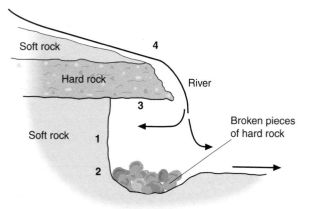

1 Hydraulic impact.
2 Abrasion of soft rock by hard fragments.
3 Lack of support by soft rock.
4 Weight of water causes unsupported hard rock to collapse.

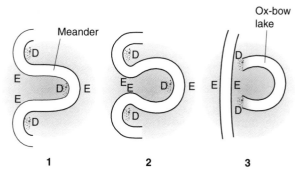

1 Erosion (E) and deposition (D) around a meander (a bend in a river).
2 Increased erosion during flood conditions. The meander becomes exaggerated.
3 The river breaks through during a flood. Further deposition causes the old meander to become an ox-bow lake.

Transportation and deposition

Deposition

Deposition occurs as a river slows down and it loses its energy. Typically, this occurs as a river floods across a **floodplain**, or enters the sea or lake, or a reservoir behind a dam. It is also more likely during low-flow conditions (such as in a drought) than during high-flow (flood) conditions – as long as the river is carrying sediment. The larger, heavier particles are deposited first, and the smaller, lighter ones later. Features of deposition include deltas, levées, slip-off slopes (point bars), ox-bow lakes, braided channels, and floodplains.

Levées

When a river floods its speed is reduced, slowed down by friction caused by contact with the floodplain. As its velocity is reduced the river has to deposit some of its load. It drops the coarser, heavier material first to form raised banks, or **levées**, at the edge of the river. This means that over centuries the levées are built up of coarse material, such as sand and gravel, while the floodplain consists of fine silt and clay.

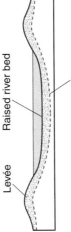

Levée   Raised river bed

Gravel and sand

Braided channels

Braiding occurs when a river transports a very heavy load in relation to its velocity. If a river's discharge falls, its **competence** and **capacity** are reduced. This forces the river to deposit large amounts of its load, and multi-channels, or **braided channels**, are formed. These are common in rivers that experience seasonal variations in discharge. For example, in proglacial and periglacial areas, such as southern Iceland, most of the discharge occurs in late spring and early summer, as snow and ice melt. This enables rivers to carry very large loads which are quickly deposited as discharge decreases.

Islands

Inactive channel

Submerged bar

Flow of river

Deltas

For deltas to be formed a river needs to:

- carry a large volume of sediment – for example rivers in semi-arid regions and in areas of intense human activity
- enter a still body of water which causes velocity to fall, and the water loses its capacity and competence, so deposition occurs, with the heaviest particles deposited first and the lightest last.

If the water is salty, deposition is increased. The salt particles group together, become heavier, and are deposited. Vegetation also increases the rate of deposition, by slowing down the water.

The coarser material is deposited first and the finest material last, and furthest away.

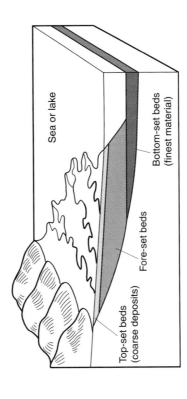

Sea or lake

Bottom-set beds (finest material)

Fore-set beds

Top-set beds (coarse deposits)

The main types of transportation

- **Suspension** – small particles are held up by turbulent flow in the river.
- **Saltation** – heavier particles are bounced or bumped along the bed of the river.
- **Solution** – the chemical load is dissolved in the flowing water.
- **Traction** – the heaviest material is dragged or rolled along the bed of the river.
- **Flotation** – leaves and twigs are carried on the surface of the river.

Light material, e.g. silts and clays held in suspension by turbulence

Dissolved material held in solution

Bedload moved by saltation (bouncing) or traction (rolling)

Bedrock

Aquatic ecosystems

Types of wetland ecosystem

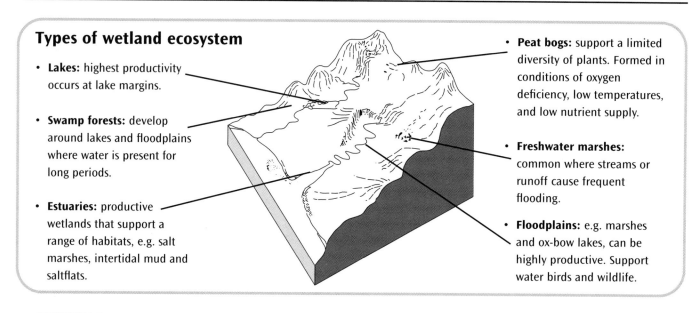

- **Lakes:** highest productivity occurs at lake margins.

- **Swamp forests:** develop around lakes and floodplains where water is present for long periods.

- **Estuaries:** productive wetlands that support a range of habitats, e.g. salt marshes, intertidal mud and saltflats.

- **Peat bogs:** support a limited diversity of plants. Formed in conditions of oxygen deficiency, low temperatures, and low nutrient supply.

- **Freshwater marshes:** common where streams or runoff cause frequent flooding.

- **Floodplains:** e.g. marshes and ox-bow lakes, can be highly productive. Support water birds and wildlife.

Ecosystem structure and functioning

The structure of an ecosystem refers to the arrangement of its parts. For example a **hydrosere** is a plant community that occupies a freshwater site. Its initial **colonisers** are highly adaptable, small species with a short lifespan, such as algae and mosses. The **climax community**, such as oak trees, develops at a slower pace. At this stage the species are in **dynamic equilibrium** with the prevailing environmental conditions.

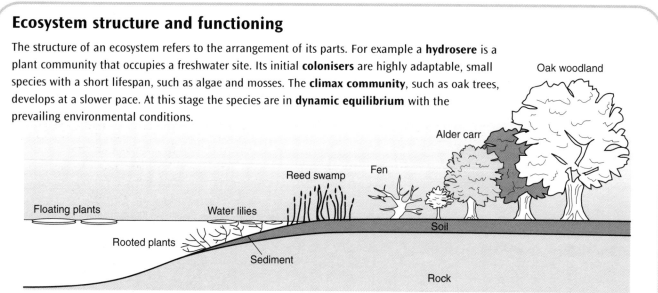

The flow of energy and nutrient cycling is part of how an ecosystem functions. A **trophic** pyramid is often used to represent ecoysystem structure, while a flow diagram is used to show the energy flow.

Peat bogs

Peat, consisting of compressed, decomposing plants, is formed in **anaerobic** (without oxygen), waterlogged conditions. Peat bogs are dominated by **sphagnum moss**, one of few plants able to grow in **oligotrophic** conditions (lacking in nutrients). A habitat for many unique birds and plants, peat bogs have been much eroded over decades and are now threatened environments. There are two main types of peat bog:

Formation of a raised peat bog

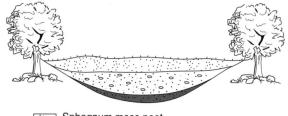

- ▒▒ Sphagnum moss peat
- ▒▒ Sedge peat
- ■ Underlying boulder clay and other glacial material

- **'Blanket bogs'** – formed in areas of high rainfall, usually in uplands. They may have been created by early farmers cutting down trees and burning grasses.

- **Raised bogs** – mounds of peat, found in lowlands, that have accumulated since the glaciers retreated 10 000 years ago. The thin strips of living vegetation on the surface rely almost entirely on rain-fed nutrients. This means that sphagnum mosses, which grow in wet, acidic conditions, dominate.

A third type of wetland, **lowland fens**, contains areas which either did not develop into bog, or where the peat has already been stripped away. The Norfolk Broads, for example, are a result of the large-scale excavation of peat in the Middle Ages.

Impacts of riverine change (1)

> Pages 15 to 18 cover environment–people interactions.
> Pages 15 to 16 ask:
> * How can changes in river landforms and river environments have an impact on people's daily lives?

Changes in a river occur naturally and as a result of human activities. **Natural changes** include climate change and river capture. **Human changes** include reservoir development and land use changes. This can have many effects, such as changes to the river channel, changing sediment loads, changes to discharge, and increased flood risk.

Floods and flooding
Key terms

* **Bankfull stage** – a condition in which a river's channel fills completely, so that any further increase in discharge results in water overflowing the banks.
* **Discharge** – the quantity of water that passes a given point on the bank of a river within a specified interval of time.
* **Flash flood** – a flood in which the lag time is exceptionally short (hours or minutes).
* **Flood** – a discharge great enough to cause a body of water to overflow its channel and submerge surrounding land.
* **Flood-frequency curve** – flood magnitudes that are plotted with respect to the recurrence interval (the size of a flood that would be expected in any given time period, e.g. the 100 year flood) calculated for a flood of that magnitude at a given location.
* **Floodplain** – the part of any river valley that is inundated during floods.

The uses of rivers

Rivers are attractive to people for a variety of reasons. They provide:

* a source of drinking water
* fertile silt for agriculture
* a line of communication and navigation
* a source of power
* fishing
* recreation.

The Thames/Cherwell floodplain

The flood hazard is extremely dangerous for people's lives and their possessions. Many settlements are built on raised ground in order to reduce the risk of flooding. Oxford is an excellent example. Much of the floodplain of the Thames and the Cherwell has not been built upon. It has been left for farming and for recreational grounds. Housing and industry have tended to locate on the higher ground free from flooding but increasingly floodplain developments are becoming more common.

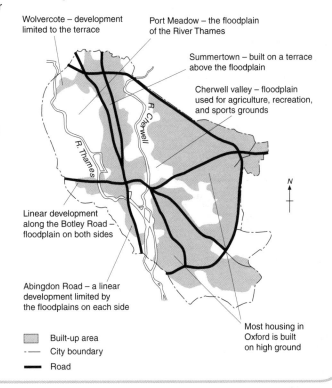

Wolvercote – development limited to the terrace

Port Meadow – the floodplain of the River Thames

Summertown – built on a terrace above the floodplain

Cherwell valley – floodplain used for agriculture, recreation, and sports grounds

Linear development along the Botley Road – floodplain on both sides

Abingdon Road – a linear development limited by the floodplains on each side

Most housing in Oxford is built on high ground

R. Thames

R. Cherwell

N

▨ Built-up area
- — City boundary
━ Road

Recurrence intervals

Recurrence intervals (or return periods) are the frequency with which large or small events take place. For example, we would expect 'average' water flows in a river in the UK for much of the time. However, very large floods or severe droughts are rare – perhaps once every 10–20 years. Catastrophic floods might occur only once in every 100 years.

By calculating flood and drought recurrence levels and employing other predictive techniques, human vulnerability to such events can be reduced. For example, information on recurrence levels can be used to plan land use and to ensure that there is adequate water provision for the future.

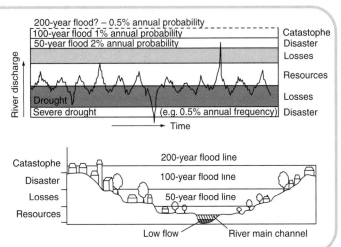

200-year flood? – 0.5% annual probability
100-year flood 1% annual probability
50-year flood 2% annual probability

River discharge	Catastophe
	Disaster
	Losses
	Resources
	Losses
Drought	
Severe drought	(e.g. 0.5% annual frequency) Disaster

Time

Catastophe — 200-year flood line
Disaster — 100-year flood line
Losses — 50-year flood line
Resources

Low flow   River main channel

Impacts of riverine change (2)

Changing sedimentation levels: the Yellow River (Hwang He)

The Hwang He River flows over a distance of more than 4000 km and drains an area of 750 000 km². Over 84 million people live in the drainage basin. Changes in the river's discharge have had a devastating impact on China's population.

The combination of this easily eroded material and the seasonal flow of the Yellow River cause many problems for the people who live in the lower parts of the catchment. It is said to have killed more people than any other natural feature. The worst flood of all occurred in 1332 – 7 million people drowned and a further 10 million died as a result of the famine that followed.

Attempts to control the river go back at least as far as 2356 BC, and there have been **levées** on the river for at least 2500 years.

Despite this long history of engineering the Hwang He has shifted its course on at least ten occasions. When it does this the place where it enters the sea can change by as much as 1100 km.

However, the river also produces some benefits:

- The sediment creates a fertile soil. As a result, 13 million ha of the drainage basin is farmed.
- Deposits dropped on the coastal plains have formed a large alluvial fan – an area which supports more than 10 million people.
- There is a huge potential for hydroelectric power. By the mid-1980s over 150 reservoirs had been built, and power stations were added to 80 of these.

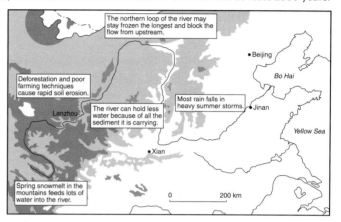

Some causes of flooding on the Yellow River

Changing channels: the impact of the Aswan Dam

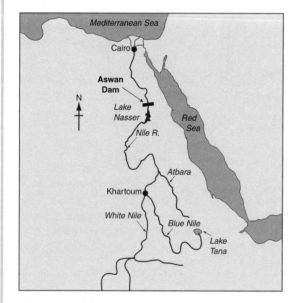

The Aswan High Dam in Egypt provides many benefits:

- **Flood and drought control** – the dam allows good crops in dry years as, for example, in 1972 and 1973.
- **Irrigation** – 60% of water from the Aswan Dam is used for irrigation and up to 4000 km² of the desert is irrigated.
- **Hydroelectric power** – this accounts for 7000 million kW hours each year.
- Improved **navigation**.
- **Recreation** and **tourism**.

It is estimated that the value of the Aswan High Dam is about $500 million each year to the Egyptian economy.

On the other hand, there are numerous disadvantages:

- **Water losses** – the dam provides less than half the amount of water that was originally expected.
- **Salinisation** – crop yields from up to one-third of the area irrigated by water from the Aswan Dam have declined due to salinisation.
- **Groundwater changes** – seepage leads to increased groundwater levels and may cause secondary salinisation.
- **Displacement of population** – up to 100 000 Nubian people were removed from their homes when the dam was built.
- **Drowning of archaeological sites** – statues of Rameses II and Nefertari at Abu Simbel had to be removed to safer locations, and the increase in the humidity of the area has led to an increase in the weathering of ancient monuments.
- **Seismic stress** – the earthquake of November 1981 is believed to have been caused by the weight of water in Lake Nasser.
- **Deposition** – infilling of Lake Nasser is taking place at about 100 million tonnes each year.
- **Channel erosion** (clear water erosion) at the base of the channel has lowered the channel by 25 mm over 18 years.
- **Erosion of the Nile delta** – this is taking place at a rate of about 2.5 cm each year.
- **Loss of nutrients** – it is estimated that it costs $100 million each year to buy commercial fertilisers to make up for the lack of nutrients.
- **Decreased fish catches** – sardine yields are down 95% and 3000 jobs in Egyptian fisheries have been lost.
- **Spread of diseases** – such as schistosomiasis (bilharzia) and malaria – due to increased stagnant water.

Human impacts (1)

Pages 17 to 18 discuss environment–people interactions.
- *How have human activities, some of which may be conflicting, influenced river environments?*

Human activities that cause river problems

Direct
- River regulation, e.g. River Nile
- Channelisation, e.g. River Thames, Oxford
- Water abstraction, e.g. the Colorado River
- Waste disposal, e.g. the Ganges
- Irrigation, e.g. Syr Darya, Aral Sea
- Drainage, especially agriculture, e.g. Fens
- Dams, e.g. Three Gorges Dam

Indirect
- Land use change, especially deforestation, e.g. Amazon rainforest; afforestation a problem in the early period when much of the ground is bare, e.g. Tennessee Valley Authority
- Urbanisation, e.g. floodplain development in Oxford
- Mining, e.g. impact on water quality
- Agricultural practices, e.g. intensive arable farming on New Bedford River

How can channelisation influence a river environment?

Most major rivers have had their natural channel artificially altered. This is often done as a flood prevention measure or to reduce erosion. Modifications include:

- straightening
- resectioning
- building levées
- bank stabilisation.

The effects of stream straightening

Natural channel

Artificial channel

Suitable water temperatures: adequate shading; good cover for fish life; minimal variation in temperatures; abundant leaf material input

Increased water temperatures: no shading; no cover for fish life; rapid daily and seasonal fluctuations in temperatures; reduced leaf material input

Pool riffle sequence

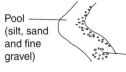

Pool (silt, sand and fine gravel)

Riffle (coarse gravel)

Mostly riffle

Sorted gravels provide diversified habitats for many stream organisms

Unsorted gravels: reduction in habitats; few organisms; made worse when concreted

The hydrological effects of dams: the Three Gorges Dam

The decision to build the Three Gorges Dam on the Yangtze River highlights some of the conflicts between people who use the river. The dam will not be completed until 2009. The dam will enable China to:

- generate up to 18 000 megawatts of power, reducing the country's dependence on coal
- supply Shanghai's 13 million people with water
- protect 10 million people from flooding (over 300 000 people died in China as a result of flooding in the 20th century)
- water levels will be raised to allow shipping above the Three Gorges (formerly rapids).

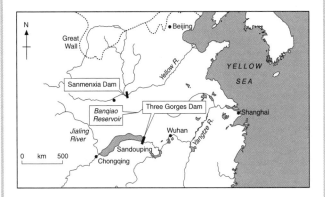

Protest against the Three Gorges Dam

- Most floods in recent years have come from rivers that join the Yangtze below the Three Gorges Dam.
- The region is seismologically active and landslides are frequent.
- The port at the head of the lake may become silted up as a result of increased deposition and the development of a delta at the head of the lake.
- Up to 1.2 million people will have to be moved to make way for the dam.
- Much of the land available for resettlement is over 800 m above sea-level, and is colder, with thin infertile soils on relatively steep slopes.
- Dozens of towns will be flooded, for example Wanxian and Fuling with 140 000 and 80 000 people respectively.
- Up to 530 million tonnes of silt are carried through the Gorge annually – the first dam on the river lost its capacity within seven years.
- The dam will interfere with aquatic life – the white flag dolphin is threatened with extinction.
- Archaeological treasures will be drowned, including the Zhang Fei temple.

Human impacts (2)

Water quality: the Ganga River basin

The Ganga River in India is over 2500 km long and drains an area of over 1 million km². Upwards of 250 million people live in the basin, and although it is mainly rural, it does contain a number of large cities such as Kolkata, Kanpur, and Varanasi. The water in the basin is used for a variety of purposes:

- **Irrigation** – there is a vast network of canals helping to irrigate India's rice crop.
- **Domestic use** – for drinking water and sewage disposal.
- **Industrial use** – there is a large concentration of tanneries, petrochemical, and fertiliser complexes, rubber, jute, and textile industries.

- **Disposal of waste water** – from industrial, residential, and agricultural areas.
- **Navigation**.
- **Religious practices** – such as the disposal of dead bodies.

Consequently, water quality is low. Untreated urban waste water is the biggest offender, followed by industrial waste. The use of fertilisers and pesticides to feed high-yielding varieties of crops is increasing the problem. Water quality deteriorates during the dry season. In addition, large urban centres, with high population densities, make water quality worse. **Biochemical oxygen demand** (BOD) levels are very high, often exceeding 10–20 mg/l. River quality decreases during periods of low flow (winter) because there is less water to dilute the polluting materials.

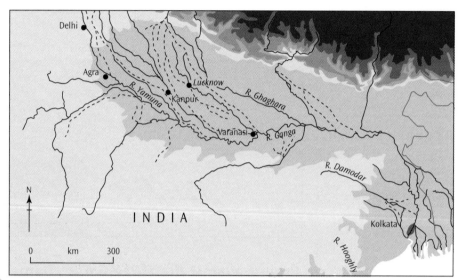

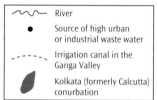

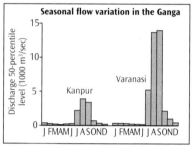

Over-extraction: Bangkok

In Thailand, excessive extraction of groundwater has caused the water table to drop rapidly. The three sectors consuming the largest amount of water are **agriculture, industry**, and **domestic use**. Unsustainable use of groundwater reserves has caused a number of problems:

- **Land subsidence** – Bangkok is sinking by 10 cm per year. This is causing major structural damage to buildings and roads.
- **Shortage of safe drinking water** – the shallow aquifers in Bangkok have become contaminated with salt water from the nearby ocean.
- **Increased risk of flooding** – aggravated by land subsidence.

Without immediate action, it is estimated that many parts of the city will be under water all-year-round in 17 years' time. To alleviate its problems Bangkok would have to reduce its groundwater extraction rate by at least one-half – a formidable challenge, because water demand is expected to grow rapidly in the coming decades.

The effects of urbanisation on flood frequency

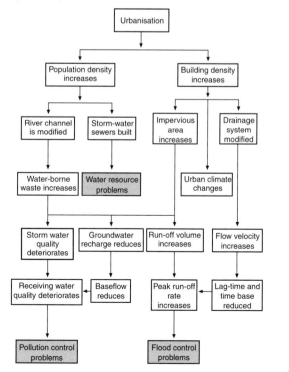

River management (1)

Pages 19 to 21 discuss river management and the future.
*   *How does the management of river systems pose a continuing challenge for people?*

Human pressures on drainage basins create the need for management schemes. Successful management requires an understanding of landform systems and processes and can be evaluated in terms of cost and benefits.

Engineering solutions: the Colorado

The Colorado river is 2333 km long and drains an area of over 630 000 km². It was the first river in the USA to be used for multi-purpose development. A number of large dams, such as the Hoover and Parker Dams, were built in the early 20th century. State or federal authorities fund the dams, and an holistic approach has been adopted. The dams are used for:

*   **Irrigation** – 800 000 ha of farmland are now fed by the Colorado.
*   **Flood and silt control** – the Colorado once carried 130 million tonnes of suspended sediment to the sea, now it hardly carries anything. Flood peaks and discharge have been reduced since the dams were built.
*   **Power** – the dams produce 120 million kW of electricity each year.
*   **Domestic and industrial water supplies** – the Colorado now supplies the demands of over 40 million people in seven US states and Mexico.
*   **Recreation** –the lakes behind the dams attract many tourists.

The Colorado is one of the first rivers in the world to have its entire flow used up before it reaches its estuary, in the Gulf of California.

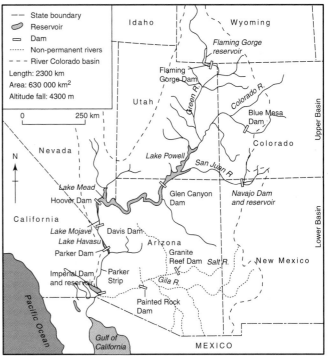

Changing waterflow in the Colorado

Distance from source (km)	River flow (m³/sec)	
	1920	2000
100	5	200
300	124	220
600	409	370
1200	905	430
2000	1003	170

Management problems

*   Water supply has failed to meet demand. Up to 25% of water is lost through **evaporation** and **leakage**, and more through wasteful irrigation techniques. Significant population increase in the west and south-west of America has put further pressure on supplies. **The Central Arizona Project**, for example, now distributes 1.85 trillion litres of water each year to farms, Indian reservations, industries, and residential homes, over a distance of 570 km.
*   Sediment has become trapped behind the dams, which is expected to shorten their useful life.
*   Once-established wildlife is disappearing along stretches of the river. The Colorado Delta, for example, is now dry for much of the year and has become starved of sediment. As a result bird, plant, and fish populations which previously thrived are now dying out (i.e. wetland loss).
*   Recycling methods have resulted in some farmers receiving highly saline water that has been damaging to their crops. Desalinisation techniques are expensive.
*   Flooding has occurred, but it has been largely attributed to human mismanagement of the flow from dams.

'Soft engineering'

Several 'soft engineering' methods can be used to reduce the impact of 'hard engineering' such as dams and channelisation, e.g.
*   minimising the length of river that is altered
*   using meanders when creating new environments
*   maintaining a diversity of channel environments, e.g. pools and riffles
*   maintaining areas for the river to flood naturally
*   using natural vegetation to protect riverbanks
*   locating embankments away from the river so that flooding can be allowed and wetlands can develop
*   maintaining a complete vegetation cover
*   minimising the length of river that is lined with concrete
*   minimising disruption to vegetation.

A River environments   19

River management (2)

Methods of river management have evolved. There is now increasing emphasis on holistic management: taking the whole river catchment area into consideration, not just the river or a section of it. The realisation of the value of natural habitats and need for long-term solutions has resulted in **river restoration** projects and sustainable strategies.

The need for sustainable management

Over the last 50 years rivers have been seriously affected by urban and agricultural flood defences, land drainage, and floodplain urbanisation. The result has been:

- extensive straightening and deepening of river channels, which has damaged wildlife habitats, reduced the value of fisheries and detracted from the natural appeal of river landscapes
- a major loss of floodplains and wetlands to intensive agriculture and urbanisation, which has destroyed floodplain habitats and reduced the ability of floodplains to function as areas of flood control
- rivers being used intensively as transport routes, carriers of waste disposal, for industrial purposes, water abstraction, recreation, etc.

Natural restoration can take hundreds of years, so restoration has to be by artificial means. The benefits are greatest when natural river shapes, flows, and loads are copied.

River restoration: the River Cole

The River Cole, near Swindon, is one of three river restoration sites in Britain to have been given financial support by the European Union (EU). The aims of the River Restoration Project (RRP) are:

- to recreate natural conditions in damaged river corridors
- to improve understanding of the effects of restoration work on nature conservation value, water quality, recreation, and public opinion
- to encourage other groups to restore streams and rivers.

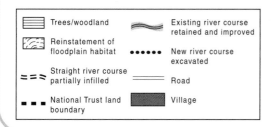

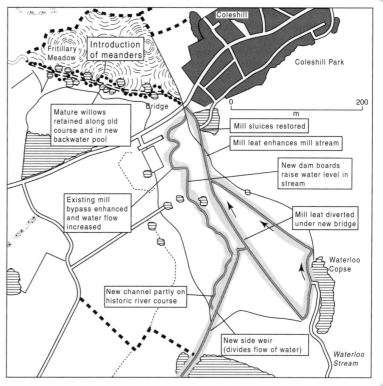

Sustainable benefits of restoration

- Increased **flood defence** – additional flood storage provided by the enlarged floodplain.
- More opportunities for **recreation** – public perception is largely in favour of natural landscapes.
- Improved **water quality** – due to natural settling of sediments on the floodplain and river bed, and increased interception of pollutants by vegetation.
- Greater nature **conservation** of wildlife in the riverine environment.
- Increased **diversity** and numbers of fish.

Evaluation of the scheme

The RRP schemes show how rivers can be managed in a sustainable way:

- they are allowed to flood
- they improve the quality of the environment
- they increase biodiversity.

However, it is important to put the results into perspective. The River Cole is only a small part of the Upper Thames catchment.

In practice most restoration schemes will only partially restore or rehabilitate the river, due to the large number of human-related uses of the floodplains. In addition, these schemes can be very costly. The perceived advantages of river restoration – better water quality, etc. – must be weighed against the potential costs when deciding whether to instigate such schemes.

River management (3)

Changing river management: the Kissimmee River

Between 1962 and 1971 the 160 km meandering Kissimmee River and flanking floodplain were **channelised** and thereby transformed into a 90 km long, 10 m deep drainage canal. The river was channelised to provide an outlet canal for draining floodwaters from the developing upper Kissimmee lakes basin, and to provide flood protection for land adjacent to the river.

Impacts of channelisation

The channelisation of the Kissimee River had several unintended impacts:

- the loss of 12 000–14 000 ha of wetlands
- a reduction in wading bird and waterfowl usage
- a continuing long-term decline in game fish populations.

Concerns about the **sustainability** of existing ecosystems led to a state- and federally-supported restoration study. The result was a massive restoration project, on a scale unmatched elsewhere.

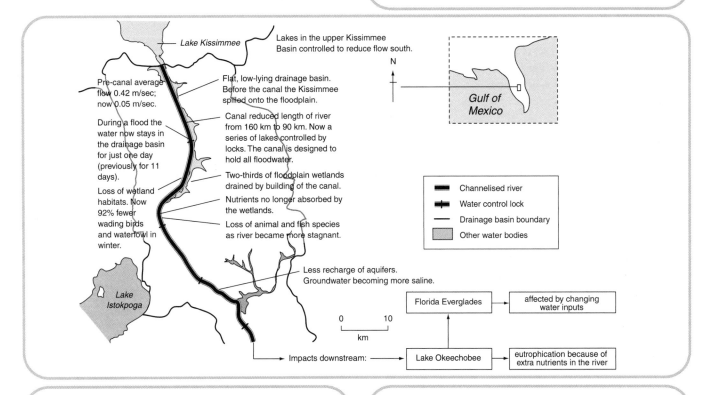

The Kissimee River Restoration Project

The aim is to restore over 100 km² of river and associated floodplain wetlands. The project will benefit over 320 fish and wildlife species, including the endangered bald eagle, wood stork and snail kite. It will create over 11 000 ha of wetlands.

Restoration of the river and its associated natural resources requires **dechannelisation**. This entails backfilling approximately half of the flood control channel and re-establishing the flow of water through the natural river channel. In residential areas the flood control channel will remain in place.

Benefits of restoration

- Higher water levels should ultimately support a natural river ecosystem again.
- Re-establishment of floodplain wetlands and the associated nutrient filtration function is expected to result in decreased nutrient loads to Lake Okeechobee.
- It is possible that restoration of the Kissimmee River floodplain could benefit populations of key avian species, such as wading birds and waterfowl, by providing increased feeding and breeding habitats.
- Potential revenue associated with increased recreational usage (such as hunting and fishing) and ecotourism on the restored river, could significantly enhance local and regional economies.

The costs of restoration

- It is estimated the project will cost $414 million (initial channelisation cost $20 million). The bill is being shared by the state of Florida and the federal government.
- Restoration, which began in 1999, will not be completed until 2010.

- Restoration of the river's floodplain could result in higher losses of water due to evapotranspiration during wet periods. Navigation may be impeded in some sections of the restored river; in extremely dry spells. It is, however, expected that navigable depths will be maintained for at least 90% of the time.

Coastal environments (1)

Pages 22 to 23 introduce coastal systems.
- What are the key features of coastal environments?
- What systems operate within coastal environments?

Coastal variety

Coastal environments are influenced by many factors, including physical and human processes. As a result there is a great variety in coastal landscapes. For example, landscapes vary on account of:

- **Lithology (rock type)** – hard rocks such as granite and basalt give rugged landscapes, e.g. the Giant's Causeway, whereas soft rocks such as sands and gravels produce low, flat landscapes, e.g. around Poole Harbour.
- **Geological structure** – **concordant** or **accordant** (Pacific) coastlines occur where the geological strata lie parallel to the coastline, e.g. the south coast of Ireland; whereas **discordant** (Atlantic-type) coastlines occur where the geological strata are at right-angles to the shoreline, e.g. the south-west coastline of Ireland.

- **Processes** – erosional landscapes, e.g. the east coast of England, have many rapidly retreating cliffs, whereas areas of rapid deposition, e.g. the Netherlands, have many sand dunes and coastal flats.
- **Sea-level changes** interact with erosional and depositional processes to produce **advancing** coasts (those growing either due to deposition and/or a relative fall in sea-level) or **retreating** coasts (those being eroded and/or drowned by a relative rise in sea-level).
- **Human impacts** are increasingly common – some coasts, e.g. in Florida, are extensively modified whereas others are more natural, e.g. south-west Ireland.
- **Ecosystem type,** such as mangrove, coral, sand dune, salt marsh, and rocky shore, add further variety to the coastline.

Coastal zones

The coastal zone includes all areas from the deep ocean, which may lie beyond political jurisdiction (up to 320 km offshore) to 60 km inland. The inland areas may affect coastal areas through sediment supply and pollution sources, as well as being affected by coastal processes such as land/sea breezes. At the coast there is the **upper beach** or **backshore** (backed by cliffs or sand dunes), the **foreshore** (periodically exposed by the tides), and the **offshore** area (covered by water).

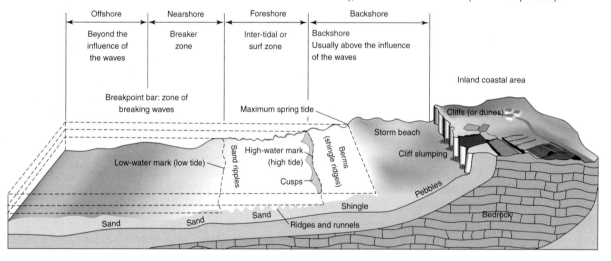

Coastal interface

The coastal zone is a dynamic area with inputs and processes from land, sea, and atmosphere, so it is, geologically, an area of very rapid change.

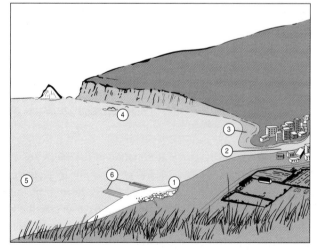

1. **Mass movements** provide large amounts of material, which may bury beaches and protect cliffs.

2. **Rivers** mostly carry sediment (fine-grained silts, clays, and sands) to the coast.

3. **Glaciers and periglaciation** – much of the shingle on beaches in the British Isles is derived from frost-shattered material from the last cold periglacial era.

4. **Erosion of cliffs** by the sea produces large amounts of material for beach building. This may protect the cliff from further erosion.

5. The **sea** may bring sediments shorewards forming offshore bars and beaches.

6. **Artificial structures** – such as groynes – interrupt the natural operation of coastal processes.

Coastal environments (2)

Coastal sediment systems

The coastal sediment system, or **littoral cell system**, is a simplified model that examines coastal processes and patterns in a given area. It operates at a variety of scales from a single bay, to a regional scale. Each littoral cell is a self-contained cell, in which inputs and outputs are balanced.

Dynamic equilibrium

This concept states that any system (or in this case littoral cell) is the result of the inputs and processes that operate within it. A change to one

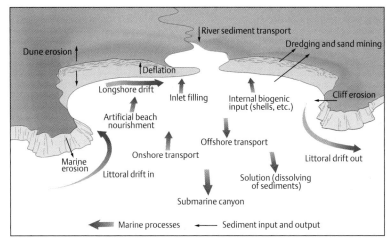

of the inputs (for example an increase in sediment to the shoreline following cliff collapse) has a knock-on effect on the processors (such as longshore drift or transport) and a resulting change in the landforms (such as stabilisation of cliffs). The balance has changed, and the processors attempt to return to a state of **dynamic equilibrium.**

Oceanside littoral cell

Inputs into this Californian sediment cell include:

- river deposits
- sediments from cliffs
- materials for beach replenishment
- north–south longshore drift.

Most of the material supplied for beach replenishment is fine-grained silt and sand.

The region is very active. Each year rip currents and offshore currents move 100 000 m^3 of sediment into the La Jolla submarine canyon and over 200 000 m^3 of material is carried southwards by longshore drift. In addition, seasonal variations in **constructive** and **destructive** waves redistribute coastal sediments, and sea-levels are rising 6–15 mm each year.

Human impacts

- Dams have reduced the supply of sediment to the beaches by 33%.
- Buildings, boats, private protection schemes, and roads are destabilising the cliffs.
- Oceanside harbour in the north is blocking the southward movement of sediment and most is now diverted to offshore currents and to the La Jolla submarine canyon.

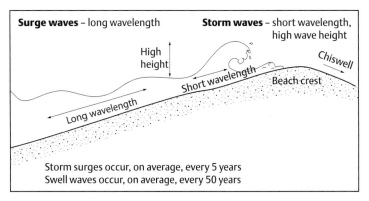

The effects of a single storm event: Chesil Beach

In December 1978, huge storm waves swept over Chesil Beach at Portland in Dorset cutting it off from the mainland for three days. This flood consisted of steep waves occurring every 12 seconds, accompanied by a strong onshore wind. On breaking, the waves plunged at a steep angle, creating a strong backwash which removed material from the beach in a seaward direction.

As the storm continued, the beach was progressively cut back which caused a lowering of the beach crest level. This was further reduced by the **overtopping** water, which also caused erosion of the landward face, assisted by the action of water percolating through the pebbles.

In February 1979 ocean swell waves of 18-second periods arrived without warning. The beach was left in a very stable condition consisting of one long continuous slope from the crest to the sea.

Coastal features in Norfolk

Pages 24 to 28 discuss process and change in coastal environments, landforms, and ecosystems.
- Which physical factors and processes influence coastal landforms?
- What processes lead to change in coastal ecosystems?

What factors influence the coastline of Norfolk?

Rock type and structure

There are two main types of cliff on the Norfolk coast:

1 At Hunstanton, consolidated rocks such as chalk, Carstone, and Hunstanton Red Rock form vertical cliffs (typically 20 m high). Some debris at the base is the result of rockfall. Undercutting at the base of the cliff leads to collapse of overlying rocks.

2 In north-east Norfolk, unconsolidated sands and gravels form less steep cliffs (typically between 37° and 49°). Between Cromer and Overstrand the cliffs reach a height of over 70 m, elsewhere they are just 20–30 m. The smaller cliffs are generally steeper. The steep slopes are formed by mass movements on the cliff followed by removal by the sea.

Coastal erosion

The glacial deposits that form the cliffs are the major source of beach material. Cliffs lose about 750 000 m³/year – this represents a net rate of erosion of between 0.33 and 1.2 m/year (reaching a maximum of 2.0 m/year). The average rate at Overstrand is 0.75 m/year.

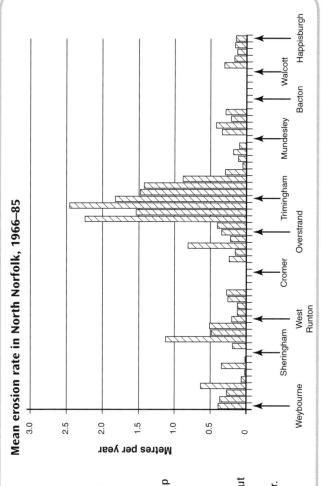

Mean erosion rate in North Norfolk, 1966–85

Metres per year (vertical axis: 0, 0.5, 1.0, 1.5, 2.0, 2.5, 3.0)

Locations (left to right): Weybourne, Sheringham, West Runton, Cromer, Overstrand, Trimingham, Mundesley, Bacton, Walcott, Happisburgh

North Norfolk marshland coast

Scolt Head Island

Scolt Head Island is a 5 km barrier beach between Brancaster harbour and Burnham harbour. It comprises a series of sand dunes that have developed on gravel ridges separated by salt marshes. The salt marshes are formed in low-energy areas of shallow water.

Northerly and north-easterly winds blowing off the North Sea drive shingle onshore at Scolt Head Island. Shingle is then moved westwards by longshore drift. **Wave refraction** at the western end of Scolt Head Island causes the ridges to swing in towards Brancaster.

Blakeney Point is a spit, 15.5 km long. In parts it is nearly 200 m wide, up to 10 m high, and contains about 9 million m³ of shingle. Sand dunes have accumulated on the shingle ridges, and there are marshes between the ridges. The shingle ridge is gradually being driven inland. This occurs mostly during

The Wash

North Sea

Land over 60 m

0 — 10 km

Places marked: Scolt Head, Brancaster, Thornham, Hunstanton, Heacham, Burnham Market, Wells, Blakeney Point, Blakeney, R. Glaven, Weybourne, Sheringham, Cromer, Cromer Ridge, R. Stiffkey, R. Wensum, Fakenham, Happisburgh

storm events. Between 1649 and 1924 the shingle moved landward at a rate of about 1 m/year. The length of the spit increased by over 80 m/year between 1886 and 1904, and by over 45 m/year between 1904 and 1925. The shingle is coarser at the eastern end (average 4 mm) and is finer – down to 1.5 mm – at the western end.

Coastal processes

Types of erosion

Coasts are shaped by the interplay of marine and sub-aerial processes.

Marine or cliff-foot, processes include: **abrasion; hydraulic impact or quarrying; solution; attrition**.

Sub-aerial, or cliff-face, processes include:

- **salt weathering** – the process by which sodium and magnesium compounds expand in joints and cracks thereby weakening rock structures
- **freeze–thaw weathering** – the process whereby water freezes, expands and degrades jointed rocks
- **biological weathering** – carried out by molluscs, sponges, and urchins. It is very important on low-energy coasts.

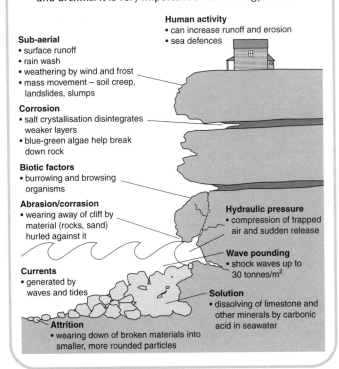

Human activity
- can increase runoff and erosion
- sea defences

Sub-aerial
- surface runoff
- rain wash
- weathering by wind and frost
- mass movement – soil creep, landslides, slumps

Corrosion
- salt crystallisation disintegrates weaker layers
- blue-green algae help break down rock

Biotic factors
- burrowing and browsing organisms

Abrasion/corrasion
- wearing away of cliff by material (rocks, sand) hurled against it

Currents
- generated by waves and tides

Attrition
- wearing down of broken materials into smaller, more rounded particles

Hydraulic pressure
- compression of trapped air and sudden release

Wave pounding
- shock waves up to 30 tonnes/m²

Solution
- dissolving of limestone and other minerals by carbonic acid in seawater

Rates of cliff erosion

Location	Geology	Erosion (m/100 years)
Holderness	Glacial drift	120
Cromer, Norfolk	Glacial drift	96
Folkestone	Clay	28
Isle of Thanet	Chalk	7–22
Seaford Head	Chalk	126
Beachy Head	Chalk	106
Barton, Hants	Barton Beds	58
Portland Bill	Limestones	0.2
Land's End	Granite	0.1

Erosion is highest where there are frequent storm waves and easily erodable material.

Constructive and destructive waves

Destructive waves

Short wavelength
High height
Circular orbit
Steep gradient

Constructive waves

Long wavelength
Low height
Elliptical orbit
Shallow gradient

- Erosional waves
- Also called 'surging', 'storm', or 'plunging' waves
- Short wavelength, high height
- High frequency (10–12 per minute)
- Circular orbit
- Low period (one every 5–6 seconds)
- Backwash greater than swash
- Steep gradient

- Depositional waves
- Also called 'spilling', 'swell' waves
- Long wavelength, low height
- Low frequency (6–8 per minute)
- Elliptical orbit
- High period (one every 8–10 seconds)
- Swash greater than backwash
- Low gradient

Wave refraction and longshore drift

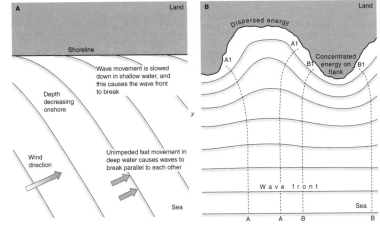

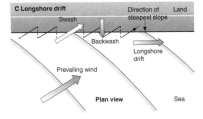

Wave **refraction** occurs when waves approach an irregular coastline or at an oblique angle (**A**). Refraction reduces wave velocity and, if complete, causes wave fronts to break parallel to the shore. Wave refraction concentrates energy on the flanks of headlands and dissipates energy in bays (**B**). However, refraction is rarely complete, and consequently **longshore drift** occurs (**C**).

Coastal features

The profile of a cliff depends upon a number of factors:
- geological structure
- subaerial and marine processes
- amount of undercutting
- rates of removal
- stage of development.

Rocks of low resistance are easily eroded and are unable to support an overhang. Jointing may determine the location of weaknesses in the rock, just as the angle of dip may control the shape of the cliff. Past processes are also important. Bevelled cliffs are found in areas affected by periglaciation.

Beach profile
Sources of material

- Material eroded from cliffs and headlands
- Offshore supplies, e.g. Chesil Beach
- River sediments
- Beach deposits from constructive waves and longshore drift

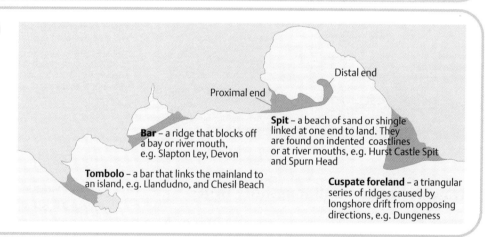

Storm beach – a noticeable, semi-permanent ridge, found at the level of the highest spring tides

Berms – small-scale beach ridges built up by successive levels of tides or storms

Cusps – semi-circular scalloped embayments found in the shingle or at the shingle/sand interface

Ripples – formed by wave action or tidal currents

Beach profiles and particle size

Material	Diameter (mm)	Beach angle °
Cobbles	32	24°
Pebbles	4	17°
Coarse sand	2	7°
Medium sand	0.2	5°
Fine sand	0.02	3°
Very fine sand	0.002	1°

Features of deposition
Essential requirements include:

- a large supply of material
- longshore drift
- an irregular, indented coastline e.g. river mouths
- low energy coastlines
- bioconstruction, i.e. the work of plants

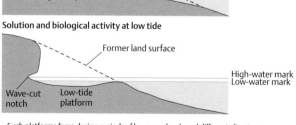

Distal end

Proximal end

Bar – a ridge that blocks off a bay or river mouth, e.g. Slapton Ley, Devon

Spit – a beach of sand or shingle linked at one end to land. They are found on indented coastlines or at river mouths, e.g. Hurst Castle Spit and Spurn Head

Tombolo – a bar that links the mainland to an island, e.g. Llandudno, and Chesil Beach

Cuspate foreland – a triangular series of ridges caused by longshore drift from opposing directions, e.g. Dungeness

Shore platforms

These include **inter-tidal platforms (wave-cut platforms)**, **high-tide platforms** and **low-tide platforms**. Wave-cut platforms are most frequently found in high-energy environments and are typically less than 500 m wide with an angle of about 1°.

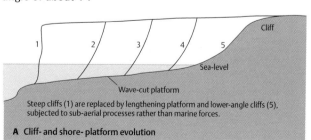

Steep cliffs (1) are replaced by lengthening platform and lower-angle cliffs (5), subjected to sub-aerial processes rather than marine forces.

A Cliff- and shore- platform evolution

Water layer weathering (salt weathering and hydration at base)

Former cliff

Former land surface

High-water mark
Low-water mark

High tide platform

Solution and biological activity at low tide

Former land surface

High-water mark
Low-water mark

Wave-cut notch

Low-tide platform

Such platforms form during periods of lower sea levels and different climates.

B Platforms formed by weathering

Short-term and long-term changes

Sea-level changes (Johnson, 1919)

Sea-levels change in response to the growth and decay of ice sheets. **Eustatic change** refers to a global change in sea-level. At the height of glacial advance, 18 000 years ago, sea-level was 100–150 m below its current position. The level of the land also varies in relation to the sea. Land may rise as a result of tectonic uplift or following the removal of an ice sheet. Localised change in the level of the land relative to that of the sea is known as **isostatic adjustment** or **isostasy.**

A simple sequence of sea-level change:

1 Temperatures decrease, glaciers and ice sheets advance and sea-levels fall eustatically.
2 Ice thickness increases and the land is lowered isostatically.
3 Temperatures rise, ice melts, and sea-levels rise eustatically.
4 Continued melting releases pressure on the land and the land rises isostatically, e.g. parts of Canada rise by up to 20 mm/year.

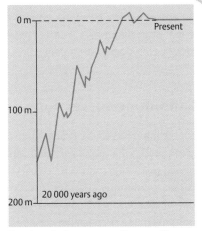

Sea-level change on the south coast of England

Features of **emerged coastlines** include:
- raised beaches such as the Portland raised beach
- coastal plains
- relict cliffs such as those along the Fall Line in eastern USA
- raised mudflats, for example the Carselands of the River Forth.

Submerged coastlines include:

- **Rias**, such as the River Fal, are drowned river valleys caused by rising sea-levels during the Flandarin Transgression (a period, from 14 000 to 7000 bp, when melting ice sheets and glaciers led to a global rise in sea levels) or due to a sinking of the land.
- **Fjords**, such as Loch Torridon and the Oslo Fjord, are glacial troughs occupied by the sea. They are common in uplifted mid-latitude coasts, notably Norway, Greenland, and Chile. An early view was that they were tectonic in origin. This has been rejected and replaced by the concept of drowning of U-shaped valleys.
- **Fjards,** or drowned glacial lowlands.

Portland island and its raised beach

Valentin's classification (1952)

- **Advancing coasts** include emerged coastlines and coasts where the deposition is rapid.

- **Retreating coasts** include submerged coasts and coasts where the rate of erosion is greater than the rate of emergence.

Villages lost through coastal retreat along the east coast of Britain since Roman times

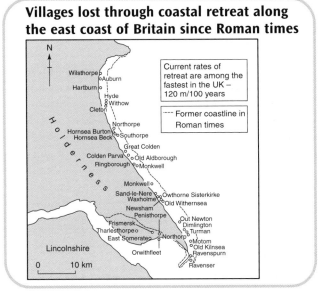

Current rates of retreat are among the fastest in the UK – 120 m/100 years

Former coastline in Roman times

Coastal ecosystems

An **ecosystem** is a set of interrelated plants and animals with their non-living environment. Coastal ecosystems include sand dunes or **psammoseres**, and salt marshes, or **haloseres** as well as coral reefs. These change spatially and temporally. The changes in micro-environment which allow other species to invade, compete, succeed, and dominate is termed **succession**.

Sand dune succession

Succession refers to the changes in plant and animal communities that occur over time and space. Over a long period the dominant species change until some form of **climax community** develops. Zonation on a sand dune shows how vegetation species change from embryo to fixed dune, so it is possible to see a spatial version of succession.

How does human activity affect sand dunes?

Sand dunes are very fragile environments that are increasingly subjected to direct and indirect human pressures. At Studland in south Dorset, for example, there is:

- recreation – walking, trampling, taking picnics, educational trips
- burning – both intentional and accidental
- trampling, leading to blowout dunes
- construction of buildings and infrastructure such as cafés, toilets and car parks
- the introduction of exotic species such as rabbits in Norman times, which has had a serious impact on the growth of vegetation
- attempts to manage sand dune systems using duckboards, information boards, fencing off selected areas, restoration of dunes, prohibition of bonfires.

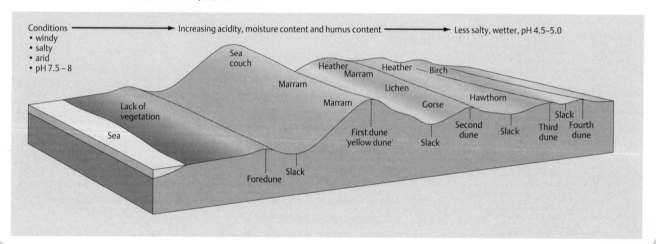

Salt marsh succession

Salt marshes are very productive and fertile ecosystems because of their high oxygen content, nutrient availability, light availability, and the cleaning action of the tides. These allow photosynthesis to take place at all levels of the salt marsh – even when it is covered with water. Examples of salt marsh succession include Scolt Head Island in East Anglia and Newtown on the Isle of Wight

I Colonisers on bare mudflats: algae, eel grass, and marsh samphire (salicornia) increase the amount of deposition of silt. Plants can tolerate alkaline conditions and regular inundation by seawater.

II Halophytic vegetation such as rice grass and spartina (cord grass) build up the salt marsh by as much as 5 cm per annum. Their roots anchor into the soft mud; the vegetation is taller and longer living than salicornia but not as salt tolerant.

III Sea lavender grasses: inundated only at spring tides. Less salt tolerant.

IV A raised salt marsh with creeks may be formed, including turf grasses such as fescue and rushes (juncus). Inundation is rare.

V Inundation absent: ash and alder.

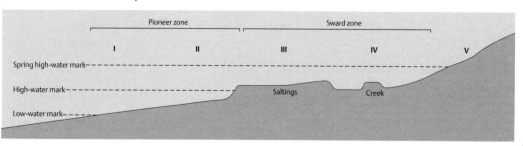

Impacts of coastal change (1)

Pages 29 to 32 look at environment–people interactions.
- *Pages 29 and 30 ask:*
- *How can change in coastal landforms have an impact on people's daily lives?*

Short-term change

There are many short-term changes that affect people's lives. These include:

- rapid erosion, e.g. the east coast of England
- changing depositional landforms, e.g. the barrier islands of the USA
- changing deltaic environments, e.g. the Nile
- coastal flooding, e.g. Towyn in North Wales.

Flooding at Towyn

In February 1990 the coastal resort of Towyn in North Wales was overcome by a storm surge. Floodwater reached 2 km inland and ruined over 750 residential and commercial buildings.

The storm surge was caused by a deep low pressure system. Air rises in a low pressure system. As air rises over oceans it actually raises the level of the sea surface. For every 10 mb drop in pressure the water level rises by 10 cm. The low pressure system that brought heavy rain and strong winds was between 950 and 960 mb. This meant that the sea's surface was at least 50 cm higher than normal. The combination of stormy winds, heavy rain, high tides, and high water levels produced severe floods.

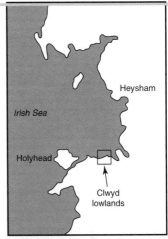

Why was the flood so disastrous?

The area around Towyn is vulnerable to floods as most of it is flat and low-lying – less than 5 m above sea-level. Human mismanagement has not helped. The Chester–Holyhead rail link, opened in 1847, has disrupted the natural movement of sediment. Between 1872 and 1899 parts of the coast eroded by 60 m. To protect the coast, sea walls were built, although these did little to create a protective beach. So when the 1990 storms struck at Towyn, there was little to absorb the sea's energy. Most of the damage was on the lower ground. There had been much speculative building, and many holiday developments had been established. Buildings on a shingle road close to the sea were spared, whereas many caravans and bungalows on land below 5 m were flooded or destroyed.

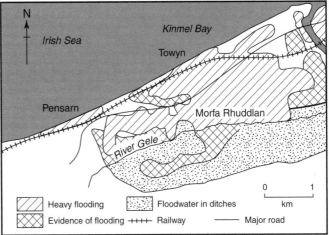

The Nile Delta

Erosion of the Nile Delta has been a problem for over a century. Between 1902 and 1960 the delta retreated 1800 m at Ras-El-Bar. Retreat began with the construction of delta barrages in 1861, followed by scores of dams and irrigation and drainage channels, all trapping sediment.

Before the construction of the High Dam at Aswan, the Nile carried up to 124×10^6 tonnes of sediment to the Delta. Now it carries negligible amounts. Between 1970 and 1987 the Rosetta Point retreated at a rate of between 80 and 120 m/yr. Other promonteries, such as Damietta, were similarly affected.

In addition to the depletion of sediment, the low-lying delta is vulnerable to rising sea levels, increased storm frequency and intensity and natural subsidence. Its ability to provide arable land for Egypt's population is in doubt.

B Coastal environments 29

Impacts of coastal change (2)

Long-term change

Many countries worldwide are under threat from rising sea-levels. This is a longer-term consequence of global climate change. Some of the areas most at risk are LEDCs. Low-lying MEDCs are also at risk, but they may have the resources to combat the perceived risk.

The effects of global climate change

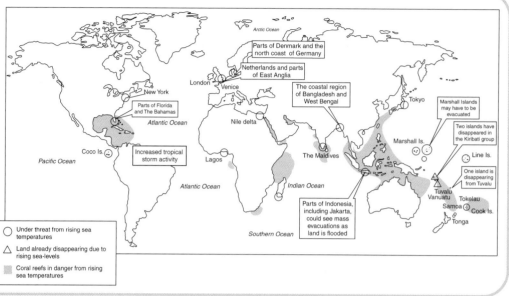

How do rising sea-levels affect Bangladesh?

Bangladesh is a densely populated, low-lying country covering an area of about 144 000 km². It consists largely of the delta of three main rivers: the Ganges, the Brahmaputra, and the Meghna. It suffers recurrent climate-related disasters – floods in 1987/88 and a cyclone in April 1989 are good examples.

The physical impacts on Bangladesh of sea-level rise are difficult to predict. This is because the coastal system responds dynamically as sea-levels rise. Huge quantities of sediment – about 1–2.5 billion tonnes per year – are carried by the rivers (whose combined flood-level can exceed 140 000 m² per second) into Bangladesh from the whole of the Himalayan drainage system. About two-thirds of this sediment goes into the Bay of Bengal and over the long term causes land subsidence within the delta. Consequently the delta is changing. As a result of this it is debatable whether residents would even notice a rise of 6 mm a year. Indeed, if sedimentation rates keep pace with sea-level rises the delta may remain very similar to its present state.

The main problem for Bangladesh is the increase in storms, especially extreme events that cause major storm surges.

Impacts of coastal change on Bangladesh

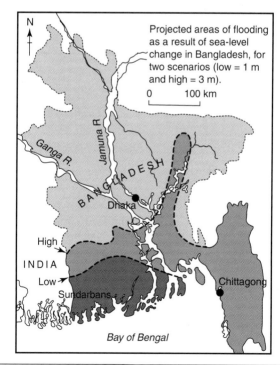

1 Rising sea-levels
- One of the most important changes will be the rise in sea-level. This will have a great impact on low-lying areas such as Bangladesh. Sea-levels are rising not just as a result of global warming and the thinning of the ice sheets, but also due to the thermal expansion of water as it becomes warmer (known as the 'steric effect'). This is about 1 mm/year.

2 Inlets and estuaries
- will be enlarged and deepened
- salt levels will increase, affecting agriculture

3 Low-lying areas
- will be permanently flooded
- loss of fertile agricultural land

4 Flood protection
- increased costs for protection of cities

5 Hazards
- flooding caused by storm surges will increase and intensify
- flood heights will be higher

6 Population
- a 1 m rise will flood over 11% of the whole country and affect 9% of the population
- a 3 m rise will flood 29% of the land and affect 21% of the population

7 Coastal erosion
- a rise in sea-level will lead to an increase in beach erosion

Human impacts (1)

Pages 31 to 32 examine the questions:
- *How have human activities, some of which may be conflicting, influenced coastal environments?*
- *What are some of the consequences?*

Relationships between human activities and coastal zone problems

Human activity	Agents/consequences	Coastal zone problems
Urbanisation and transport	Land use changes, e.g. for ports, road, rail, and air congestion; dredging and disposal of harbour sediments; water abstraction; wastewater and waste disposal	Loss of habitats and species diversity; visual intrusion; lowering of groundwater table; water pollution; human health risks; eutrophication; introduction of alien species
Agriculture	Land reclamation; fertiliser and pesticide use; livestock densities; water abstraction	Loss of habitats and species; diversity; water pollution; eutrophication; river channelisation
Tourism, recreation, and hunting	Development and land use changes, e.g. golf courses; road, rail, and air congestion; ports and marinas; water abstraction; wastewater and waste disposal	Loss of habitats and species diversity; disturbance; visual intrusion; lowering of groundwater table; saltwater intrusion in aquifers; water pollution; eutrophication
Fisheries and aquaculture	Port construction; fish processing facilities; fishing gear; fish farm effluents	Overfishing; impacts on non-target species; litter and oil on beaches; water pollution; eutrophication; introduction of alien species; habitat damage and change in marine communities
Industry (including energy production)	Land use changes; power stations; extraction of natural resources; processing of effluents; cooling water; windmills; river impoundment; tidal barrages	Loss of habitats and species diversity; water pollution; eutrophication; thermal pollution; visual intrusion; decreased input of fresh water and sediment; coastal erosion

The USA's changing eastern seaboard

Many beaches along the east coast have disappeared since 1900, such as Marshfield, Massachusetts. As the sea-level rises, the beaches and barrier islands that line the coasts of the Atlantic Ocean and the Gulf of Mexico from New York to the Mexican border, are in retreat.

The problem is that much of the shore cannot be allowed to retreat naturally because industries and properties worth billions of dollars are built here. Many important cities and tourist centres, such as Miami, Atlantic City, Galveston (Texas), are sited on barrier islands. Consequently, many shoreline communities have built sea defences to protect them from the power of destructive waves.

- **Relief** – the flat topography of the coastal plains from New Jersey southwards means that a small rise in sea-level can allow the ocean to advance a long way inland.
- **Changing sea-levels** – much of the North American coast is sinking relative to the ocean, so local sea-levels are rising faster than global averages.
  The tide-levels along the coast show that subsidence varies between 0.5 and 19.5 mm a year. By contrast, the west coast of the USA, in particular Alaska, is rising.
- **Coastal development** – extensive coastal development has accelerated erosion. By 1990, 75% of Americans lived within 100 km of a coast.
- **Erosion and tourism-related developments** – erosion is evident at many places along the coast of the Atlantic and the Gulf of Mexico. Major resorts such as Miami Beach and Atlantic City have pumped in dredged sand to replenish eroded beaches. Erosion threatens islands to the north and south of Cape Canaveral, although the Cape itself appears safe. Resorts built on barrier beaches in Virginia, Maryland, and New Jersey have also suffered major erosion.
- **Rates of erosion** – overall losses are not well known. Massachusetts loses about 26 ha a year to rising seas. Nearly 10% of that loss is from the island of Nantucket, south of Cape Cod. However, these losses pale into insignificance when compared with Louisiana, which is losing about 15 500 ha a year.

Barrier islands along the east coast of the USA

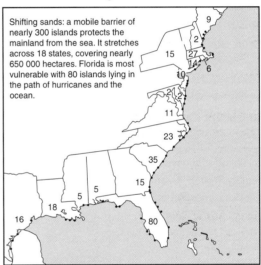

Shifting sands: a mobile barrier of nearly 300 islands protects the mainland from the sea. It stretches across 18 states, covering nearly 650 000 hectares. Florida is most vulnerable with 80 islands lying in the path of hurricanes and the ocean.

Relative sea-level change in the USA (mm/pa)

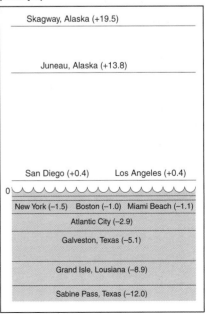

Skagway, Alaska (+19.5)

Juneau, Alaska (+13.8)

San Diego (+0.4)   Los Angeles (+0.4)

0

New York (−1.5)   Boston (−1.0)   Miami Beach (−1.1)

Atlantic City (−2.9)

Galveston, Texas (−5.1)

Grand Isle, Lousiana (−8.9)

Sabine Pass, Texas (−12.0)

Human impacts (2)

Problems in LEDCs

Human activities in LEDCs have had a profound impact on the physical environment. These impacts will intensify in forthcoming decades as a combination of population growth, decreasing land per person, rising sea levels, increased storm frequency and intensity put an increasing strain on the coast.

The ability of LEDCs do pay for coastal defences is compromised by demands to fund other forms of social and economical development.

Human activity and longshore drift in West Africa

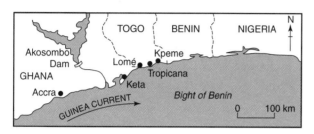

1 Natural causes

The Guinea Current is among the strongest in the world, and is removing approximately 1.5 million m³ of sand each year between the Ivory Coast and Nigeria. The effect upon Ghana, Benin, and Togo is especially catastrophic. Ocean currents along the coast of West Africa have removed huge amounts of the coastline between Ghana and Nigeria.

2 Human causes

The increase in coastal retreat has been blamed on the construction of the Akosombo Dam on the Volta River in Ghana. It is just 110 km from the coast and disrupts the flow of sediment from the River Volta and stops it from reaching the shore. Thus there is less sand to replace that which has already been washed away, so the coastline retreats due to erosion by the Guinea Current. Towns such as Keta, 30 km east of the Volta estuary, have been destroyed as their protective beach has been removed.

Erosion in southern Nigeria

Lagos is located at a break in the coast, and developed rapidly in the 19th and early 20th centuries. Dredging started in 1907 and the harbour was begun in 1908. Breakwaters and a jetty provide a deepwater channel for large ships.

These developments interrupted the west–east longshore drift along the coast of West Africa. As a result, there has been an increase of deposition on Lighthouse Beach (on the western updrift side of the jetty) and also on the eastern downdrift side of the jetty.

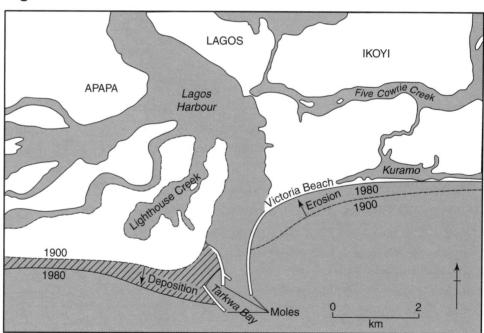

Victoria Beach has been eroded by almost 70 m/year, and over 2 km of beach has been lost.

Victoria Beach is much used as a recreational area by the people of Lagos. Beach replenishment has been actively applied since 1976.

The problems of Victoria Beach are difficult to solve because Lagos must be kept open for shipping. This stops the eastward drift of sediment, and therefore promotes erosion of the eastern beach. However, continued deposition on Lighthouse Beach will lead to deposition beyond the jetties of Tarkwa Bay, thus cutting off the deep channel of Lagos Harbour.

Erosion of the Niger Delta

	m/year
Western delta	18–24
Central delta	15–20
Eastern delta	10–24

Coastal management (1)

Pages 33 to 35 look at coastal management and the future.
- *In what ways does the management of coastal environments pose a continuing challenge for people?*

Human pressures on coastal environments create the need for a variety of coastal management strategies. These may be long-term or short-term, sustainable or non-sustainable. Successful management strategies require a detailed knowledge of coastal processes. Rising sea-levels, more frequent storm activity, and continuing coastal development are likely to increase the need for coastal management.

Shoreline management plans (SMPs)

SMPs in the UK are designed to develop sustainable coastal defence schemes. Sections of the coast are divided up into littoral cells and plans are drawn up for the use and protection of that zone. Defence options include:

- do nothing
- maintain existing levels of coastal defence
- improve the coastal defence
- allow retreat of the coast in selected areas.

Coastal defence

Coastal defence covers protection against coastal erosion (coast protection) and flooding by the sea.

The coastal zone is a dynamic system that extends seawards and landwards from the shoreline. Its limits are defined by the extent to which natural processes and human activities occur. **Coastal zone management** is concerned with the whole range of activities that take place in the coastal zone and promotes integrated planning to manage them. Conflicting activities in coastal areas include housing, recreation, fishing, industry, mineral extraction, waste disposal, and farming.

Coastal management

Coastal management involves a wide range of issues:

- coastal protection
- cliff stabilisation and ground movement studies
- coastal infrastructure, including sea walls, esplanades, car parks, paths
- control of beaches and public safety
- recreational activities and sport
- beach cleaning
- pollution and oil spills
- offshore dredging
- management of coastal land and property.

Hard engineering structures

The effectiveness of sea walls depends upon their cost and their performance. Their function is to prevent erosion and flooding but much depends on whether they are:

- sloping or vertical
- permeable or impermeable
- rough or smooth

and of which material they are formed (clay, steel, or rock for example).

In general, flatter, permeable, rougher walls perform better than vertical, impermeable, smooth walls.

Cross-shore structures such as groynes, breakwaters, piers, and strongpoints have been used for decades. Their main function is to stop the drifting of material. Traditionally, groynes were constructed from timber, brushwood, and wattle. However, modern cross-shore structures are often made from rock. They are part of a more complex form of management that includes beach nourishment and offshore structures.

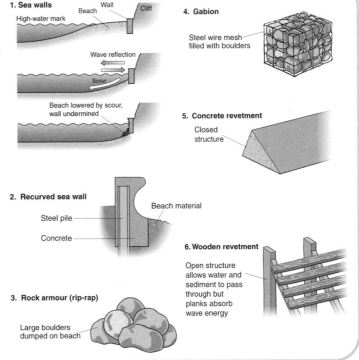

1. **Sea walls** — High-water mark, Beach, Wall, Cliff; Wave reflection; Scour; Beach lowered by scour, wall undermined

2. **Recurved sea wall** — Steel pile, Concrete, Beach material

3. **Rock armour (rip-rap)** — Large boulders dumped on beach

4. **Gabion** — Steel wire mesh filled with boulders

5. **Concrete revetment** — Closed structure

6. **Wooden revetment** — Open structure allows water and sediment to pass through but planks absorb wave energy

Managed natural retreat

The cost of protecting Britain's coastline was up to £60 million annually until the mid-1990s. Since then government cuts have reduced this. Part of the problem is that southern and eastern England are slowly sinking while sea-level is rising. The risk of flooding and hence the cost of protection are rising. **Managed retreat** allows nature to take its course – erosion in some areas, deposition in others. Benefits include less money spent and the creation of natural environments. In parts of East Anglia, hard engineering structures are being replaced by brushwood defences, and some farmland is being sacrificed to erosion and being allowed to develop into salt marsh.

Coastal management (2)

Strengths and weaknesses of different types of coastal management

Types of management	Aims/methods	Strengths	Weaknesses
Hard engineering	**To control natural processes**		
Cliff-base management	*To stop cliff or beach erosion*		
• Sea walls	Large-scale concrete curved walls designed to reflect wave energy	Easily made good in areas of high density	Expensive. Lifespan about 30–40 years; foundations may be undermined
• Revetments	Porous design to absorb wave energy	Easily made; cheaper than sea walls	Lifespan limited
• Gabions	Rocks held in wire cages absorb wave energy	Cheaper than sea walls and revetments	Small-scale
• Groynes	To prevent longshore drift	Relatively low cost; easily repaired	Cause erosion on downdrift side; interrupt sediment flow
• Rock armour	Large rocks at base of cliff to absorb wave energy	Cheap	Unattractive, small-scale; may be removed in heavy storms
• Offshore breakwaters	Reduce wave power offshore	Cheap to build	Disrupt local ecology
• Rock strongpoints	To reduce longshore drift	Relatively low costs; easily repaired	Disrupt longshore drift; erosion downdrift
Cliff-face strategies	*To reduce the impacts of subaerial processes*		
• Cliff drainage	Removal of water from rocks in the cliff	Cost-effective	Drains may become new lines of weakness; dry cliffs may produce rockfalls
• Cliff regrading	Lowering of slope angle to make cliff safer	Useful on clay (most other measures are not)	Uses large amounts of land – impractical in heavily populated areas
Soft engineering	**Working with nature**		
• Offshore reefs	Waste materials, e.g. old tyres weighted down, to reduce speed of incoming waves	Low technology and relatively cost-effective	Long-term impacts unknown
• Beach nourishment	Sand pumped from seabed to replace eroded sand	Looks natural	Expensive; short-term solution
• Managed retreat	Coastline allowed to retreat in certain places	Cost-effective; maintains a natural coastline	Unpopular; political implications
• 'Do nothing'	Accept that nature will win	Cost-effective!	Unpopular; political implications
• Red-lining	Planning permission withdrawn; new line of defences set back from existing coastline	Cost-effective	Unpopular; political implications

Coastal management (3)

The North Norfolk coastline is mostly composed of Quaternary (Ice Age) deposits underlain by chalk bedrock. Although chalk is a relatively soft rock it is more resistant to erosion than the Quaternary deposits. The North Norfolk cliffs are mostly formed of soft, heterogeneous sand and clay deposits which are very vulnerable to **wave erosion** and **undercutting** (they have a low shear strength). The sand and gravel components of the cliffs are permeable but the clays are impermeable. This causes ponding of water within the cliff, which leads to saturation of the clay, an increase in porewater pressure, and cliff failure through landslides and slumps.

Pressures on the North Norfolk coast

- Storm surges
- Rising sea-levels
- High tides
- Increasing storm frequency and intensity as a possible result of global warming

Human features

- Tourism
- Cliff-top agriculture
- Gas terminal at Bacton
- Villages and towns
- Ministry of Defence
- Nature conservation

The defences along the North Norfolk coast take many forms. These range from natural shingle beaches to concrete sea walls and revetments. Sea walls have evolved from vertical-faced walls to sloping, recurved walls. Increasingly rock armour is used to protect the base of sea walls, while revetments are positioned in order to reduce wave energy. Groynes interrupt the movement of material, and so help maintain large, healthy beaches. In addition, offshore breakwaters prevent storm waves from striking the shoreline. On the cliffs, drains and boreholes are used to stop the build-up of excess water within the clay strata.

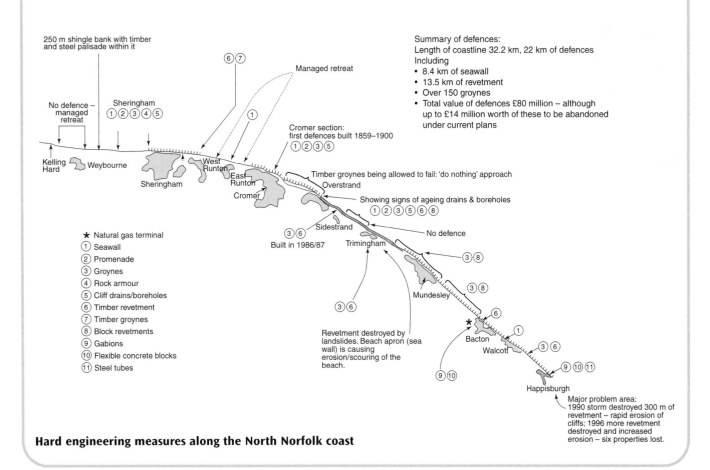

Hard engineering measures along the North Norfolk coast

Question

This question is a typical Unit 1 (6471) Question 3 which requires you to show knowledge, understanding, and skills across both the river and coastal sections.

Study the diagram. It shows a stretch of a river entering the sea.

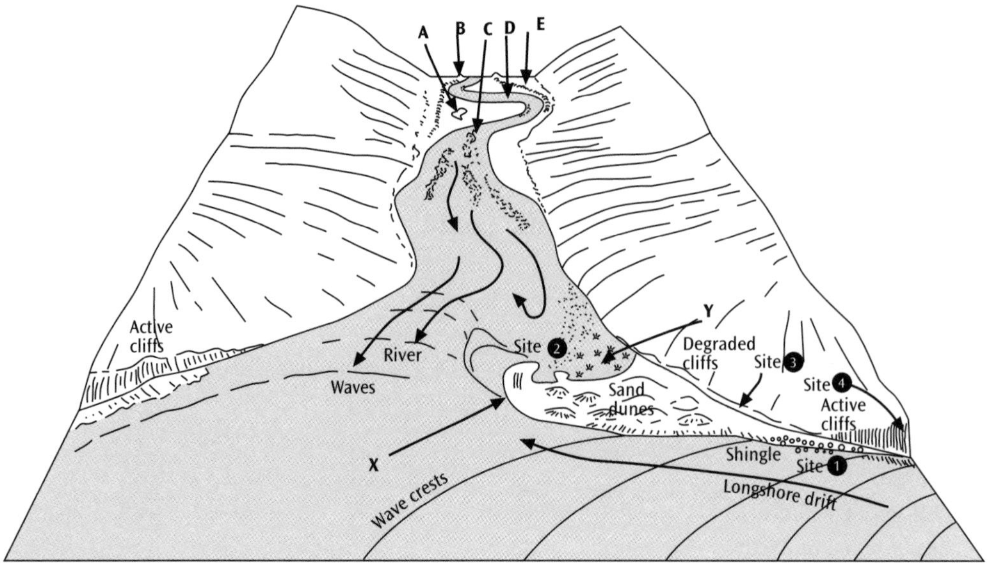

(a) (i) Identify the river features A to E.

A _____ B _____

C _____ D _____

E _____ [5]

(ii) Choose **one** of these features. Choice _____
- Describe its key features.
- Explain how it was formed. [5]

(b) (i) Name the following:

Coastal feature X _____

Coastal ecosystem Y _____ [2]

(ii) Explain why coarse shingle is found at site (1) whereas fine silt is found at site (2). [3]

(iii) Describe and suggest reasons for the **contrasting** cliff profiles at sites 3 and 4. You should annotate the diagrams below to support your answer. [5]

Site (3)

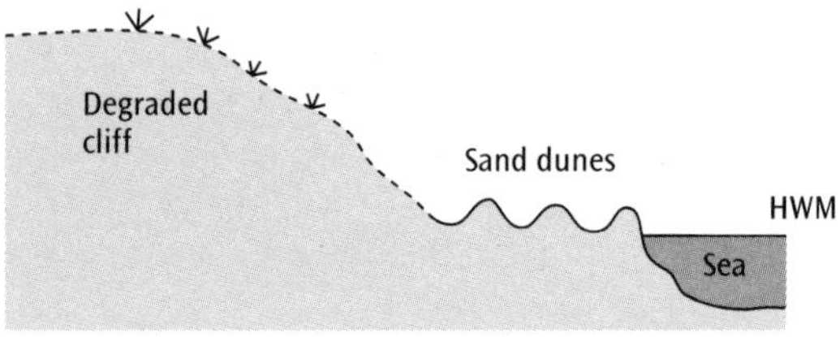

Site (4)

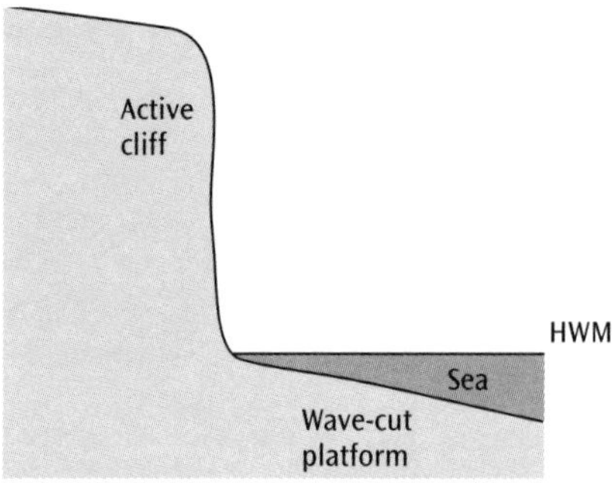

(c) A severe storm (200 mm rainfall in 18 hours, with gale-force onshore winds) occurred in the area shown in the sketch. Examine the likely impacts of such a storm on both river and coastal features. [10]

Total marks 30

Answer

(a) **(i)** A = ox-bow lake; B = levée; C = ayot (braiding); D = meander; E = floodplain (terrace) [5]

(ii) **Example**: maximum 3 marks for either description or explanation.

Crescent-shaped$^{\odot}$ abandoned meander loop$^{\odot}$, lateral erosion, $^{\odot}$ sinuosity → formation of swan's neck$^{\odot}$, often breached in time of flood → $^{\odot}$ cut off, sealed off by deposition. May dry up to form a mort lake. [5]

(b) **(i)** X = spit   Y = salt marsh [2]

(ii) Site 1 – likely to be fed from cliff fall, or longshore drift along coast, moved by swash and backwash along shore.

Site 2 – eddy currents carry fine material only in suspension, deposited when loss of energy as river current meets tide. [3]

Marks

3	Sound technical understanding of differing processes at both sites.
2	Has some understanding of both sites, or is very strong on one only.
1	Has a basic understanding of one site.

(iii) Site 3 is degraded with a gentle slope, usually grassed over because it is only affected by **sub-aerial** processes as the sand dunes prevent active marine erosion. Site 4, on the other hand, has a vertical cliff face, active abrasion, and hydraulic action from the sea, which leads to cliff retreat and the formation of a wave-cut platform. [5]

Marks

5	Clear comparison, showing understanding of both sites using terminology.
4–3	Describes what is going on at both sites. Sound process. No comparison.
2–1	Has a basic idea of processes (for two at both sites), e.g. sand dunes protect cliff.

(c) **Information for examiners**

The severe storm will lead to river flooding, bursting of levées. As the river floods it may bring down much coarse material (moved by traction) and large quantities of silt. It may erode salt marsh areas, and even breach the spit. At the same time the heavy rainfall may lead to widespread slumping and land-slipping on the cliff face. The strong onshore winds will lead to destructive onshore waves, carrying away any beach deposits, and possible breaching of the sand dune area to form slacks. Rapid cliff retreat is likely. Both storms and floods upset the dynamic equilibrium. [10]

Marks

10–9	Clear understanding of the role of dynamic equilibrium and of the role of winds and rain. Makes appropriate suggestions for both changes in the river and coast.
8–5	Shows some understanding of the impact of a storm on both the river and coastal features. May lack terminology or all aspects of storm. Maximum 6 marks for river or coastal only.
4–1	One or two basic suggestions for the impact of the storm. Likely to be generalised and not well related to the diagram.

Total marks 30

Rural and urban

Page 38 introduces rural and urban environments.
• What are rural and urban environments?

Definitions

- **Urban** – having specific characteristics such as: a large population, high percentage employed in manufacturing and services, large built-up area, specific administrative functions, defined as urban by the government.
- **Rural** – areas characterised by low population densities, primary industries, small settlements.
- **Urbanisation** – the process whereby the proportion of a country's population that is classified as urban, increases.
- **Urban sprawl** – an increase in the area covered by urban activities and settlement.
- **Counterurbanisation** – the movement from urban areas to towns and villages in rural areas.
- **Ruralisation** – an increase in the proportion of people classified as rural.
- **Re-urbanisation** – revitalisation of urban areas and movement of people back into urban areas.
- **Suburbanisation** – the growth of urban settlements at their edge; also the spread of urban values/way of life into semi-rural settlements.

Perceptions of rural and urban

The decline of traditional rural economic activities combined with the growth of personal mobility has changed rural communities so much that some claim that there are no significant differences between rural and urban populations. However, there are widely held perceptions of the differences between rural and urban, and of the quality of life in each.

A simplified index of rurality and urbanism in an MEDC

Indicator	Rural characteristic	Urban characteristic
Population density	Low	High
% change in population between 1951/61 and 1961/71	Decrease	Increase
% total population over 65 years	High	Low
% total population: males 15–45 years	Low	High
% farmers in total population	High	Low
% farm workers	High	Low
% residents in employment outside the rural district	Low	–
% population resident for less than 5 years	Low	High
Dominant land use	Farming	Residential, commercial manufacturing

The rural–urban continuum

The rural–urban continuum is the range of settlement types from remote (extreme) rural, through accessible rural, rural–urban fringe, suburban, inner city to central business district.

According to the sociologist Pahl (1966), 'the terms rural and urban are more remarkable for their ability to confuse than their power to illuminate'. As increasing numbers of middle-class commuters moved into rural settlements, they changed the characteristics of these settlements. *Urban* and *rural* are no longer defined by place or location, but by way of lifestyle and behaviour. Hence it is increasingly difficult to distinguish between urban and rural. Although two extreme forms can be identified, it is better to think of an **urban–rural continuum**.

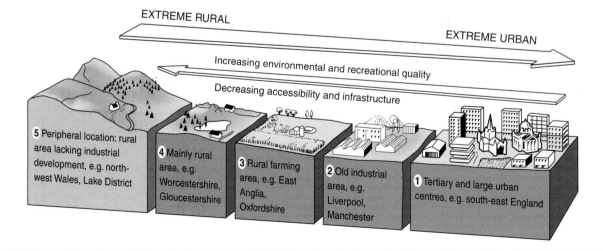

EXTREME RURAL

EXTREME URBAN

Increasing environmental and recreational quality

Decreasing accessibility and infrastructure

5 Peripheral location: rural area lacking industrial development, e.g. north-west Wales, Lake District

4 Mainly rural area, e.g. Worcestershire, Gloucestershire

3 Rural farming area, e.g. East Anglia, Oxfordshire

2 Old industrial area, e.g. Liverpool, Manchester

1 Tertiary and large urban centres, e.g. south-east England

The rural mosaic (1)

Pages 39 to 40 discuss process and change in rural environments.
* *How and why do rural environments vary in landscape and character?*

The variety of rural landscapes stems, in part, from basic differences in the location, and physical, socio-economic, and cultural factors.

Recent changes in rural settlements in the UK

Changes include repopulation, fewer farms, a changing agricultural land base, counterurbanisation, and long-distance commuting. In addition, new roads, airports, housing schemes, and theme parks have been constructed. Key factors explaining rural change are:

* improvements in transport
* increased standards of living
* decreased size of households
* greenfield sites.

In addition, industry and retailing are moving to accessible rural areas. Reasons for this include:

* a growing dissatisfaction with urban lifestyles
* an increase in car ownership
* improving technology.

One of the greatest changes has been brought about by improvements in transport, both public and private. There is a definite relationship between the type and rate of change that is occurring in rural settlements, and distance from large urban areas. The most accessible villages have grown the most. Many villages have grown at an alarming rate and have lost their original character, form, and function. These are often described as **dormitory**, **commuter**, or **suburbanised villages**.

Changes in the suburbanised village

Characteristics	Original village	Suburbanised village
Housing	Detached, stone-built houses with slate/thatch roofs; some farms, most over 100 years old; barns	New, mainly detached or semis; renovated barns or cottages; expensive planned estates, garages
Inhabitants	Farming and primary jobs; labouring or manual jobs	Professionals/executives; commuters; wealthy with families or retired
Transport	Bus service; some cars; narrow winding roads	Decline in bus services as most families have one or two cars; better roads
Services	Village shop, small junior school, public house, village hall	More shops, enlarged school, modern public houses, and/or restaurant
Social	Small, close-knit community	Local community swamped; village may be deserted during the day
Environment	Quiet, relatively pollution free and open space	More noise and risk of more pollution; loss of farmland

The relationship between accessibility from large urban centres, and rural change, e.g. the Oxford area

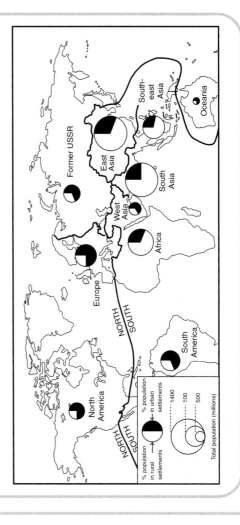

Rural and urban areas associated with development

The rural mosaic (2)

Planned rural settlements in the Netherlands

To overcome the shortage of land in the Netherlands, the Dutch reclaimed land from the sea. These areas, known as **polders**, were used for farming as well as for the development of new settlements.

First generation settlements

In the planning of the north-east polder the central settlement was located at the intersection of a skeletal road system with smaller service centres on the periphery. In 1948 it was decided that 5 km was the maximum distance that people would be prepared to travel from outlying districts to the villages. A plan was devised to develop 11 villages with populations of 1000–2000 and a main town of 10 000 at Emmeloord.

Despite careful planning there have been problems. The growth of mechanised agriculture has meant that there are fewer jobs in agriculture than had been expected. Although Emmeloord has developed faster than anticipated, seven of the villages failed to reach 700 in size, and six of these have declined since 1970. Much of this decline is due to wider socio-economic changes including:

- increasing affluence
- greater mobility
- higher demands for the provision of services.

Second generation settlements

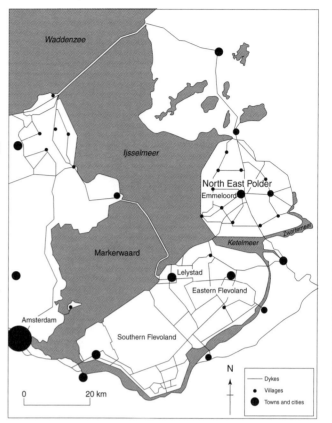

The Dutch polder settlements

By 1957, when the Eastern Flevoland had been drained, the planners had gained from their experiences. They planned to have:

- a number of 'A' centres (local service function)
- a single 'B' centre, having a district service function
- a 'C' centre having a regional function serving four polders.

Lelystad, a 'C' centre, was later to become one of the most important towns to accommodate overspill from the urban agglomeration of Randstad. As a result of this planning, there is a very regular size and spacing of rural settlements in the Dutch polders.

Rural settlements in the Eastern Cape, South Africa

In rural areas of South Africa only 33% of the population have good-quality housing. Up to 10 million people live in informal houses and sub-standard huts. These houses are often overcrowded, with little access to facilities such as running water, sanitation, and electricity.

Welcomewood is a village in the Eastern Cape province of South Africa. Parts of the area were originally used for commercial farming but much of the land is too hilly and steep. The village of Welcomewood was developed to house black people who had been displaced by the apartheid system. It is a village of about 2000 people and contains a primary school, health clinic, and two water taps.

Population densities are high, and as a result farming suffers from a combination of:

- overcrowding
- use of steep slopes
- overgrazing
- soil erosion
- declining yields
- declining standards of living.

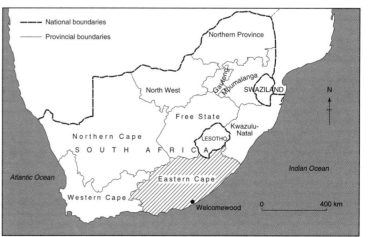

Change in rural areas

Pages 41 to 44 ask:
• What are the processes of change which affect rural areas?
• How are these leading to change and conflict in rural areas?

Migration and change

Rural populations are subject to constant change. The large-scale movement from rural areas to urban areas is a feature of developed and developing countries. Push–pull factors are clearly in operation.

Restricted social and welfare amenities

Decline in agricultural employment due to mechanisation

PUSH FACTORS

Poor housing

Low wages

Better housing and schools

Superior shops and entertainment

PULL FACTORS

More employment opportunities

Higher wages

However, the evidence for **return migration** is clear. For many people living in large cities, small towns and rural areas are very attractive. **Ruralisation** refers to an increase in the proportion of people classified as rural. **Rural turnaround** refers to an increase in the rural population in certain rural districts.

However, in remote areas there is still some evidence of population decline. Even where the population is now largely stable (in all but very remote areas), services continue to decline. A vicious circle is evident.

Decreasing numbers → Closure of village schools → Run-down bus services → Transfer of many services to larger towns → Depopulation → Decreasing numbers

A vicious circle of rural decline

Housing developments

There are great pressures on rural areas for housing developments. There are also pressures for economic and transport developments.

The increase in the demand for housing occurs throughout the country. Between 1991 and 2001, a further 460 000 new homes were needed.

Increased demand for housing is generated by:
• longer life expectancy
• young people leaving home earlier
• more families splitting up and moving into separate homes
• more people preferring modern houses with good facilities.

Large urban areas are no longer desirable because they are seen as expensive, polluted, and unsafe. By contrast, in a rural area or a small town, property costs less and larger plots of land are available. The process by which people leave large settlements for smaller ones is known as **counterurbanisation**. Much of the new housing is being built in new towns, overspill towns, and small towns.

Pressures for housing developments in England

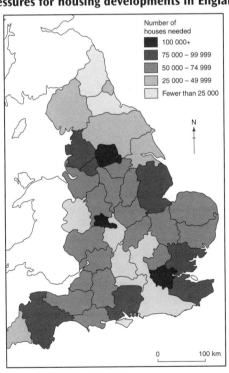

Number of houses needed
- 100 000+
- 75 000 – 99 999
- 50 000 – 74 999
- 25 000 – 49 999
- Fewer than 25 000

N

0   100 km

Where should new homes be built?

Greenfield sites		Brownfield sites	
Advantages	Disadvantages	Advantages	Disadvantages
• Land may be accessible	• Habitat destruction	• Redevelopment of disused land	• Land may be contaminated
• Cheaper land	• Reduction in biodiversity	• Does not harm the environment	• Widespread air and water pollution
• People prefer more space and pleasant environments	• Increased pollution	• Creates jobs locally	• Congestion
• Allows planners a free reign	• Increased impermeability leads to flooding	• Provides a boost to local economies	• Overcrowding
• Easier to plan for infrastructural developments	• Increased traffic on the road, and cross-city commuting	• May use existing infrastructure	• Land is expensive

Rural conflicts (1)

Rural deprivation

Rural deprivation is the result of long-term depopulation (up until the 1970s), poverty, and limited transport and access to services. There are a number of similarities between remote rural areas and inner cities. These include:

- decreased demand for labour
- unemployment
- low wages
- a decline in services
- limited new investment
- population decline
- reduced morale
- inaccessibility
- a high dependency ratio
- high cost of public services.

Unlike inner cities where these features are concentrated spatially, in rural areas they are spread over a large part of the country.

Rural settlement: thresholds and functions

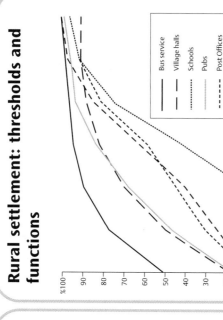

Definitions

- **Rural deprivation** – a lack of economic, social and political well-being resulting in impacts on physical and mental health.

- **Rural disadvantage** – the inability of individuals or households to share in the lifestyle of the majority.

- **Rural exclusion** – the process(es) whereby social integration fails, for example failure of employment provision or housing schemes.

- **Rural poverty** – the inability of individuals or households to share in the lifestyle of the majority due to a lack of financial resources.

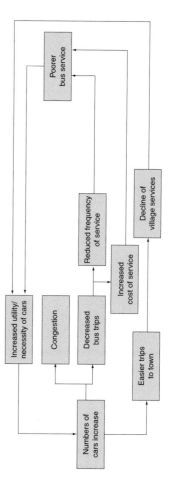

related to economic problems. In addition, many local authorities lack sufficient funding to provide adequate services.

Declining transport in rural areas

Many rural areas have experienced a decline in the number of shops and services that they contain. This is partly related to the increase in private transport. For those without a car there are some options, but these do not provide the same service, comfort, and guarantee as one's own transport. Options include:

- subsidised fares
- integrating transport with other services, such as post buses (taking passengers on post vans)
- car sharing
- mobile services
- concentration of services in key settlements.

Small settlements have many advantages, such as standards of behaviour, social cohesion, and environmental attributes. There are, however, many social problems and these are closely

Rural conflicts (2)

Rural deprivation

Rural deprivation takes three forms:

- **Household deprivation** – the hardships of individuals and households. The experience of tenant farmers in less favoured areas is an excellent example. Others include those on state pensions, and/or low incomes. Poor housing standards and high levels of income support are common.
- **Opportunity deprivation** – refers to the lack of access to education, health, retailing, and social services. For those without transport, the problem is compounded.
- **Mobility deprivation** – the lack of transport, and the difficulty in obtaining key services, such as education and health care, as well as in getting to work.

Managing rural deprivation

National governments are keen to manage rural environments in a physical as well as social and economic ways. In the UK there were a number of programmes aimed at supporting rural areas. For example:

- **Rural development areas** – such as parts of Cornwall and the North Pennines: these areas have had severe social and economic problems, and benefit from grants for improving employment opportunities.
- **Rural challenge grants** – for imaginative projects.
- **European Union funding** – for the most deprived rural regions.
- **European Regional Fund** – for community initiatives.
- **Rural transport partnership scheme** – to produce bus partnerships.
- **Village shop development scheme.**
- **Millennium Fund** – to renovate village halls and community centres.

In 1999 the **Countryside Agency** was formed to draw together a range of rural initiatives. Its vision includes:

- providing support for sustainable farming
- providing sustainable transport
- providing sustainable recreational areas
- eradicating pockets of poverty
- maintaining the diverse character and beauty of rural areas.

In 2000 the UK government issued a White Paper on rural issues. There were a number of proposals known as the **Blueprint for Revival**:

- £37 million to revitalise small towns and market towns as key settlements (providers of key services)
- new funding for rural buses, village taxis, dial-a-ride and community buses
- providing support for diversity in farming and promoting local speciality products
- building affordable houses and stemming rural out-migration
- tackling social exclusion
- making use of brownfield sites in order to protect greenfield sites
- providing more support for National Parks and Areas of Outstanding Natural Beauty (AONBs)
- providing a £15 million Community Service Fund to safeguard village services
- improving rights of access to the countryside.

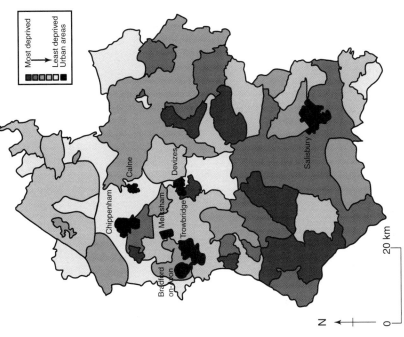

Rural deprivation in Wiltshire

Rural conflicts (3)

Definition of second homes

'Second homes' generally refers to properties that are owned by people who have their main residence elsewhere. Second homes are defined as:

- a specialised form of holiday accommodation in remote rural areas beyond the travelling limit for weekend recreation

or

- a seasonal–temporal extension of suburbia that is occupied for two or three days of the week throughout the year.

They do not include caravans and mobile homes.

Demand for second homes

A number of factors have led to a greater demand for second homes:

- increasing standards of living
- increased leisure time
- increased accessibility
- advertising
- the availability of suitable housing.

Second homes are bought for a variety of reasons: rural appreciation, an investment, a retirement home, and for recreation. In Britain, second homes account for about 2% of all properties, and the number is growing at about 15 000 annually. Most second homes are old houses that have been converted or redeveloped.

Spatial patterns

Second homes are more likely to be found in certain environments:

- at considerable distance from large urban centres yet accessible for weekends
- where the landscape quality is high
- close to water (two-thirds of second homes)
- where there are recreational opportunities
- where land is available
- where the climate is pleasant.

The pattern of second home ownership shows an important **distance decay** function. In the USA, 66% of second homes are within 160 km of the main residence and up to 95% are within 320 km. In Sweden, up to 66% are within 15 km of the main home!

Advantages of second homes	Disadvantages of second homes
• They are a rational alternative for the economic development of backward rural areas. For example, land can be sold off at higher prices to urbanites; rural authorities obtain additional taxes from second home owners, and business may increase in local shops, cafés and garages. • Second home owners are not a burden on local services that are aimed at the permanent population. However, the taxes from second homes help to support these services. • The competition between second home owners and young people may not be as great as generally assumed. Most second home owners require an isolated home without electricity or a bath, so that they can renovate it.	• House and land prices escalate. Property owners are generally very willing to sell land to the second home market because of greater profitability. • Weekenders do not buy their provisions from local stores, yet they demand piped water and mains sewerage, the cost of which is mostly borne by the local population. • There may be conflict in relation to services, between the permanent and temporary populations. • Roads become congested and there is an increase in the number of accidents. • The local environment may deteriorate due to increased visitor pressure. • New buildings may not fit in with the local surroundings.

Second homes in England

Second homes in England and Wales are concentrated in Wales, the Lake District, and parts of Cornwall. In Wales the number of second homes fell from 22 000 in 1991 to 19 500 in 2002. In Devon and Cornwall the distribution of second homes is related to National Parks and scenic coastal areas. For example, in Treyarnon Bay near Padstow up to 70% of the properties are second homes. In Exmoor, 10% of the properties are second homes, and in places this rises to 40%. Average incomes in Exmoor are 76% of the national average, yet house prices are out of the reach of local people.

Issues surrounding second homes

There are a number of key questions regarding second homes:

- Are they a justifiable call on resources, given that up to 4 million people in the UK live in sub-standard housing?
- What are the effects of second homes on local communities?
- Are they a justifiable use of public money?

Managing rural environments (1)

Pages 45 to 47 discuss rural planning issues.
- What are the challenges of managing rural environments?
- Who should decide how rural areas should develop?
- How do planners and decision makers attempt to resolve conflicts in a variety of locations?
- How successful are the strategies of planners and decision makers in managing change and conflict?

Managing the countryside for recreation and tourism

Tourism and recreation are vital parts of the rural economy, especially as farming in many countries is in decline. In the UK, scares over BSE and foot and mouth disease in 2000, have made alternative forms of employment crucial to the rural future.

This issue has been thought through carefully in Northern Ireland. In 1993 the Northern Ireland Tourist Board (NITB) published the report *Tourism in Northern Ireland: A Sustainable Approach*. Main development priorities were seen as:

1 relating tourism to the environment
2 involving the local community
3 needing to aim for quality
4 needing all parties to work together.

Sustainable tourism: the benefits

Benefits for the visitor

- The development of a quality tourism service.
- Better relationships with the local community.
- Closer involvement with and better understanding of both the people and the holiday destination.

Benefits to the tourism industry

- Economic benefits for operators, e.g. reducing energy by installing efficient insulation.
- Enhanced appeal of Northern Ireland for visitors from market areas that have ecologically aware consumers.
- Opportunities for the development and promotion of environmentally friendly activity tourism, e.g. conservation holidays.

Benefits to the environment

- Safeguarding the resource for the benefit of future generations.
- The protection and enhancement of the special landscapes which form much of Northern Ireland's appeal to visitors.

Benefits to the community

- Opportunities for community involvement in tourism and the creation of a better climate for development.
- Supporting the local economy and local services, e.g. helping to support local transport systems in rural areas.
- Creating new business opportunities.

Tackling rural deprivation and rural poverty in South Africa

- **Reasons** for rural poverty include poor location (inaccessible), poor economic structure (such as marginal farming), poor-quality people (e.g. in some parts of South Africa rural areas were seen as 'dumping grounds' for unwanted 'surplus people').
- **Strategies** for counteracting rural poverty include: rural employment schemes, affordable housing, community housing, village participation, and small-scale grass roots schemes such as earthen dams and brick-making factories.

The Eastern Cape of South Africa is an underdeveloped part of the most depressed region in the country. It has few raw materials, few towns and a poor infrastructure. It is distant from the main markets in South Africa. Many people have left the area for the richer Johannesburg–Gauteng region, leaving behind a population that includes large numbers of elderly and infirm people, children, and people without qualifications.

Government intervention

To improve the area the South African government created **development points**, and selected locations such as Dimbaza, where there were incentives for factories to locate. Businessmen were encouraged to locate here, with the provision of cheap loans, tax-free concessions, grants, and subsidies. Although many jobs were created, wages were low and in some cases were not enough to cover household income.

Despite government intervention, industrial development has not been successful, and many of the firms have either closed down or moved to the core areas. The real problem may be that the 'solutions' did not cover the basic problems of the area – accessibility, lack of raw materials, and a poor population structure.

Managing rural environments (2)

Rural development in Botswana
The impact of mineral discovery

Botswana is an African success story. Since its independence in 1966 it has been transformed from a largely rural society dependent on livestock, to a middle-income country with a **diversified rural economy**. Its success is largely due to the discovery of diamonds in 1967, and the investment of its wealth into social and infrastructural projects. There has been some success in creating jobs in textiles and car manufacturing – but not enough to absorb all the unemployed (21% in 2001).

The impact of minerals, especially diamonds, has been considerable. Not only does the mining industry create jobs, but it also earns foreign exchange, acts as a catalyst for industrial development, and helps develop the infrastructure.

Cattle ranching

Cattle remain an important part of the rural economy, providing employment, draught animals, milk, and a traditional form of savings. They are especially important where arable farming is limited or marginal – which it is in much of Botswana. Cattle ranching has spread westwards into marginal areas as boreholes have tapped groundwater reserves. However, the national herd of 2.5 million exceeds the carrying capacity of the land. Botswana has an extensive network of veterinary cordon fences that have been built to control the movement of animals and to stop the spread of foot and mouth disease. As a result of this, wildlife migration routes are blocked, causing undue pressure on National Parks.

Problems related to mining and cattle ranching

- The diamond reserves are finite.
- Development based on diamonds has led to inequalities – 54% of the rural population live below the poverty line.
- The benefits of commercial ranching have been limited to a minority (3% of the households own half the national herd!).
- Overgrazing has caused desertification.
- Cattle ranching conflicts with the needs of wildlife.

Population growth is rapid: the population total was 1.3 million in 1991, and likely to exceed 2 million by 2011. The population is youthful, although there has been an increase in the number of people with AIDS. This is disproportionately affecting the working population. Partly as a result of mining development, there is increasing rural–urban migration, especially of young adults. This is having severe implications in rural areas.

According to the Botswana National Conservation Strategy, there are a number of environmental issues confronting Botswana:

- Growing pressure on water resources.
- Degradation of range and pasture resources.
- Depletion of both commercial and domestic wood resources.
- Overuse or exploitation of some grassland products.
- Pollution of air, water, soil, and vegetation resources.
- Resource pressures due to the growth in human population.
- Depletion and conservation of wildlife resources.
- The need to improve public awareness about natural resource problems and opportunities.

Botswana factfile

Land use	1% arable, 0% permanent crops, 99% other	Life expectancy	35 years
Population (2002)	1.59 million	HIV prevalence rate	35.8% (1999 est.)
Age structure	0–14 years = 4.0%, 15–64 years = 55.8%, 65+ years = 4.2%	GDP by sector	Agriculture 4%, Mining 36%, Manufacturing 8%, Services 52%
Birth rate	28%	PPP*	$7,800/head
Death rate	26%	Unemployment	21%
Infant mortality rate	6.5%		

* PPP = purchasing power parity

Managing rural environments (3)

Managing rural environmental problems generated by agriculture

Problems created by modern intensive farming include: the impacts of agro-chemicals such as eutrophication; soil erosion; desertification; hedgerow removal; loss of biodiversity; BSE; foot and mouth disease; social problems such as those caused by the Green Revolution, e.g. the widening rich/poor gap in many LEDCs.

Feature	Likely impact on landscape
Plant and animal breeding to produce higher-other uses, e.g. afforestation	• Has meant some agricultural land has become redundant and available for yielding varieties
Use of large quantities of fertiliser, especially nitrates, to increase yields	• Problems of increased pollution of watercourses, eutrophication
Use of pesticides (herbicides and insecticides) to cut down losses of crops	• Loss of biodiversity of herb meadows • Poisoning and killing of wildlife • Many improved pastures lack diversity
Improvements in farm technology, e.g. more effective driers and harvesters	• Removal of hedgerows to make way for mechanisation • Increased arable farming has led to massive soil erosion, and 'cover' is removed
Changes in farming practices	• Creation of large unsightly buildings for 'factory farming' • New extensive farming practices can lead to many hectares of less favoured land being taken out of use

The Green Revolution

The Green Revolution is the application of science and technology to increase crop productivity. It came about in the 1950s and 1960s in response to food shortages in many countries, particularly in Asia. It includes a variety of techniques such as genetic engineering to produce higher-yielding varieties (HYVs) of crops and animals; mechanisation; pesticides; herbicides; chemical fertilisers; and irrigation. Essentially it transfers high-tech farming practices to LEDCs that have environmental problems.

The consequences

The main benefits are:
• yields are higher and more food can be produced
• up to three crops can be grown each year
• more food should lead to less hunger
• more exports create more foreign currency.

However, there are many problems:

• Not all farmers adopt HYVs – some cannot afford the cost, and as the price has risen, indebtedness has increased.
• Rural unemployment has increased due to mechanisation.
• Irrigation has led to salinisation – 20% of Pakistan's and 25% of Central Asia's irrigated land is affected.
• Soil fertility is declining because HYVs use up all the nutrients: replacement fertilisers are expensive.
• LEDCs are dependent on many MEDCs for the inputs.

The Green Revolution and inequality

1 Rapid adoption by farmers with plenty of land and/or money. Land is used as security to buy seeds, irrigation pumps, fertilisers, pesticides, HYVs, etc. so small farmers cannot benefit at first.
2 Adoption by smaller farmers caused by:
• government-backed agricultural development projects
• new seeds targeted for more environments
• continued population pressure creating extra demand for more food.
3 Diffusion of new techniques to most farmers. Widespread adoption.

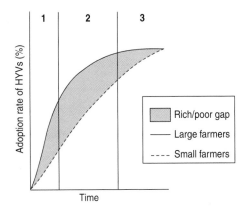

The problem

Population growth is more rapid than the increase in food production. For example, the population of India exceeded 1 billion in 2000, and is expected to reach 1.3 billion by 2020. Food production will need to increase by 40% to match demand. But much of India's land is of limited potential.

The effects of the Green Revolution in South India

Use of fertiliser	+138%
Human labour	+111%
Paddy rice	+91%
Sugar cane	+41%
Income	+20%
Subsistence food	−90%
Energy efficiency	−25%
Casual employment	−66%

Rural futures (1)

Pages 48 to 51 discuss rural futures.
• *What is the future for rural areas?*

Sustainable development strategies are needed to improve the quality of rural environments and the lives of the rural poor. Innovative solutions are required to ensure the survival of many rural areas.

Development in the Gaelteacht areas of Ireland

What and where is the Gaelteacht?

The Gaelteacht covers extensive parts of counties Donegal, Mayo, Galway, and Kerry, together with parts of counties Cork, Meath, and Waterford. The term 'Gaelteacht' describes those areas where the Irish language is the community language. All of the population of some 86 000 is also fluent in English.

Who is responsible for planning issues in the Gaelteacht?

Udaras na Gaeltachta is a state agency responsible for promoting the economic and social development of the Gaelteacht in order to facilitate the preservation and extension of the Irish language as the principal language of the region. It was established in 1980.

What is the Gaelteacht's economy?

Gaelteacht economic activities include agriculture, fishing, aquaculture, other natural resources, textiles, engineering, electronics, audio-visual activities, and telecommunications. However, employment in the traditional manufacturing sector is declining. The main sources of the 930 job losses (or 11% of total employment) in 2000 were recorded in the traditional

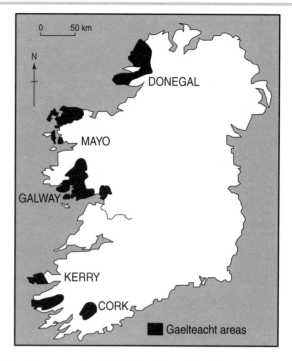

sectors. Decades of outmigration have left a larger than average ageing population.

What is being done to attract new industries and keep existing ones?

New and expanding businesses in the Gaelteacht area may be eligible for financial and non-financial assistance from Udaras na Gaeltachta. The Gaelteacht's success in attracting mobile international investment is due to the financial and tax incentives on offer in a modern infrastructural setting.

Summary of assistance available to new and expanding businesses

General financial assistance includes:

• employment grants
• capital grants on new equipment and buildings
• training grants
• rent subsidies on leased premises.

Non-financial incentives include:

• Accommodation – ready-to-occupy factories and offices on individual sites and within industrial parks are available; assistance available for custom-built accommodation.
• Advice – assistance available in negotiations with financial institutions and preparation of financial projections.
• Recruitment and training – help available in selection, recruitment, and training of staff; assistance available in management training for small companies.

How successful has it been?

In 1999, job creation in Gaelteacht areas reached a plateau, and a decline in the level of job creation – and consequently in the numbers employed – was forecast. Reasons for the

employment slowdown included labour shortages, lack of skilled personnel for the growth sectors, and the absence of basic infrastructural requirements.

What is the way forward?

The Gaelteacht needs to be made:

• more accessible
• more attractive to young people
• more competitive with urban areas in the rest of Ireland.

The Gaelteacht also needs to attract new economy-based projects that will stem the outflow of graduates and educated young people from the area. There is intense competition for new investment from other parts of the region and of the country, most of which have a much more advanced telecommunications infrastructure than the coastal Gaelteacht areas. In recent times a number of such projects approved for Gaelteacht locations decided to locate elsewhere, having failed to attract the required numbers of skilled employees in the Gaelteacht. Effectively, many parts the Gaelteacht are excluded from the employment benefits that flow from the modern services economy, which is based almost exclusively in the urban areas.

Rural futures (2)

Bottom-up development, run *by* local people *for* local people

Features	Examples
• Gives great self-determination to rural areas: – localised decision making – small scale and geared to local needs	• Grameen Bank, Bangladesh, which provides for rural women
• Uses limited funding effectively	• NGOs (see page 135), e.g. Cafod, Oxfam
• Serves basic needs, e.g. water, health, education	• Rural health programmes (Operation Hunger in South Africa); school programmes (Tanzania)
• Land reform redistributing land to the landless	• Some programmes have been questionable, e.g. Zimbabwe 2000–2002
• Use of appropriate technology (acceptable and affordable)	• Farm Africa in Sudan and Kenya • Brickmaking in Eastern Cape, South Africa • Water tanks, Uganda
• Use of external resources limited	• Diguettes (stone banks) in Burkina Faso
• Improved rural-to-urban communications and inter-village links	• Solar radios in South Africa • Village telephones in India
• Labour-intensive industrialisation	• Craft industries in former homelands of South Africa • Knitting cooperatives in Peru, Malawi
• Sustainable development projects	• Ecotourism in Namibia and Botswana • ActionAid in Tarata, Peru and Altiplano, Bolivia

Rural development in Bangladesh

Bangladesh is one of the world's most densely settled states. It is also one of the world's poorest countries.

Bangladesh factfile

Population	13 million
Growth rate	1.6 per annum
Birth rate	25.3 births/1000 population
Child death rate	8.6 deaths/1000 population
Infant mortality rate	69.9 deaths/1000 live births
Life expectancy	60.5 years (60.7 male, 60.3 female)
Fertility rate	2.78 per woman
Literacy	56%
GDP	$1570/head
Population below poverty line	35%

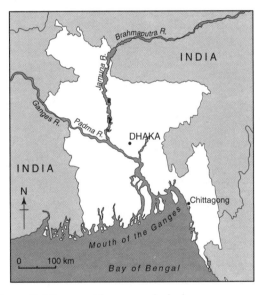

The problem

Rural poor people frequently lack funds and equipment to raise productivity. Many are deeply in debt. Many governments and agencies recognise the importance of providing easily available and relatively cheap credit as a means towards reducing rural poverty and promoting development.

The solution

The Grameen Bank was founded in 1976 to tackle Bangladesh's serious indebtedness, through providing loans to households that owned less than 0.2 ha of land. It now helps over 2 million poor people in over 34 000 villages.

The bank was founded on the principle that if the poor received financial help at reasonable terms and conditions, they could then generate productive self-employment without external assistance. In contrast, some households were paying back small loans with an interest rate up to 10% per month.

The 'essential Grameen' focuses exclusively on:

• the poor, with preference given to poor women
• simple loan procedures
• small loans repaid weekly

to be used for any income-generating activity chosen by the woman herself through groups, and organised with strict credit discipline and close supervision.

The bank's default rate is less than 3%, compared with default rates of 40–60% in other rural credit programmes in developing countries.

In order to receive loans, people must organise themselves into groups, and be prepared to interact with each other. Weekly meetings are held with the bank representative in attendance. In 1984 a social development programme was introduced to promote discipline, unity, and hard work, and to improve living standards.

Rural futures (3)

Ecotourism in Nepal

Deforestation on the steep slopes of the Himalayas in Nepal has led to severe erosion, removal of topsoil, and flooding. The Nepalese Government has encouraged a number of community reforestation schemes, one of which is the Annapurna Conservation Area Project (ACAP). It has four distinctive characteristics:

1 It covers a large area, over 2200 km², and involves over 40 000 people.
2 It is managed by local people since the government believes that it will only work if it involves and benefits the local community.
3 It is based on land use zoning.
4 Part of the funding comes from the tourist trade.

Mountain tourism

There are few roads in the Nepalese Himalayas, so tourists must walk, or 'trek', to enjoy the mountains. Except on the more popular routes, trails are in poor condition; acute deforestation has led to frequent landslides; board and lodging facilities are poor; and clean drinking water is not always available. However, tourism is the country's second highest foreign exchange earner (after carpet exports), contributing nearly 4% of its gross domestic product, so the government is keen to attract more tourists.

The Annapurna Conservation Area Project (ACAP) – a success story?

Land use zoning in the Annapurna Range

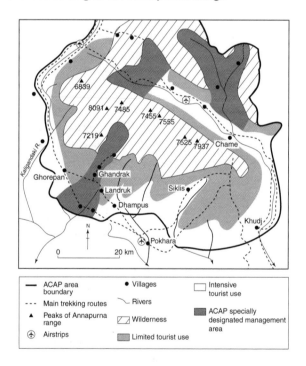

—— ACAP area boundary	• Villages	☐ Intensive tourist use
- - - Main trekking routes	╲ Rivers	
▲ Peaks of Annapurna range	▨ Wilderness	▨ ACAP specially designated management area
✈ Airstrips		▨ Limited tourist use

Village control of forests

ACAP was established in 1986. The conservation area does not exclude human habitation; the needs of the local people are integral to the project. After initial scepticism, local people have come to realise that they can gain from the project.

The traditional method of managing Nepal's forests (known as *ritithi*) involves balanced cutting and growth. However, the practice died out and decades of deforestation ensued as the population grew. Since the formation of ACAP, however, the responsibility of managing forests and wildlife has been handed back to villagers.

New ideas

Fees paid by trekkers who pass through the Annapurna area fund the ACAP. It has devised many simple fuel-saving devices, including solar-heated showers, and runs health-related workshops. These workshops include hygiene (the necessity of boiling water or digging latrines), and using flues to prevent buildings filling up with smoke and contributing to one of the biggest health problems, tuberculosis.

Consequences?

The Annapurna Conservation Area is visited by over 80 000 people a year. Over 700 tea shops and lodges have been built. Today, the local people are learning to maintain a high level of control over their resources and their future by building an endowment fund from entry fees to the area, and working together on education, community development, biodiversity, and energy conservation projects.

The concern of mountain people is that, as tourism develops, they will lose control over their culture, their economy, and their environment. Merely restricting tourism cannot be the solution to this imbalance, because people's desire to see new places will not disappear. Instead, mountain communities must achieve greater control over the rate at which tourism grows.

The effects of tourism in Nepal

Rural futures (4)

Sustainable development in rural areas

Sustainable development is defined as: *development that meets the needs of people at present (and improves basic standards of living) without compromising the needs of future generations.* Sustainable development implies social justice, equity, resource conservation, and empowerment of local communities.

Options for sustainable agriculture in LEDCs

Rural areas are especially important in LEDCs. They account for a large proportion of the workforce as well as providing food and export earnings. For about one-fifth of the population of LEDCs, environmental concerns and development needs are focused upon immediate survival.

Rural aid for Barca Province, Eritrea

- Financial advice promoted by NGOs
- Establishment of three plant nurseries for demonstration projects
- Development of veterinary services
- Construction of 56 km of new roads to enable farmers to market produce
- 'Barefoot' doctors and provision of 'health for all'
- Farm schools planned in an area with widespread illiteracy
- Construction of two flourmills to reduce workload of women
- Irrigation using hand pumps and hand-dug wells and diversion channels from rivers
- Local purchase of seeds to suit local environment
- Locally forged tools for 3000 families
- Integrated planning of farming, irrigation, soil and water conservation, reforestation, health and education

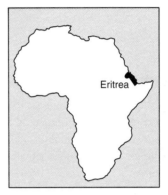

A profile of agriculture in the Eastern Cape, South Africa

In general the Eastern Cape is an area of arable agriculture rather than pastoral farming. Most cultivation is of a subsistence nature. Agricultural productivity is low and variable for a number of reasons:

- low and irregular rainfall
- poor soils
- limited vegetation quality
- steep slopes
- limited access to the land
- high cost of seeds and water
- lack of fences to deter domestic animals
- shortage of labour
- theft, and the high risk of operations, further reduced the incentive to farm the land.

Increasing agricultural productivity

There are many possibilities for improving agricultural productivity in the region. Irrigation schemes can be expensive but there are cheaper options, for example:

- **Establishing small-scale gardens and subsistence farms** – if such gardens are integrated with improvements in harvesting and storage there ought to be a much larger supply of quality food at very little cost.
- **Developing farming cooperatives** – there is a pool of skilled people, who could share the cost of tools and seed, and use the produce for their subsistence needs.
- **Erection of fences or barbed wire** – this would help prevent theft and trampling of crops by livestock.
- **Using drought-resistant fodder crops**, such as American aloe – pastureland is especially fragile owing to a combination of drought, overgrazing, population pressure, and the absence of land ownership policies. Trying to decrease herd size has proved unpopular and unsuccessful.

Essential oils

The production of essential oils holds considerable potential as a form of sustainable agricultural development. The raw materials can be grown in this region, and it is a labour-intensive industry which would utilise a large supply of unemployed and underemployed people.

The essential oils industry has a number of advantages:

- It is a new or additional source of income for many people.
- It is labour intensive and the raw material can be grown locally.
- Many plants are already known and used by the local people as medicines, and they are therefore culturally acceptable.
- In their natural state the plants are not very palatable nor of great value and so are unlikely to be stolen.
- Many suitable species are looked upon as weeds. Removing these regularly improves grazing potential as well as supplying raw materials for the essential oils industry.

Characteristics of urbanisation

Pages 52 to 54 introduce urban environments.
- What are the characteristics of urban environments?
- How and why do contrasting urban environments develop?
- How do the nature and importance of urban environments vary spatially?

What is urbanisation?

Urbanisation is an increase in the percentage of a population living in urban areas. It is one of the most significant geographical phenomena of the 20th century. It takes place when the urban population is growing more rapidly than the population as a whole. It is caused by a number of interrelated factors, including:

- migration to urban areas
- higher birth rates in urban areas due to the youthful age structure
- higher death rates in rural areas due to diseases, unreliable food supply, famine, decreased standard of living in rural areas, poor water, hygiene, and medication.

Urban classifications

Urban populations are those living in areas that have a census definition as 'urban'. The criteria used to specify what is an urban area vary widely and it is not possible to give a single definition. However, there are a number of underlying principles:

- population size
- specific urban characteristics, such as a CBD and residential zones
- predominant economic activities, such as manufacturing and services
- an administrative function.

The process of urbanisation

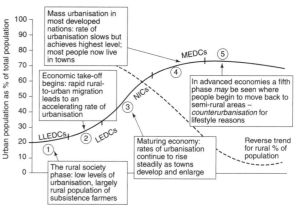

Source: Warn, S. *Managing Changes in Human Environments*, Philip Allan Updates 2001

Stages in urbanisation in MEDCs

In many developed countries the process of urbanisation is almost at an end, and the proportion of urban dwellers is beginning to fall. The progress has followed an S-shaped curve and it seems to have tailed off at 80% of the total population. For many MEDCs there appears to be a cycle of **urbanisation**, **suburbanisation**, **counterurbanisation**, and **reurbanisation**.

Levels of urbanisation 1950–2000

	1950	1970	1990	2000
Phase 5				
Australia	75	85	86	85
Sweden	66	81	93	90
UK	84	89	93	90
Phase 4				
Brazil	35	56	77	81
Japan	50	71	77	78
South Korea	21	41	72	86
Phase 3				
Greece	37	53	63	68
Mexico	43	59	73	78
Pakistan	18	25	32	38
Phase 2				
China	11	20	21	35
Indonesia	12	17	29	40
Senegal	31	33	40	45
Phase 1				
Ethiopia	5	9	12	15
Uganda	3	6	11	14
Vietnam	12	18	22	22

Trends in selected countries

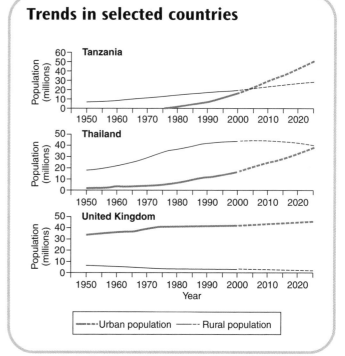

Rapid urbanisation

Causes and consequences of rapid urbanisation in Cairo

Cairo illustrates many of the causes and consequences of rapid urbanisation. Other cities showing these problems include Mumbai, Mexico City, Lima, and Rio de Janeiro. In the case of Cairo:

- population reached 13 million in 2000
- rapid expansion of Cairo from 1950s onwards
- growth is due to natural increase (70%) and rural-to-urban migration (30%).

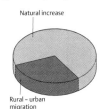

Source of population growth in modern Cairo

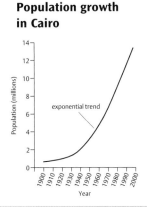

Population growth in Cairo

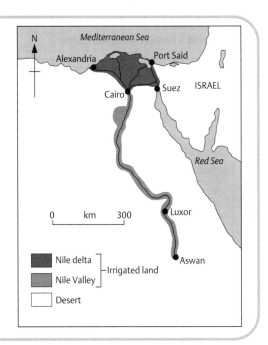

Problems

Housing

- Informal housing accounts for 80% of Cairo's housing
- 2–3 million people live in the Cities of the Dead
- Population density reaches over 30 000/km²

Traffic congestion

Lack of jobs/low salaries

Water and air pollution

- Vehicle fumes – smog
- Groundwater pollution
- Leaking sewers
- Rotting buildings

Environmental hazards

- In 1992, 30 000 buildings collapsed in an earthquake

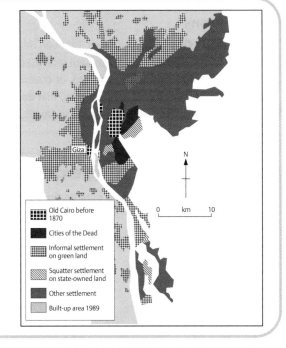

Solutions

- New satellite and dormitory towns built, such as 10th Ramadan and 15th May
- Massive ring road built to relieve pressure on the city centre
- Metro line provided, used by more than 1 million commuters every day
- Sewers repaired
- Refuse collection improved

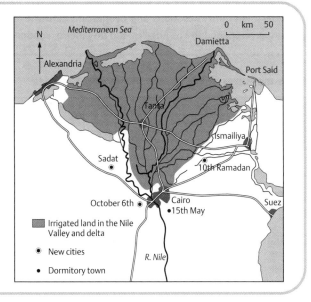

Urban areas in MEDCs

Case study – Urban development in Ireland

Ireland's urbanisation is characterised by being at a relatively low level and occurring relatively late. Until the 1960s the rate of rural-to-urban migration was low and primarily to large cities such as Dublin, Cork, and Limerick (most rural migrants moved to destinations overseas). This changed with the government's commitment to **modernisation**, which has brought new functions and renewed growth to many urban centres, and urbanisation is now increasing rapidly.

Urbanisation in Ireland shows a high degree of **urban primacy** – the Dublin metropolitan area accounts for over a third of the national population, and it could grow by a further 560 000 (nearly 50% of its current size) by 2015. It is the favoured destination of rural migrants and returning migrants.

Dublin

The rapid growth of Dublin has brought many of the problems experienced by other urban centres in MEDCs.

Population change

- In the inner city areas population has fallen to 20% of its 1900 total as high- and middle-income groups have moved out.
- Inner city areas contain a high proportion of substandard housing and slum conditions, mostly rented from the local authority.
- High-rise apartment blocks (municipal estates) have been built outside the city centre, such as at Crumlin.
- In inner Dublin over 50% of homes were built before 1919, 30% are overcrowded, and 30% require modern bathroom facilities.
- There is a strong social polarisation between the wealthy suburbs and impoverished inner city areas.
- Rapid suburban growth has absorbed discrete villages, such as Blanchardstown, Clondalkin and Lucan.
- Availability of greenfield land at comparatively low prices and the ready availability of mortgages has encouraged this process.

Industrial decline and the growth of the service sector

- Traditionally, industry was centred on the ports and the inner city, due to advantages from the transport infrastructure and the large working populations located nearby.
- Since then, however, land prices have increased and Industries have had to close down or re-locate, leaving an inner city that is economically disfunctional.
- The suburbs attracted many of these industries, providing the space needed at a lower cost, with better accessibility.
- Over 25% of establishments found in suburbs relocated there from the inner city.
- The suburbs have also attracted activities related to the service sector, such as retailing and office developments (the first out-of-town retail development was opened in a suburb south of the city centre in 1966).
- However, almost 50% of Ireland's office employment remains in central Dublin as a consequence of centralisation of decision-making.
- The growth of the service sector has not necessarily addressed the problems caused by **deindustrialisation** – namely high unemployment and poor job prospects for poorly educated blue-collar workers.

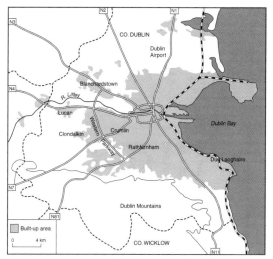

Districts of Dublin

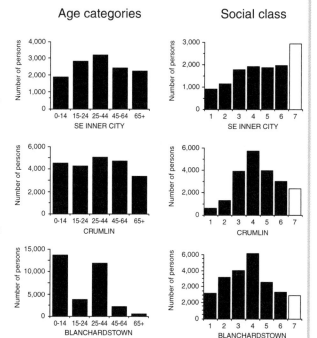

Statistics for selected Dublin districts

1 = Higher professional – managerial
2 = Lower professional – managerial
3 = Other non-manual
4 = Skilled manual
5 = Semi-skilled manual
6 = Unskilled manual
7 = Unknown

Segregation and gentrification

Segregation

Segregation implies a degree of isolation or separation of one particular group of people from another. This can be at a national scale or at an urban or local scale. Segregation is evident in Belfast in Northern Ireland between Catholics and Protestants, although in most MEDCs segregation is largely based on colour. This is clearly the case in Los Angeles, USA.

Measures of segregation over time in selected US cities
(100 equals total segregation)

	1970	1980	1990
Los Angeles	91.0	81.1	73.1
New York	81.0	82.0	82.2
Chicago	91.9	87.8	85.8
Washington DC	81.1	70.1	66.1
Detroit	88.4	86.7	87.6

A new index

The 'segregation dissimilarity index' was a comparison of residential segregation between blacks and whites in various American cities. A recent survey, 'Racial Integration in Urban America: A Block Level Analysis of African-American and White Housing Patterns', focuses on black/white integration, not segregation. Using data from the 2000 census, the study examined all America's 8.2 million blocks – the smaller units into which cities and country areas are divided. Blocks provide a better measure of interaction between races.

Most integrated metropolitan areas in the USA, 2000

Ranking, based on residential integration*	% of total population residing on integrated streets*	% black population in metro. area
1 Norfolk, VA	38.6	31.5
2 Columbia, SC	33.5	32.3
3 Charleston, NC	32.3	31.1
4 Richmond, VA	26.4	30.5
5 Memphis, TN	23.5	43.6
6 Raleigh, NC	23.1	23.0
7 Charlotte, NC	21.5	20.7
8 Jacksonville, FL	20.9	21.9
9 Wilmington, DE	20.3	18.2
10 Little Rock, AR	20.2	22.2
73 New York, NY	4.7	23.8
89 Los Angeles, CA	2.5	10.0
97 Orange County, CA	0.1	1.8

* Where a street's residents are at least 20% black and 20% white

The fact that most of America remains racially segregated – almost a third of blacks and more than half of whites live in blocks whose inhabitants are at least 90% of their own race – is not surprising. Metropolitan areas such as St Louis, Birmingham, Philadelphia, and Indianapolis, which rank near the bottom on the old indices, come out in the top third on a block-by-block ranking. Others previously praised as less segregated, such as Albuquerque, Honolulu, and Orange County, drop to near to the bottom, partly because relatively few black people live there.

Gentrification

Gentrification is the reinvestment of capital into inner city areas. It refers mostly to an improvement of residential areas, although there is an economic development too. Gentrification may also lead to the social displacement of poor people – as an area becomes gentrified, house prices become unaffordable. As they move out, young upwardly mobile populations take their place.

Gentrification has occurred in many large old cities throughout the world, such as in New York (Greenwich Village), London (Fulham and Chelsea), Tokyo and São Paulo. This was partly the result of state-sponsored **suburbanisation** (governments want people to leave overcrowded, unhygienic inner city areas for better-quality housing in the newly developed suburbs). This process dominated the decades between the 1930s and the 1970s. By the 1970s inner city land prices had devalued and the middle class reinvaded. Gentrification had begun.

Gentrification in Sydney

Inner suburbs such as Paddington, Balmain and Glebe experienced out-migration of working-class families with children, who were replaced by in-migration of childless people. Many of the new households were working couples. The newcomers were generally well-off, mobile and relied less on local facilities and services than their predecessors. Consequently, the economic and service base of the inner city declined. The overall effect of first losing its population and then losing its services has been termed the 'doughnut effect' – i.e. an empty hole characterised by a loss of services, community facilities, and people.

Lower-income migrants move into deteriorated housing (previously owned by middle-income groups)

Lower-income groups gradually move up housing scale

CBD →

Gentrification: upper-middle-income groups move to old housing

Redevelopment area: low status

Older housing occupied by lower-income groups

Better housing occupied by middle-income groups

Best housing occupied by upper middle-income groups

Expansion: new houses built for upper middle-income groups

Filtering occurs as housing deteriorates and it moves downwards through the social groups.
Gentrification reverses this process as middle-income groups upgrade older city properties by renovating them.

The LEDC city

Land use zoning in LEDCs

A number of models describe and explain the development of cities in LEDCs. There are several key points:

- The rich generally live close to the city centre whereas the very poor are more likely to be found on the periphery.
- Higher-quality land is occupied by the wealthy.
- Segregation by wealth, race, and ethnicity is evident.
- Manufacturing is scattered throughout the city.

Primate cities

Many cities in LEDCs are characterised by a high degree of **primacy**. This occurs when the largest or top-ranking city, in terms of population size, dominates the rest of the national urban system, e.g. Mexico City. Primacy is generally achieved by:

1 **Colonial inertia** – developed by colonial powers to function as centres of trade and administration.
2 **Export dependency** – gateway ports dominate the urban system.
3 **Urban bias theory** – development of manufacturing in urban areas results in rural-to-urban migration – increasing inequalities between the two.

Zones in LEDCs: Mexico City

Latin American city structure

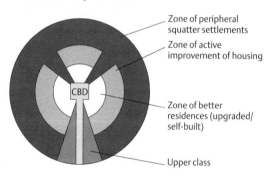

The CBD in many LEDCs displays a concentration of commercial, political, financial, and service functions. Inner areas are frequently inhabited by the rich, owing to the better access to employment and services. However, in some cities the rich and some services are moving to out-of-town '**edge cities**' due to congestion in the city centre, e.g. Barra da Tijuca outside Rio de Janerio. Thus **centrifugal forces** take place both in LEDCs and MEDCs.

In most LEDC cities there is a considerable amount of **informal** or **shanty housing**. There is great variety within shanty towns. **Slums of hope** and **slums of despair** are a further distinction of shanty towns.

- **Slums of hope** are the self-built houses where migrants are consolidating their position in the informal urban economy by improving their housing, e.g. in Mexico City these are the *Colonias Paracondistas*.
- **Slums of despair** have little room for improvement because incomes are low, rents are high, leasing arrangements are insecure, and there are environmental problems, e.g. in Mexico City these are the *Ciudades Perdidas*.

Mexico City can be split into zones, sectors, and nuclei. The old city core is surrounded by the tenements of the urban

Housing areas in Mexico City

poor (*vecindades*). In general, the poor dominate the north and east, the middle classes are found mostly in the south central area, and the highest class is found in the west. Hence, within nuclei there are class variations organised in a **preindustrial** fashion, namely a centralised elite and a peripheral lower class.

There has been some suburban development to the west and north of Mexico City, and small satellite communities have clustered in the south. There has also been peripheral development of low-quality housing. In 1954 the Federal District prohibited the subdivision of land within the city limits. This led to the development of shanty towns on the edge of the city at Naucalpan, Ecatepec, and Netzahualcoyotl.

Managing change in an LEDC city

Kingston, Jamaica

Kingston was founded in 1692 and soon became Jamaica's most important trading port. It had a number of advantages, such as:

- a sheltered harbour
- good links with the rest of the island
- a site with room for expansion and further development
- good building land.

Kingston's population has grown from about 5000 in 1700 to around 650 000 today. With this increase the city has expanded.

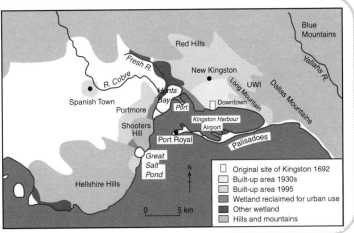

Legend:
- □ Original site of Kingston 1692
- Built-up area 1930s
- Built-up area 1995
- Wetland reclaimed for urban use
- Other wetland
- Hills and mountains

0   5 km

Decentralisation

Until the 1950s Kingston's offices and large shops were concentrated in the downtown CBD. Since then there has been large-scale **decentralisation**. New Kingston, a private development built on a former racecourse, has become the preferred location for many big businesses. Reasons for this include:

- the scarcity of large downtown sites in a decent condition
- the proximity of New Kingston to the residence of most of the workers
- New Kingston is safer and has a lower crime rate than the downtown area
- New Kingston has easier parking and is less congested.

The port

The old port was located south of the CBD and consisted of 'finger piers' where ships could dock. The new port at Newport West, built on reclaimed land, offers facilities for dealing with large container ships. There are also many export industries located near the port in the two adjacent Free Zones.

Retailing

Downtown Kingston is characterised by small shops, some department stores, and the main market. However, new retailing malls, such as those close to New Kingston, are on large suburban sites.

Downtown

Attempts to prevent downtown Kingston from becoming too run-down include:

- **redevelopment** of the Old Waterfront into office buildings, a shopping centre, and luxury apartments
- retaining the market area as a vibrant part of the retail economy; it is still the main destination for fresh produce from the countryside
- infrastructural improvements: road widening, the extension of the sewerage system, new parking facilities, and upgrading of the bus terminus.

Urban expansion

Kingston's further expansion is limited:

- land to the north and east is mountainous
- land to the west, near the Rio Cobre, is swampy and subject to flooding
- some land is valuable for farming, e.g. the Caymanas Estate.

Although available land is plentiful some distance from Kingston, it is too far away for daily commuting and would require considerable upgrading of infrastructure.

The new housing development in Portmore, just west of Kingston Harbour, has grown rapidly. Its population increased from 5000 in 1970 to over 100 000 by 1990. The scheme consists of 10 000 low-cost two- and three-bedroom homes and includes a number of schools, a police station, a post office, a shopping centre, and a health centre.

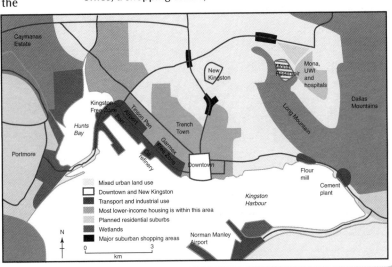

Legend:
- Mixed urban land use
- □ Downtown and New Kingston
- Transport and industrial use
- Most lower-income housing is within this area
- Planned residential suburbs
- Wetlands
- Major suburban shopping areas

0   3 km

Land use in Kingston

Urban land use in an LEDC city

Case study – Rio de Janeiro

Rio became the political and economic centre of Brazil in the 1700s with the gold boom, but it was in the 20th century that industrial growth resulted in a rapid increase in population and a spreading outwards. By 2000 the city had a population of 10.6 million people.

The expansion, particularly in the outer urban and suburban areas, resulted primarily from:

- in-migration of rural dwellers
- natural increase
- the decentralisation of lower-income residents from the centre or suburbs of Rio.

The consequence of this change has been the concentration of some of the poorest groups of the population in these zones. The distribution of population reveals a concentric pattern of wealth differences, generally coinciding with the four functional zones of the city:

- the centre (*nucleo*) – the historic core of the city which includes the CBD, the high-class residential areas and the industrial port complexes where the city's main functions are located
- the inner urban area (*zona imediata*) – older suburbs with a good infrastructure and a mix of traditional and modern industry
- the outer urban area (*zona intermediata*) – the newer outer fringes of the expanding urban area, including Nova Iguaçu and Duque de Caxias, both industrial cities in their own right
- the rural–urban fringe (*zona distante*) – a less urbanised zone beyond the commuting zone of Rio.

Social segregation

Wide inequalities of wealth and of the provision of urban services are evident. The core and suburban areas show a concentration of wealth, high-quality accommodation, the provision of municipal services, and access to the CBD and the popular beachfronts, while the city's margins are poorly provided with basic services, transport and electricity

networks. The even poorer informal squatter settlements (**favelas**) are also found outside the urban area, or interspersed in the central area on land that is unsuitable for development, such as steep hill slopes.

Decentralisation

Barra da Tijuca represents the most recent example of the decentralisation of the rich, containing many attractions for Rio's expanding middle and higher-income groups, with its pleasant environment of mountain views, forest, lagoons and 20 km of beaches. It is an area four times larger than the increasingly congested and polluted central zone, but still only 30 minutes away by motorway. The area expanded from 2500 inhabitants in 1960 to 98 000 in 1991. Accommodation consists of low-rise residential areas interspersed with clusters of high-rise apartments, centred on two commercial cores with shopping malls and hypermarkets.

Favelas

The rise of the favelas as an urban feature of Rio has been rapid. The official definition of such settlements is: *residential areas lacking formal organisation or basic services, containing 60 or more families who are squatting illegally on the site*. In 1992 just under 1 million people (nearly 20% of the total population) lived in 765 favelas of varying sizes. The largest has an estimated total population of 80 000.

Upgrading favelas

In 1990 a programme of electrification was started, as a means of improving conditions in the favelas. While long-established favelas, some dating back to 1940, have a mix of commercial services serving a more diverse socio-economic population, the worst conditions are still found in the most recent favelas. Here there is a complete absence of basic services, people have low incomes, and there is a high unemployment rate.

Location of favelas and edge towns in south-west Rio de Janeiro

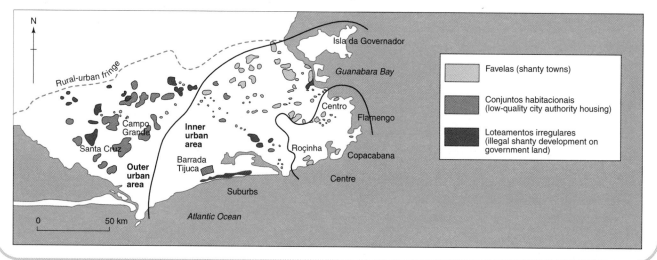

The CBD

Core and frame elements of the CBD

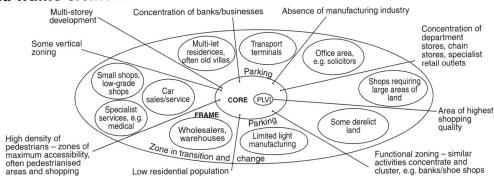

PLVI = peak land value intersection: the highest rated, busiest, most accessible part of a CBD

Factors influencing CBD decline

Adapted from: Warn, S. *Managing Change in Human Environments*, Philip Allen Updates 2001

Case study – change in Oxford's CBD

Traffic congestion and rising land prices in Oxford have forced many companies to move to out-of-town sites. Some were **greenfield sites**, e.g. Heyford Hill, whereas others were **brownfield sites**, e.g. the retail park on part of the former Rover works. There is also evidence of **centripetal forces** (movement in towards the city centre). Within the CBD, department stores occupy prime sites (highest pedestrian flows), whereas legal, administrative, and other services are found on the edge. Charity shops once dominated George Street but this has been redeveloped largely for theme pubs and other recreational uses.

Managing Oxford city centre

The objectives of Oxford's City Centre Management are:

- to promote a safe, accessible and pleasant city for residents and visitors
- to improve access for residents and visitors to the city centre, its buildings, and open spaces
- to promote the provision and use of public transport for residents and visitors
- to create a safe city centre through sensitive policing and introducing appropriate technology
- to create and maintain an attractive, signposted, clean, and safe environment
- to attract inward investment
- to market the city
- to monitor progress.

Achieving all this in a city of over 115 000 people, with an estimated daytime population of 180 000 (including 38 000 full-time students), over 5 million visitors each year, and over 100 000 m² of retail space, presents many problems. This is especially so as the City Centre Manager has no powers apart from persuasion.

The results of Oxford City Centre Management

Access
- *colour coding of park-and-ride bus stops*
- *installation of signposting in the city centre*
- *ring road signage for park-and-ride schemes.*

Crime
- *decrease in recorded crime*
- *introduction of radio link to reduce shoplifting*
- *increased use of CCTV*
- *removal of strong beer and sherry from a number of city centre off-licences*

Environment
- *black street furniture throughout the city centre*
- *increased cycle rack provision*
- *anti-flyposting initiatives (more street murals)*

Air quality
- *general decrease in concentrations of pollutants, notably PM10s and NOx*

New investments
- *Said Business School (next to railway station) £40 million*
- *Oxford Prison to be redeveloped*

Urban zones

Every city is unique, although there are many similarities in their land use. Large cities, such as London, have very complex patterns, which reflect their long history. The main types of land use in MEDC cities include offices, retail, industrial, residential, recreation, and transport.

Land use in Bradford

Bradford's urban structure shows elements of the concentric model and the sector model. Recent edge-of-town developments have made the model less clear.

Urban land use in Bradford shows a number of characteristics:

- a CBD on the site of the original village; there are three distinct areas: the wool warehousing and office area, the banking and retail area, and the entertainment and educational area
- the inner city areas such as Manningham, where large numbers of immigrants are located
- outer areas of suburban development and council housing, facilitated by improvements in transport and slum clearances in the 1950s
- a commuter zone, including villages such as Allerton, Eccleshill and Wibsey

- sectors of industry along the Bradford Beck to Frizinghall and Bowling; along the Clayton Beck to Thornton; the Bowling Beck towards Bowling; and along the railway towards Thornbury.

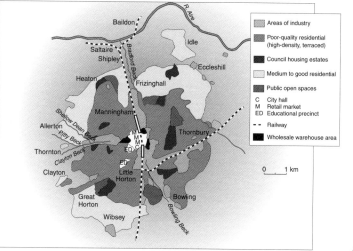

Land use in Prague
Urban land use in Prague

Prague is the capital and the largest city in the Czech Republic. It has a population of about 1.2 million and covers an area of about 500 km^2.

- The main commercial centre is located on the banks of the Vlatva (Moldau) and this is surrounded by residential areas and some green areas.
- The main industrial areas are located on the edge of the town, although smaller areas are located close to motorways and main roads.
- Some small-scale industries are located close to the city centre.
- Most of the residential areas are located in the flatter parts of the Vlatva and its tributaries.
- Open areas, woodland and green areas are also located on the higher ground and upper parts of the tributaries.

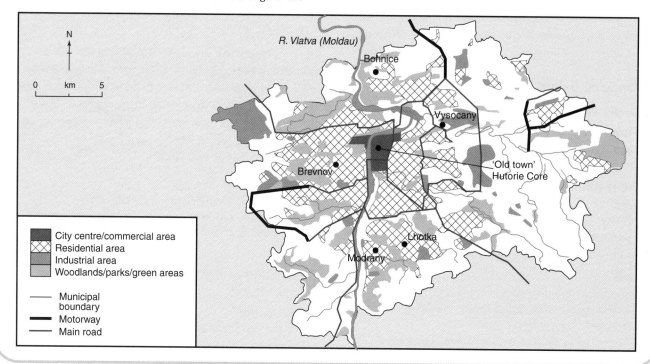

The rural–urban fringe

Pressures

Pressures on the rural–urban fringe include:

- urban sprawl
- more housing
- industrial growth
- recreational pressures for golf courses and sports stadia
- transport
- agricultural developments.

The nature of the pressure depends on the type of urban fringe, e.g. in an area of growth such as southern England compared with an area of decline such as parts of South Wales.

Issues in the urban fringe

Land use	Positive aspects	Negative aspects
Agriculture	Many well-managed farms and smallholdings	Farms often suffer litter, trespass and vandalism; some land is derelict in hope of planning permission for development
Development	Some well-sited, well-landscaped developments	Some developments, such as out-of-town shopping areas, cause heavy pollution; many unregulated businesses (e.g. scrap metal, caravan storage)
Urban services	Some, such as reservoirs or cemeteries, may be attractive	Mineral workings, sewage works, landfill sites, and Sunday markets (car boot sales), can be unattractive and polluting
Transport infrastructure	Some cycleways improve access and promote new development	Motorways destroy countryside, especially near junctions
Recreation and sport	Country parks, sports fields and golf courses can lead to conservation	Stock-car racing and scrambling erode ecosystems and create localised litter and pollution
Landscape and nature conservation	Many SSSIs and AONBs	Much degraded land, e.g. land ruined by fly-tipping; many SSSIs under threat

Source: Warn, S. *Managing Change in Human Environments*, Philip Allen Updates, 2001

Oxford's rural–urban fringe

There is little doubt that Oxford's rural–urban fringe is in crisis. Superstores and science parks used to be seen as the biggest threat. Now housing, roads, golf courses, and recreation facilities are seen as bigger threats. Developments on Oxford's rural–urban fringe include:

- an all-weather athletics tracks at Horspath
- a sports field at Kidlington (Stratfield Brake)
- Oxford United's new sports ground is located on urban fringe land
- large areas of the Cherwell Valley are seen as particularly vulnerable to the expansion of college sports grounds
- park-and-ride schemes add to the pressure to release more fringe land – the Pear Tree park-and-ride and service station covers 12 ha of rural–urban fringe
- there is a substantial housing development at Blackbird Leys
- the Oxford Science Park is a 30 ha site on the rural–urban fringe
- a golf course at Hinksey Hill opened in the mid-1990s.

Pressures on Oxford's rural urban fringe

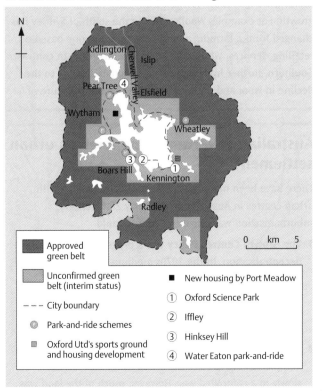

■ Approved green belt	
▨ Unconfirmed green belt (interim status)	■ New housing by Port Meadow
- - - City boundary	① Oxford Science Park
◉ Park-and-ride schemes	② Iffley
▦ Oxford Utd's sports ground and housing development	③ Hinksey Hill
	④ Water Eaton park-and-ride

Managing urban areas (1)

Pages 66 to 69 discuss the challenge of managing urban environments.
- *What are the challenges of managing urban environments?*
- *How do planners and decision makers attempt to resolve these challenges?*
- *What is the balance between private and public provision?*
- *How successful are the strategies of planners and decision makers in improving the quality of life for all urban dwellers?*

Economic development and urbanisation

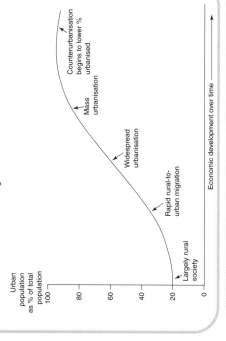

Managing the housing stock in MEDCs

In many MEDCs there is an urgent need to provide more affordable housing. In some cases **gentrification** of old buildings is a good way of improving the housing stock. However, these may also become too expensive as a location's image changes. Many of Britain's suburbs are beginning to show signs of **urban decay**. Solutions for this have changed: large-scale house building, which characterised the early part of the 20th century, has been replaced by renewal schemes. Funding has also changed, from state-sponsored initiatives to a mix of private and public support.

The City Challenge Scheme

This scheme was established in 1991 to encourage local authorities to compete for funding. It is open to local authorities with the most severe urban problems. In Leicester, for example, the City Council and De Montfort University designed a project transforming the derelict inner city into a 'showpiece' area with new shops, facilities, and houses. Critics argued that government policy had lost steam and that it was asking other organisations for suggestions on how to tackle the inner city problem.

The housing crisis in LEDCs

Provision of enough quality housing is also a major problem in LEDCs. There are at least four aspects to the management of housing stock:

- quality of housing – with proper water, sanitation, electricity, and space
- quantity of housing – having enough units to meet demand
- availability and affordability of housing
- housing tenure (ownership or rental).

Some idea of the crisis can be gleaned from the example of Mexico City below.

Overcrowding in Mexico City

Population growth in Mexico City has been very rapid (its current population is 18 million). There are many problems with much of its housing: lack of access to water, adequate sanitation, a reliable and safe power supply, adequate roofs, solid foundations, secure tenure (i.e. the residents are at risk of eviction).

The main reason that people migrate to Mexico City is to search for employment. Many of Mexico's rural areas are very poor and there are few jobs available. Migrants to Mexico City tend to be young (under 30) and as a result the city's birth rate is high and the death rate is low.

All these problems fall on the city's authorities and planners to solve. There is immense pressure to provide sufficient housing, employment, schools, water, and decent levels of sanitation. However, all these things are expensive – there are just too many people with too low standards of living to provide for.

Possible solutions to the housing problem

- Government support for low-income self-built housing
- Subsidies for home building
- Flexible loans to help shanty town dwellers
- Slum upgrading in central areas
- Improved private and public rental housing
- Support for the informal sector/small businesses operating at home
- Site and service schemes
- Encouragement of community schemes
- Construction of health and educational services.

Low-income households in Mexico City

Low or no income   No electricity

Low or no income

☐ Lowest concentration ☐ ☐ ☐ ■ Highest concentration

Managing urban areas (2)

Managing movement in cities

Traffic problems in MEDC and LEDC cities

MEDCs	LEDCs
• Increased number of motor vehicles • Increased dependence on cars as public transport declines • Major concentration of economic activities in CBDs • Inadequate provision of roads and parking • Frequent roadworks • Roads overwhelmed by sheer volume of traffic • Urban sprawl results in low-density built-up areas, and increasingly long journeys to work • Development of out-of-town retail and employment leads to cross-city commuting	• Private car ownership is lower • Less dependence on the car, but growing • Many cars are poorly maintained and are high polluters • Centralisation and development of CBDs increases traffic in urban areas • Heavy reliance on affordable public transport • Journeys are shorter but getting longer • Rapid growth has led to enormous urban sprawl and longer journeys • Out-of-town developments are beginning as economic development occurs
Carrots	**Sticks**
• Park-and-ride schemes – parking at the terminal for a major bus or train route, e.g. Oxford, Brisbane • Subsidised public transport systems, e.g. Oxford, Zurich, Brisbane • Modern electronic bus systems with consumer information on frequency, e.g. Curitiba in Brazil; rapid transit systems: supertrams on dedicated tracks, e.g. Zurich, or underground trains, e.g. Newcastle, Cairo • Providing bus lanes to speed up buses, e.g. Oxford, London	• High car parking charges in city centres, e.g. Copenhagen, London, Oxford • Restricted city-centre parking, e.g. Copenhagen, Cambridge • Road tolls and road pricing (congestion charges), e.g. Durham, Bergen (Norway) and central London (2003) so that people have to pay to drive through congested areas of the city centre

Source: Warn, S. *Managing Change in Human Environments*, Philip Allen Updates, 2001

Oxford's park-and-ride scheme

Oxford's transport problem is severe.

• Up to 80 000 vehicles a day converge on the city and its 15 000 parking spaces.
• Asthma has been linked to the rise in air pollution – Oxford has one of the highest rates of asthma in the UK.

In 1973 Oxford City Council opened the Redbridge Park and Ride Scheme. **Congestion** and **pollution** forced the planners to develop this scheme:

• Over 35% of visitors to central Oxford arrive by car.
• Park-and-ride intercepts 18% of Oxford-bound cars during off-peak times and 38% at peak times.
• The city has over 15 000 parking spaces: park-and-ride has **added** more rather than **replacing** inner city ones.
• Oxford has the highest bus usage for a city its size, and the second highest use of bicycles.
• Park-and-ride takes up to 12 ha of good-quality green belt land.

There needs to be:

1 restricted parking in the city centre
2 more bus routes and bus lanes
3 users of park-and-ride should pay so as to increase revenue to pay for public transport.

The **Oxford Transport Strategy** is the result. So far there has been:

• a decline in the number of shoppers in Oxford city centre

Results of the Oxford Transport Strategy

Traffic		Car parking	
Entering city centre	−20/30%	City centre (public spaces)	
High Street	−75%	Sept/Oct 1999	−20%
Science area	−14%	Nov 1999	−12%
Buses			
Passengers	+9%		
Travel: faster and more reliable			

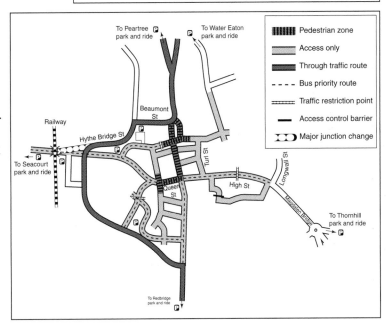

Access to the city centre following the Oxford Transport Strategy

• an increase in the cost of parking in the city centre, and fewer cars going into the city centre
• an improvement in air quality.

Managing urban areas (3)

Managing the Brown Agenda

There are a range of environmental problems in urban areas. These vary over time as economic development progresses. The greatest concentration of environmental problems occurs in cities experiencing rapid growth. This concentration of problems is referred to as the **Brown Agenda** (see page 73). It has two main components:

- issues caused by limited availability of land, water, and services
- problems such as toxic hazardous waste, pollution of water, air and soil, and industrial 'accidents' such as at Bhopal in 1985.

Urban challenges

Environmental	• Atmospheric pollution from a variety of sources, especially from industrial, domestic, and transport services • Traffic congestion – moving the daily flow of commuters • Sewage and waste disposal • Water pollution • Rapid urban sprawl, causing loss of land and creating wide areas of slums • Dereliction • Flooding or landslides affecting especially poor people who cannot choose to live in safe locations
Socio-cultural	• Zones of poverty within the city – can become areas of high crime and social deprivation • Ghettoisation of low income and ethnic groups, leading to friction between groups • Creation of an urban underclass with limited powers to improve their quality of life and health
Economic	• Providing resources for the large numbers of new arrivals • Services such as health, education, housing, employment, water, and sewerage are increasingly costly to provide
Political	• The difficulties of governing cities effectively to cope with the range of problems; declining incomes from rates

Environmental problems in urban areas

Problems	Causes	Possible solutions
Waste products and waste disposal: 25% of all urban dwellers in LEDCs have no adequate sanitation and no means of sewage disposal	• Solids from papers, packaging, and toxic waste increase as numbers and living standards rise • Liquid sewage and industrial waste both rise exponentially • Contamination and health hazards from poor systems of disposal, e.g. rat infestation and waterborne diseases	• Improved public awareness – recycling, etc., landfill sites, incineration plants • Development of effective sewerage systems and treatment plants, including recycling of brown water for industrial use • Rubbish management
Air pollution, e.g. air in Mexico City is 'acceptable' on fewer than 20 days annually!	• Traffic, factories, waste incinerators, and power plants produce pollutants • Some specialist chemical pollution • Issues of acid deposition	• Closure of old factories and use of clean technology, e.g. filters • Use of cleaner fuels • Re-siting of industrial plants, e.g. oil refineries in areas downwind of settlements
Water pollution, e.g. untreated sewage into the Ganga from cities such as Varanasi	• Leaking sewers, landfill and industrial waste • In some LEDCs, agricultural pollution from fertilisers and manure is a problem	• Control of point sources of pollution at source by regulation and fining: development of mains drainage systems and sewers • Removal of contaminated land sites
Water supply, e.g. overuse of groundwater led to subsidence and flooding in Bangkok	• Aquifer depletion, ground subsidence and low-flow rivers	• Construction of reservoirs, pipeline construction from long-distance catchment, desalination of saltwater • Water conservation strategies

Source: Warn, S. *Managing Change in Human Environments*, Philip Allen Updates, 2001

Managing urban areas (4)

Restoring the environment

Environmental problems that most cities have to deal with include problems of water quality, dereliction, problems of air quality, noise and environmental health of the population.

Attempts to turn cities green can be expensive. Increasingly local governments are monitoring the environment to check for signs of environmental stress, and then applying some form of **pollution management, integrated management**, or **conservation order** to protect the environment.

Camley Street Natural Park

Opened in 1983, this park was once an important part of the King's Cross and St Pancras stations, but the site had become derelict when railways, rail freight, and coal declined in importance. Approved by the Greater London Council Planning Committee in 1982, the area now includes an ecological area, picnic area, field centre, and a footbridge over the local canal to the towpath. The area of open water was enlarged and the range of aquatic habitat increased.

Camley Street Natural Park is an ecologically important haven at a local level. It also provides much needed recreational facilities in an area of London that has a serious deficiency in open space and where dwellings have very limited access to gardens.

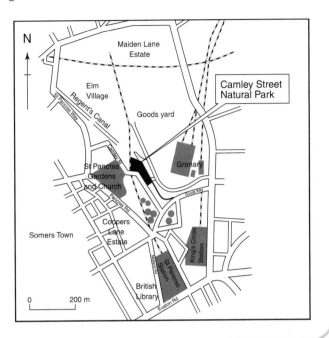

Managing inequalities and social problems

Examples of the many social problems found in cities include:

- access to services for the underclass
- problems related to crime
- ethnic and religious divisions causing social and economic polarisation.

Some examples are striking, such as religion in Belfast and Jerusalem, ethnicity in Bradford and Oldham; others, such as crime, are more widespread.

Issues of crime

The majority of criminal activity is concentrated in the most urbanised and industrialised areas and, within these, the poorest working-class neighbourhoods. Some, such as fraud and sexual offences, are relatively more common in lower-density neighbourhoods with lots of open spaces and a limited police presence.

Crime prevention methods in city centres and neighbourhoods include:

- the introduction of a radio link between shops to warn about known and possible shoplifters
- increased use of CCTV (closed circuit television)
- greater street lighting to provide safety in the evening and at night
- more police officers on the beat
- neighbourhood watch schemes.

Common attributes of known offenders

Category	Indicator	Subgroup at risk
Demographic	Age	young
	Sex	male
	Marital status	single
	Ethnic status	minority group
	Family status	broken home
Socio-economic	Family size	large
	Income	low
	Occupation	unskilled
	Employment	unemployed
Living conditions	Housing	substandard
	Density	overcrowded
	Tenure	rented
	Permanence	low

Distribution of crime in Oxford

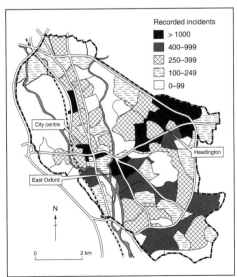

Urban futures (1)

Pages 69 to 72 look at urban futures.
- *What will the future hold for urban areas?*
- *Can urban areas be made sustainable?*

Regenerating and redeveloping urban environments

Many cities, and parts of cities, have been regenerated, attracting new industries, creating new homes, and improving the environment. Some have been very high-profile, such as London Docklands, while others, such as tourism developments in Bradford, have been less so, but equally successful.

There are many reasons why urban areas need to be redeveloped and regenerated:

- **Economic reasons** – large job losses following deindustrialisation; migration of industry to greenfield sites; concentration of unemployment and low-paid jobs in the inner city.
- **Social reasons** – increasing inequalities within cities (the rich/poor gap); social exclusion of certain groups.
- **Environmental reasons** – extensive areas of dereliction, contamination, and pollution.
- **Political reasons** – perceived neglect by government of the urban poor.

To regenerate urban areas there has been a long history of planned action. Some of these policies have targeted social problems (such as education and health) while others have earmarked economic development as the key to success. Some have improved the environment, while **flagship projects** – prestige developments such as London Docklands, Cardiff Bay, and Birmingham city centre – have revitalised small areas at vast expense, and not necessarily to the benefit of local residents.

Criticisms of urban policy

1 **Insufficient funding** – resources have stood still or been reduced.
2 Renewed **public sector involvement** is needed.
3 The approach is too **fragmentary** and lacks a clear focus.
4 The consistent emphasis on helping **small areas** appears unsuccessful.
5 Government policy is simply **not doing enough** for most inner cities.

Regeneration in Manchester

The Castlefield area of Manchester was an important industrial area, but it declined with the closure of Manchester Central Station in 1966 and the Goods Depot in 1975. The Greater Manchester Council bought the area in 1978 and embarked on a campaign to promote its rich industrial heritage. This was seen as the key to the regeneration of the area:

- The City Exhibition Hall was repaired and in 1982 it became Britain's first urban heritage park.
- In 1983 the first phase of the Castlefield Museum of Science and Industry was opened.
- Canals and towpaths were restored.
- New housing was built.
- An array of restaurants opened.
- The Victoria and Albert Warehouse was refurbished and opened as a hotel.
- Deansgate was restored and opened as a recording studio.

In other parts of Manchester, the Higher Education Precinct is an expansion of universities and colleges. It caters for 35 000 students and covers 135 ha. In East Manchester, Olympic and Commonwealth Games Bids have been used to develop large-scale sporting venues with housing developments in a bid to attract the Games to Manchester. It attracted the 2002 Commonwealth Games, improved the amount and type of housing, and upgraded the infrastructure all at the same time.

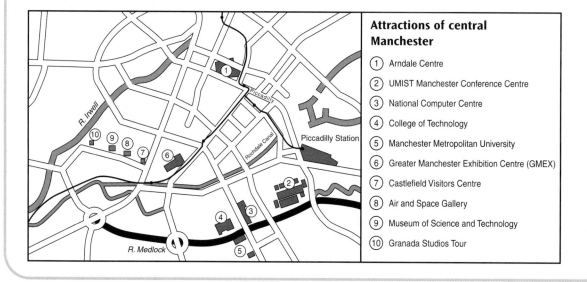

Attractions of central Manchester

1. Arndale Centre
2. UMIST Manchester Conference Centre
3. National Computer Centre
4. College of Technology
5. Manchester Metropolitan University
6. Greater Manchester Exhibition Centre (GMEX)
7. Castlefield Visitors Centre
8. Air and Space Gallery
9. Museum of Science and Technology
10. Granada Studios Tour

Urban futures (2)

Sustainable development in Curitiba

Curitiba, a city in south-west Brazil, is an excellent model for sustainable urban development. It has experienced rapid population growth, from 300 000 in 1950 to over 2.1 million in 1990, but has managed to avoid all the problems normally associated with such expansion. This success is largely due to innovative planning:

- Public transport is preferred over private cars.
- The environment is used rather than changed.
- Cheap, low-technology solutions are used rather than high-technology ones.
- Development is through the participation of citizens (bottom-up development) rather than top-down development (centralised planning).

The location of Curitiba in Brazil

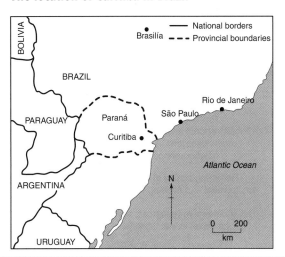

Sustainable solutions to flooding in Curitiba, Brazil

Problems (1950s/60s)	Solutions (late 1960s onwards)
• Many streams had been covered to form underground canals which restricted water flow. • Houses and other buildings had been built too close to rivers. • New buildings were built on poorly drained land on the periphery of the city. • Increase in roads and concrete surfaces accelerated runoff.	• Natural drainage was preserved – these natural flood plains are used as parks. • Certain low-lying areas are off-limits. • Parks have been extensively planted with trees; existing buildings have been converted into new sports and leisure facilities. • Bus routes and bicycle paths integrate the parks into the urban life of the city.

Transport

The approach to transport in Curitiba is very integrated. The road network and public transport system have structural axes. These allow the city to expand, but keep shops, workplaces, and homes closely linked.

There are five main axes of the three parallel roadways:

- A central road with two express bus lanes – Curitiba's mass transport system is based on the bus. Inter-district and feeder bus routes complement the express bus lanes along the structural axes. Everything is geared towards the speed of journey and convenience of passengers.
- A single fare allows transfer from express routes to interdistrict and local buses.
- Extra-wide doors allow passengers to crowd on quickly.
- Double- and triple-length buses allow for rush-hour loads.

The rationale for the bus system was economy and sustainability. A subway would have cost $80–$70 million per km; the express bus routes were only $200 000 per km. The bus companies are paid by the kilometres of road they serve and not the number of passengers. This ensures that all areas of the city are served.

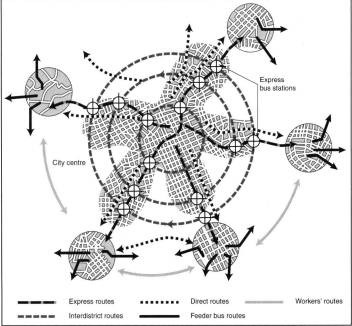

Curitiba's transport system

Question

This question is a typical Unit 2 (6472) Question 3, which requires you to show knowledge, understanding, and skills across both rural and urban sections.

Study the diagram. It shows a population pyramid for a village of 900 people which has experienced recent rural depopulation.

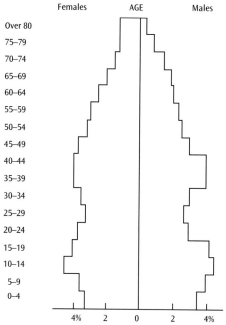

(a) (i) Define *rural depopulation*. [2]

(ii) Suggest **three** ways in which the population pyramid shows rural depopulation. You may annotate the diagram to show the key features. [3]

(iii) With reference to examples, explain why rural depopulation has occurred in some villages. [5]

(b) Recently there have been three new developments in the village.

(i) A new housing estate of 50 high-quality bungalows.

(ii) A time-share complex – phase 1 consists of 60 units and a central facilities area (bar, office, cafeteria, etc).

(iii) A vital village project, with combined post office, cyber café, and new village store, run by community members.

Choose **two** of these projects and evaluate their likely impact on the development of the village. [10]

(c) With reference to a named **urban** area, examine the processes that have led to recent population change. [10]

Total marks 30

Answer

(a) **(i)** **Rural depopulation** refers to the decline in numbers in a rural area or village as people move away.① Often, as these are younger people, there is an absolute decline in numbers because of an ageing population①.
1 mark for basic answer and 1 mark for any extension/example. [2]

(ii) Waisted profile at 20–35 years①. Regressive base (declining birth rate) ①, ageing population, high % over 65①.
[3 × 1]

(iii) Expect details of:
- **push** factors (deprivation – lack of transport, services, employment) [5]
- **pull** factors (employment, available housing, services).

Marks

5	A well-exemplified explanation, with appropriate details of push and pull factors.
4–3	Understands some push and pull factors may be unbalanced, and more generalised.
2–1	One or two basic ideas, lacks exemplification.

(b) **(i)** **New bungalows** would lead to a minimum of 100 new arrivals (10% increase). **Quality** would suggest they are not affordable housing for village people; also, **bungalows** may be targeted at retired people. Could even be bought as second homes. So may not be especially beneficial to vitality of village. Limited multiplier effect.

(ii) **Time share**. Tourism development – increased traffic, may be loss of attractive land. Could generate some employment (possibly low pay/seasonal cleaning, etc). May contribute little to village survival (likely not to use village services).

(iii) **Vital village** aimed at village regeneration – self-help. Survival of basic services **plus** additional modern services to encourage teleworking, education, etc. Innovative solution likely to be of great benefit.
5 each for 2 projects = [10]

Marks

5	Evaluates the project with sound linkage to village development. Shows a good range of ideas.
4–3	Shows understanding of the chosen project, some linkage to village development.
2–1	One or two basic ideas of impact, but lacks linkage to village development.

(c) So much depends on the chosen area. Needs to be well linked to chosen urban area or district in an urban area.
LEDC likely to be rapid **urbanisation** → rapid **growth**, shanty towns, urban sprawl.
MEDC likely to be inner city decline/**deurbanisation** and possible **reurbanisation**/gentrification, **filtering** and **suburbanisation**/**urban sprawl**, even counterurbanisation (decline). [10]

Marks

10–9	Sound examination of named processes, well linked to chosen urban area.
8–5	Some understanding of processes, may lack terminology at lower end. Not well linked to chosen area.
4–1	One or two basic rather generalised descriptive processes. Will lack terminology and linkage to chosen area.

Total marks 30

Environmental investigation (1)

The **focus** of this investigation must be linked to one or more of the following environments studied at AS:

- river
- coastal
- rural
- urban

Students will have studied these environments in AS Units 1 and 2. This investigation must link environmental geography with physical and/or human processes. The focus of the investigation should be **small-scale**. Whilst the fieldwork may be done in groups or individually, the write-up must be individual work.

The investigation must include evidence of **primary data** (fieldwork) supported by appropriate use of **secondary** sources.

Students are encouraged to prepare an **action plan** for their route to enquiry, especially if they are hoping to achieve key skills, using form GB2 (AS).

1 Purpose of investigation – developing a focus (10 marks)

The purpose of the enquiry should be clearly focused on one or two key questions.

This section should:

a introduce the question, issue, or problem (based on a clearly defined individual site)

b outline the key questions in the route for enquiry and put them in a geographical context

c provide details of the location of the investigation, including an annotated site map.

Choosing a fieldwork topic

- Read through your notes on the relevant parts of Units 1 and 2.
- Read an article or section in a book on the topic.
- Revisit the site and think about what seems to be significant to you.
- Browse through articles, newspapers, radio, television, internet, CD-ROMs.
- Talk to outsiders about possible investigations.
- Focus on a question, issue, or problem, and then devise one or two key enquiry questions.

Remember also:

- The topic must be manageable (work on a small stream will be more manageable and much safer than on a major river).
- Explain the geographical context of your investigation. (What are the main features of the physical and human environment that are relevant to your investigation?)

Useful titles

Environment	Questions
Rivers	
	• How and why does velocity/bedload/suspended load/width-depth ratio [pick one] change downstream?
	• In what ways does human activity influence the discharge (or other characteristics) of an urban stream?
	• How does water quality vary above and below a sewage treatment plant?
Coasts	
	• How and why do beach profiles vary between location X and Y?
	• How and why does beach material vary
	(a) with distance from the shoreline, and
	(b) along a coastline?
Rural	
	• To what extent is **x** (*a village in your local area*) a suburbanised village?
	• What is the relationship between population size and the number of services for selected settlements in a small rural area?
Urban	
	• How and why does quality of life vary between two wards (or enumeration districts) in a small town/city?
	• How do the characteristics of retailing differ between the CBD and out-of-town sites?
	• How has the physical geography of a small area affected urban land use?
	• To what extent do different types of shops show elements of clustering in a small town/CBD?

Environmental investigation (2)

Group investigations

Primary investigations may be carried out as group work but you must then develop your own question, issue or hypothesis. Generally, a range of issues can be investigated for a single fieldwork destination.

Physical geography

Human geography

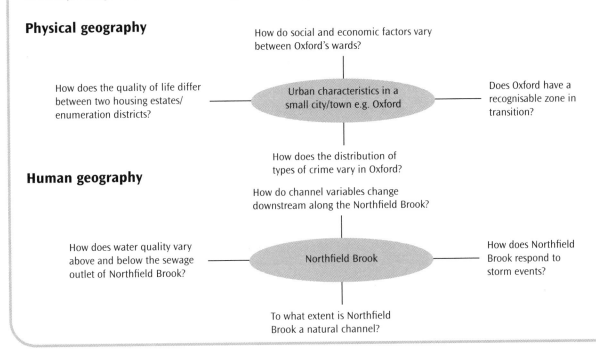

How do social and economic factors vary between Oxford's wards?

How does the quality of life differ between two housing estates/enumeration districts?

Urban characteristics in a small city/town e.g. Oxford

Does Oxford have a recognisable zone in transition?

How does the distribution of types of crime vary in Oxford?

How do channel variables change downstream along the Northfield Brook?

How does water quality vary above and below the sewage outlet of Northfield Brook?

Northfield Brook

How does Northfield Brook respond to storm events?

To what extent is Northfield Brook a natural channel?

2 Methodology of data selection, collection, and recording (15 marks)

The data will include primary field evidence, supported by appropriate secondary research (such as planning documents or management plans).

This section should:

a state the nature of the information required in order to answer the question, issue, or problem posed

b describe what kind of data was needed, and when and how it was collected – including correct use of sampling techniques and questionnaire design (if appropriate)

c note any problems encountered in data collection

d show evidence of the data collected in the field (including a research action plan, and fieldwork notes in the appendix)

e present the data record in an organised manner, with appropriate selection of information.

Note: A data methodology table would be an appropriate means of fulfilling the majority of the requirements of this section.

Figure	Technique	Data collected	Purpose	Method	Limitations	Dates
10–15	Photographic evidence	Photos were taken at all sites	To show features of erosion and deposition	Photos of inner and outer banks	Early Sept. was quite dry so there was little water in the river	10 Sept.

Top tips

- State how and why the data was selected.
- Describe the methods of sampling (random, stratified, systematic, etc.).
- Ensure the sample size is large enough.
- Construct a data methodology table to include limitations and evaluation.
- Use relevant data collection methods.
- Justify the questionnaire or survey design.
- Evaluate (assess the importance of) any problems encountered.
- Present surveys and questionnaires in a useful way.
- Use photos to calibrate scale such as quality of life.
- Focus on the subject of your title.

Environmental investigation (3)

3 Data representation (10 marks)

This section should be transitional between sections 2 and 4 and should be integrated with the analysis (section 4).

It includes the quality and variety of:

a the presentation of evidence in cartographic (map) form
b the representation of evidence in diagrammatic and photographic forms
c the representation of data in graphical form.

Note: Whilst it is entirely appropriate for students to make use of communications technology (ICT) for representation of data, credit will also be given for the quality of hand-drawn maps and field sketches, and original methods of data representation.

The main methods include:

- **qualitative maps** – land use and morphological maps
- **quantitative maps** – flow diagrams, proportional symbols, dot maps, choropleth and isopleth maps
- **diagrams and graphs** – histograms, pie charts, scatter graphs, line graphs, statistical tests
- **annotated photographs** – can often be used alongside a map.

Top tips

- Use a variety of relevant techniques.
- Draw the maps by hand.
- Make sure you understand the technique.
- Integrate your data representation with your writing.
- Annotate (label) all graphs, photographs, and diagrams.
- Present the data clearly.
- Use a variety of suitable techniques.
- Discuss, justify, and explain any techniques used.

4 Analysis and explanation (25 marks)

This section should show evidence of use of appropriate techniques of analysis and explanation. It will help to clarify the relationships between the key aspects of the question, issue, or problem under study.

This section should:

a describe and explain the results in an analytical commentary
b interpret the results using suitable techniques, including statistical analysis where appropriate
c apply or test the relevance of models, theories, or hypotheses appropriate to the enquiry
d not only analyse items individually, but also recognise overall links and trends across items.

Top tips

- Draw up a data analysis table.
- Analyse logically each piece of evidence.
- Compare and contrast pieces of evidence.
- Refer the evidence to relevant geographical concepts, theories, or models.
- Use a range of relevant geographical techniques.
- Refer frequently to your key enquiry questions.

Environmental investigation (4)

5 Conclusion and evaluation (25 marks)

This section provides the opportunity to:

a return to the question, issue, or problem defined at the beginning of the route to enquiry

b summarise and draw threads together to reach a conclusion

c evaluate specific findings

d state and evaluate, where relevant, possible solutions to the question, problem, or issue being investigated

e discuss the limitation of the enquiry by evaluation of the strengths and weaknesses of the route followed.

Top tips

- This section is worth 25% of the marks, so leave time for a thorough, thoughtful conclusion and evaluation.
- State your original aims.
- Refer to your key questions.
- Summarise your results.
- Make links between your results (bring them together).
- Evaluate what you have achieved.
- How far are your results time and place specific?

6 Quality of written communication (15 marks)

The written communication and presentation of the investigation is an important part of the complete enquiry.

Attention should be given to:

a the structure of the investigation – to include the organisation of the information into a clear and logical enquiry, with clear subdivisions into sections

b the clarity of presentation, with precise labelling (figure numbers) of all maps, diagrams, and photographs to ensure that text and figures are easily handled and capable of being read together

c the acknowledgement of data sources (both primary and secondary) and references to any planning documents, websites, or texts used

d appropriate style of writing, including high standards of grammar, punctuation, and spelling (with the use of spell check systems) and appropriate use of geographical terminology

e the ability to meet the word limit of 2500 words (latitude 10%) by the use of precise, clear communication.

Note: An investigation that is more than 2500 words long cannot achieve more than 6 marks out of 15 in this marking criterion.

Top tips

- Use clear, neat, logical writing and layout.
- Include a contents page.
- If relevant, include an appendix.
- Keep within the 2500 word limit.
- Provide a short bibliography.

Remember also to:

- use a spell check, and re-read your entire investigation
- include annotated photographs, newspaper cuttings, and maps
- divide the enquiry into sections identified in the mark scheme (it is helpful to use coloured paper or file dividers)
- place a sample of your questionnaires and/or survey sheets in the appendix
- incorporate figure numbers in the text, e.g. Fig. 1 etc.

Introduction to A2

Progression from AS to A2

The knowledge, understanding, and skills developed in the AS units form a solid base for further study at A2. In particular:

- decision-making and problem-solving skills are developed
- the increased breadth of study leads to a broadening of the interrelationships and a deeper understanding of the connections between different aspects of geography
- a greater depth of understanding through research (Unit 5)

- Units 5 and 6 require students to synthesise geographic information from various sources.

'Global challenge' is an extensive unit, and you are advised **not** to exclude any element from your studies. If you do, you may struggle in the cross-unit section and/or the synoptic paper.

Many of the topics are current affairs such as the world refugee problem, degradation of coral reefs, global warming, the debt crisis, and so on. These are summarised in the diagram below.

The specification framework

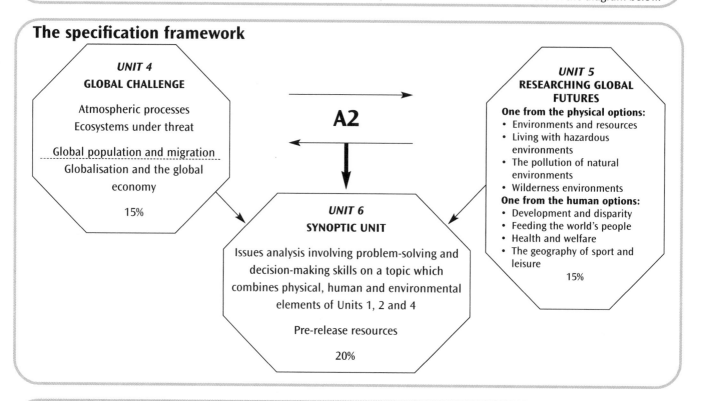

Scheme of assessment

	UNIT	STYLE OF ASSESSMENT	Duration and length	Advanced GCS (A2) weighting
A2	4 Global challenge	Students will choose three structured data and stimulus essay-style questions: one from Section A *The natural environment*, one from Section B *Population and the economy*, one from Section C, which will be cross-modular. A choice of questions will be set in each section. Sections A and B questions will be marked out of 25 marks. Section C questions will be marked out of 30 marks. The total for the unit is 80 marks.	2 hrs	15%
	5 Researching global futures	*Managing natural environments* will be assessed by a formal research-based essay written under examination conditions. One generalisation will be set (pre-released two working weeks ahead). The exam will give a choice of two titles on each generalisation. The essay will be marked out of 60.	1 hr 20 mins	15%
		Challenges for the human environment will be assessed by a coursework report. The student will choose from a list of titles published each year by Edexcel. It will show conceptual understanding and individual research (primary and/or secondary). The report will be marked out of 60.	1500 words (penalty applies above this limit)	
		All coursework for this unit will be externally marked. The total for the unit is 120 marks.		
	6 Synoptic assessment	Assessed by an issues analysis exercise – a sequence of linked tasks focused on a place, area, or environment unfamiliar to students. It will enable students to show critical understanding. Knowledge, understanding, and skills will be drawn from physical, human, and environmental geography in Units 1, 2, and 4. Students will be assessed on their ability to synthesise, and to demonstrate decision-making and problem-solving skills. They will be required to analyse resources (pre-released two working weeks ahead) and then work under exam conditions. The total for the unit is 70 marks.	2 hrs	20%

Weather and climate

Pages 81 to 82 ask:
• Why do weather and climate present a global challenge?

Definitions

- **Climate** – the average weather conditions of a place or an area over a period of not less than 30 years.
- **Weather** – the state of the atmosphere at a given time and place.

The term **climate** refers to the state of the atmosphere over a period of not less than 30 years. It includes variables such as temperature, rainfall, winds, humidity, cloud cover, and pressure. It refers not just to the averages of these variables but to the extremes as well.

By contrast, **weather** refers to the state of the atmosphere at any particular moment in time. However, we usually look at the weather over a period of between a few days and a week. The same variables as for climate are considered.

Weather systems: impact on human activity

Experiencing the weather is probably most people's most direct and frequent experience of the physical environment. This is especially true for people who live in urban areas, who are less likely to experience other aspects of the physical environment. The impact on human activity ranges from the spectacular (e.g. the sinking of the *Titanic* in poor visibility) to the mundane (e.g. the weather affects what we wear).

Human biometeorology is the study of the effects of weather and climate on people. In addition to the natural environment, it is possible to study the micro-environment of the home, school, or office on people's well-being.

Environmental determinism states that the environment to a large extent controls human response, whereas **environmental possibilism** suggests that people may operate differently within environmental parameters.

Short-term and medium-term forecasts

Extreme events can have a huge impact on human lives – the Mozambique floods of 2000 are a good example. However, it is important to forecast for a range of events, not just extreme ones. Short-term and medium-term forecasts allow people to decide whether to make decisions (e.g. whether to undertake a journey). The floods in the UK during the winters of 2000–01 and 2002–03 are an excellent example. Short-term and medium-term forecasts allowed people to move furniture upstairs, put sandbags in place, and to therefore reduce the impact of flooding in certain locations.

The challenges of weather and climate for economic activities

Primary sector	General activities	Specific activities
Food	Agriculture	Land use, crop scheduling and operations, hazard control, productivity, livestock and irrigation, pests and diseases
	Fisheries	Management, operations, yield
Water	Water disasters	Flood-, drought-, pollution-abatement
	Water resources	Engineering design, supply operations
Health and community	Human biometeorology	Health, disease, morbidity and mortality
	Human comfort	Settlement design, heating and ventilation, clothing, acclimatisation
	Air pollution	Potential, dispersion, control
	Tourism and recreation	Sites, facilities, equipment, marketing, sports activities
Energy	Fossil fuels	Distribution, utilisation, conservation
	Renewable resources	Solar-, wind-, water-power development
Industry and trade	Building and construction	Sites, design, performance, operations, safety
	Communications	Engineering design, construction
	Forestry	Regeneration, productivity, biological hazards, fire
	Transportation	Air, water, and land facilities, scheduling, operations, safety
	Commerce	Plant operations, product design, storage of materials, sales planning, absenteeism, accidents
	Services	Finance, law, insurance, sales

Source: Goudie, A. (ed.) *The Encyclopaedic Dictionary of Physical Geography*, Blackwell 1994

Climatic impacts

Managing weather and climate

Environments vary in terms of their suitability for human activity, and people try to alter weather and climate to optimise their impact. The use of air conditioners and heaters operates at a small-scale level, whereas cloud-seeding illustrates human (mis-) management at a larger scale.

An important influence of weather and climate on human activity is through the effects of **hazards**. Weather-related losses are large, and increasing. The European floods of 2002 (the worst in Europe for over 200 years) caused about 300 deaths and £18.5 billion damage.

Weather and climate have a direct impact on health and death rates. Death rates increase once a critical temperature has been reached. Morbidity (illness) rates are higher, too, in cloudy, damp, snowy places. Certain diseases have a seasonal pattern, such as respiratory problems and diarrhoea.

Climate also influences people in the very way it varies. These variations include:

- long-term changes (e.g. global warming)
- seasonal changes (e.g. decreased temperatures in winter)
- rapid, unexpected changes (e.g. the Great Gale of 1987).

As a result there is a great deal of human interest in being able to predict the weather.

Impact on economic activities

The impact of weather and climate on farming systems is well known:

- Plants require water to survive and grow – too much may cause soil erosion, too little may kill plants.
- Most plants require temperatures of over 6°C for successful germination of seeds; **accumulated temperatures** are the total amount of heat required to produce optimum yield: wheat needs about 1300°C.
- Wind can increase EVT rates and erode soil.
- Cloud cover may reduce light intensity and delay harvesting.

Farmers use greenhouses, plastic covers, hay, and straw to raise temperatures, and irrigation to make up for a shortage of water.

Increasingly, climate is having an impact on manufacturing activity. In the USA, states with warmer climates, such as Arizona and New Mexico, have a cost-advantage over colder states because firms need to spend less on heating bills. A large section of the aircraft industry has moved to the South West where there are clearer skies and heating costs in the hangars are much lower.

Comfort zones

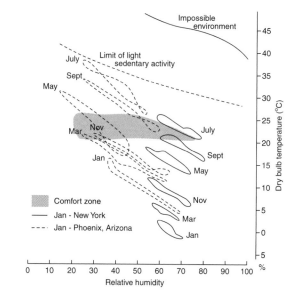

Note how the climates of New York and Phoenix fall outside the comfort zone in most of the six months plotted.

Cloud seeding

This is the process of adding silver iodide to clouds in order to make it rain. A 2001 government report suggests that the Lynmouth floods of 1952, which killed 34 people, may be attributable to the work of cloud seeding by the RAF and the Met Office. Weeks of heavy rain fell across the West Country, and on 15 August over 250 mm of rain fell in just 12 hours. Secret rainmaking experiments had taken place over Exmoor in the weeks before the floods. A major problem with cloud seeding is that it is difficult to forecast where it will rain after the clouds have been seeded.

Weather forecasts

These are made using a variety of methods:

- observations from ships, aircraft, oil rigs, buoys, and balloons, land stations and remote-sensing equipment, both on the ground and in space
- surface observations using barometers, thermometers, anemometers, rain gauges, and visual observations (e.g. cloud and weather type)
- upper-air observations using balloon-borne instruments (radiosondes)
- radar
- satellites – **polar-orbiting satellites** pass around the earth from pole to pole at a height of about 870 km, and **geostationary satellites** remain over the equator, stationary with respect to the earth.

Mid-latitude weather

Pages 83 to 91 look at atmospheric processes – a management challenge.
Pages 83 to 85 ask:
- *Why do mid-latitude areas such as the UK experience such changeable weather?*
- *What management problems does this changeable weather cause?*

The mid-latitudes are located at the convergence of subtropical air masses and polar air masses. This means that areas such as the UK are affected by warm air at certain times and cold air at other times. Often the two air masses meet and produce a **depression** or **cyclone**.

The **polar front** refers to the boundary between the warm air mass and the cold air mass. At high altitude there is a **polar front jet stream**. This is a very fast meandering thermal wind that causes air to rise and sink. In a low pressure system air is rising, whereas in a high pressure system air is sinking.

Air masses and weather types

The climatologist H. Lamb has identified seven main air masses which bring different conditions to the UK's weather.

Type	General weather
Westerly (Pm, Tm)	Unsettled weather: variable wind directions as depressions cross the country. Mild and stormy in winter, cool and cloudy in summer.
North-westerly (Pm)	Cool changeable conditions. Strong winds and showers affect windward coasts, but southern parts of Britain may have dry, bright weather.
Northerly (Am)	Cold weather at all seasons. Snow and sleet showers in winter, especially in the north and east.
Easterly (Pc, Tc)	Cold in the winter, sometimes severe snow and sleet in the south and east. Warm in summer with dry weather. Occasionally thundery.
Southerly (Tm, Tc)	Generally warm and thundery in summer. In winter it brings mild, damp weather from the Atlantic, or dry conditions from central Europe.
Cyclonic (Pm, Tm)	Rainy, unsettled conditions often accompanied by gales and thunderstorms caused by the rapid passage of depressions or the persistence of a deep depression.
Anticyclonic (Tc, Pc)	Warm and dry in summer apart from occasional thunderstorms. Cold in winter with night frosts and fog, especially in autumn.

Average air mass frequency at Kew in January

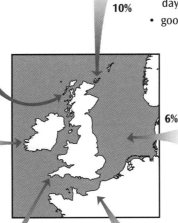

Polar maritime (returning)
- originates in cold polar regions
- travels south then veers north
- passage over the North Atlantic drift causes lower layers to become cooler and more stable
- moving north the lower layers become cooler and more stable

Polar maritime (Pm)
- an unstable air mass
- cool, showery weather – especially in winter
- gains moisture over the sea, warms up, leading to unstable air
- 'nice morning, bad day' cumuliform clouds
- in winter often about 8°C – warmed by the North Atlantic Drift
- in summer about 14°C to 16°C – cooled by the North Atlantic Drift
- visibility is excellent

Tropical maritime (Tm)
- a stable air mass brings warm air from low latitudes
- commonly forms warm sector of depressions
- in winter, air is unseasonably mild (11°C) and damp
- stratus or stratocumulus cloud with drizzle
- summer temperatures are 16°C to 18°C
- visibility is poor – solid particles remain near the ground

Arctic maritime (Am)
- extreme weather – cold severe frosts at night but clear blue skies by day: mostly dry and sunny so days can be warm.
- good visibility

Polar continental (Pc)
- affects British Isles between December and February
- very cold, dry air from Siberia around 0°C in January (absent in summer)
- picks up moisture from the sea and can lead to snow showers, especially on the east coast (as air becomes unstable over the North Sea)
- wind chill factor (dry air) exaggerates coldness

Tropical continental (Tc)
- warmest air entering the British Isles: 13°C in January, 25°C in July
- can lead to heatwaves or late summer warming – the September 'Indian summer'
- can lead to instability and thunderstorms caused by convectional instability – the ground becomes so hot that it causes air to rise rapidly, cool and produce thunderstorms
- in winter it can bring fine, hazy, mild weather
- originates in North Africa
- moderate visibility

10%

44%

6%

4%

36%

Adapted from: Barry, R. & Chorley, R. 1998

Depressions

A **depression** is a low pressure system, in which warm air is forced to rise over cold air. They are caused when two different types of air mass meet. A **front** is a boundary between cold and warm air. Severe depressions are potential hazards.

No two fronts are the same. In general, the greater the difference between the temperatures of the air masses involved, the greater is the frontal activity. Two main types can be distinguished.

- **Anafronts** occur where there is a strong contrast in the air masses involved, and uplift is vigorous
- **Katafronts** develop when there is little difference between the fronts involved, and uplift is limited.

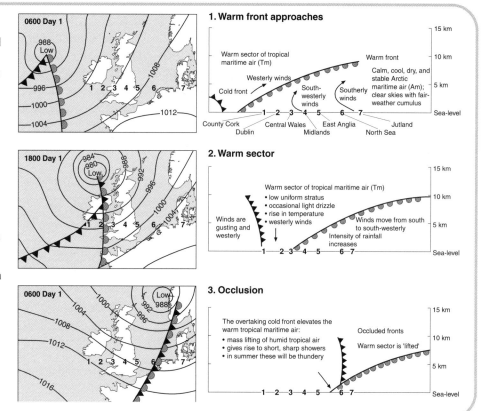

Severe storms and gales in Britain

The Great Gale of 1987 was one of the most severe storms ever to hit the south of Britain. It started as a low pressure system off the coast of Spain but was dragged north-eastwards to Britain by high-level jet streams. Warm waters from the Bay of Biscay supplied some of its energy.

The strongest gusts (up to 104 mph) were experienced during the night – had they been during the daytime the effects would have been much greater. The total cost of insurance claims was over £860 million.

Several elements affect the nature of a disaster:

- the time of day – it is more difficult to warn or evacuate people in the middle of the night
- areal extent of the storm – the wider the area affected the greater the potential damage
- the time of year – trees in leaf may intercept rain, but not deciduous trees in winter
- awareness of the event – people who are aware of the event can take precautionary measures
- precautions taken – such as leaving the area, etc.
- the duration of the event – the longer it goes on the greater the risk of damage
- the strength of the storm or hazard – the more extreme the event the greater the damage inflicted.

There are many management problems to deal with: disruptions to transport and communications; localised flooding; damage to properties; injury and loss of life, and the psychological impacts these have; insurance claims;

preparing to meet bigger, more serious storms partly as a result of global warming.

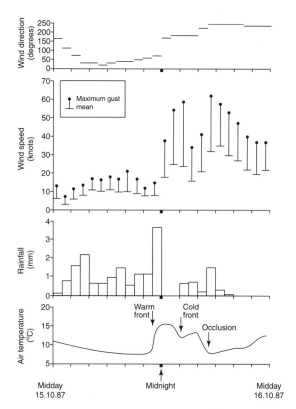

Weather data collected in Oxford during the Great Gale of 1987

Source: Coones, P. *The Great Gale of October* 1987, Geography Review vol. 1, issue 3, 1987

High pressure (anticyclones)

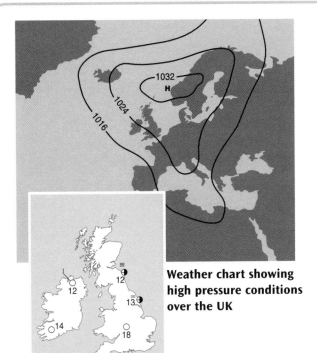

Weather chart showing high pressure conditions over the UK

High pressure

Air stability and instability refers to the buoyancy characteristics of air. High pressure is associated with stable conditions (stability) or **descending air,** whereas low pressure systems are characterised by unstable conditions (instability) or **rising air**.

High pressure systems or **anticyclones** act very differently to low pressure systems or **depressions**. An anticyclone is a large mass of subsiding air, which causes high pressure at the surface. High pressure systems produce hot, sunny, dry, calm days in summer and cold, sharp, crisp days in winter. Nights are cold in winter as the lack of cloud cover allows heat to escape. Frost and fog are common in winter and autumn. Winds in a high pressure system blow out from the centre of high pressure in a clockwise direction. The winds are light, so the isobars on a high pressure weather chart are circular and spaced far apart.

High pressure systems bring clear, dry, stable conditions but they also cause problems, notably fog, low-level ozone, and, increasingly, skin cancer and cataracts.

Anticyclonic weather in the UK

Winter weather (polar source)

- Low daytime temperatures – usually below freezing to a maximum of 6°C.
- Very cold night-time temperatures with frost.
- Clear skies by day and night with low relative humidities.
- Stable conditions, so fogs may form, especially radiation fogs in low-lying areas.
- High levels of atmospheric pollution in urban areas, caused by subsiding air and lack of wind.
- Pollutants are trapped.

Summer weather (tropical source)

- High daytime temperatures – over 23°C.
- Warm night-time temperatures – may not fall below 15°C.
- Generally clear, sometimes cloudless skies.
- Some mists and fogs in early morning, especially at the coast where they may be persistent – these are advection fogs caused by differences in temperature between sea and land.
- Thunderstorms may result from convectional uplift, usually in the late afternoon or early evening
- Large amounts of low-level ozone, and formation of photochemical smog, are a major pollution hazard.

Air pollution and health

Air pollution is associated with high pressure because winds in a high pressure system are usually weak. Hence pollutants remain in the area and are not dispersed. It has been linked with health problems for many decades. Those at risk include asthmatics, those with heart and lung disease, infants, and pregnant women. This accounts for 20% of the population in MEDCs and an even higher proportion in LEDCs. The death rate from asthma has increased from between 40% and 60% in recent decades and it is now one of the most common causes of hospital admissions for children.

Nitrogen oxide

There are many types of nitrogen oxide. They can cause coughs and sore throats, and can have an effect on asthmatics and people with bronchitis. Nitric oxide (NO) and nitrogen dioxide (NO_2) (jointly termed NOx) are gases formed in combustion processes both from the nitrogen present in fuels and from the oxidation of nitrogen in air.

Ozone

Ozone is formed by a complex series of reactions between nitrogen oxides and volatile organic compounds (VOCs) in the presence of sunlight. In the lower atmosphere (troposphere) ozone is formed by sunlight splitting oxygen molecules into atoms which regroup to form ozone.

Ozone concentrations are greatest during the day, especially during warm, sunny, stable conditions. Above 20°C reactions are accelerated.

Ozone can harm lung tissue, impair the body's defence mechanism, increase respiratory tract infections, and aggravate asthma, bronchitis, and pneumonia. Even at relatively low levels, coughing, choking, and sickness increase. The long-term effects include the premature ageing of the lung. Children born and raised in areas where there are high levels of ozone can experience up to 15% reduction in their lung capacity.

Seasonal variations in climate

Pages 86 to 89 ask:
- *Why do seasonal variations of climate occur?*
- *What management problems does the seasonality of climates cause?*

The **heat equator** refers to the zone of maximum insolation. It largely reflects the migration of the overhead sun.

During late March and late September it is over the equator. At that time trade winds blow in towards the equator from the subtropics. As the NE trades and the SE trades are similar in character they form a **convergence zone** rather than a front. The **inter-tropical convergence zone** (ITCZ) or **inter-tropical discontinuity** marks the position of the thermal equator.

Impact on ecosystems

Seasonal variations in the thermal equator have an impact on rainfall and on the distribution and type of ecosystems. In general, with increasing distance from the equator there is increasing seasonality of rainfall, and a longer dry season. The vegetation changes from rainforest to savanna to desert. There is also a change of vegetation with altitude. The variation in the nature and range of ecosystems with climate is mirrored by a transect from the equator to the Sahara in which seasonality of rainfall is mirrored by changes in ecosystems. An **ecotone** is a narrow transition zone between habitats, while an ecocline represents a broader area of transition across an environmental gradient.

Main vegetation zones of Africa

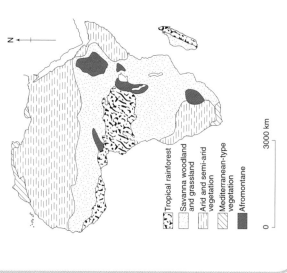

- Tropical rainforest
- Savanna woodland and grassland
- Arid and semi-arid vegetation
- Mediterranean-type vegetation
- Afromontane

0   3000 km

N

Pressure and winds in July

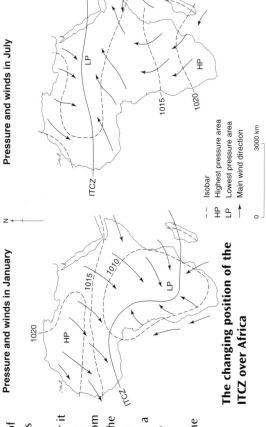

Pressure and winds in January

N

1020

HP

1015

1010

ITCZ

LP

1010

LP

ITCZ

1015

1020

HP

- – – Isobar
- HP Highest pressure area
- LP Lowest pressure area
- → Main wind direction

0   3000 km

The changing position of the ITCZ over Africa

Seasonal variations

Latitudinal variations in the ITCZ occur as a result of the movement of the overhead sun. In June, the ITCZ lies further north whereas in December it lies in the Southern Hemisphere. The seasonal variation in the ITCZ is greatest over Asia, which is a very large land mass. By contrast over the Atlantic and Pacific Oceans its movement is far less. Winds at the ITCZ are generally light – known as the doldrums, they are broken by occasional strong westerlies, generally in the summer months.

Seasonal patterns of rainfall in Africa

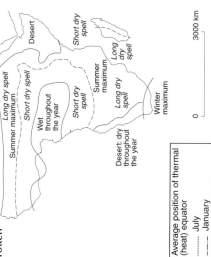

N

- Winter maximum
- Desert: dry throughout the year
- Summer maximum
- Wet throughout the year
- Short dry spell
- Long dry spell
- Desert
- Short dry spell
- Summer maximum
- Long dry spell
- Short dry spell
- Long dry spell
- Desert: dry throughout the year
- Winter maximum

0   3000 km

Average position of thermal (heat) equator

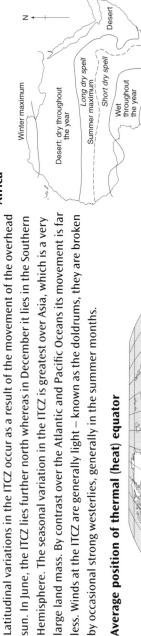

Average position of thermal (heat) equator
- ······· July
- – – – January

Equator

Managing water supplies in dry areas

Water supply and demand

Water **supply** and **demand** depend on many factors:

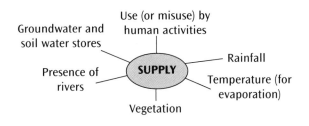

Water can be 'mined' in many ways. The main ones are:
- extraction from rivers and lakes
- it can be trapped behind dams and banks
- it can be pumped from aquifers (water-bearing rocks)
- desalinisation (changing salt water to fresh water).

These can be achieved using either high-technology or low-technology methods.

Water harvesting refers to making use of available water before it drains away or is evaporated. Efficient use or storage of water can be achieved in many ways, for example:
- irrigation of individual plants rather than of whole fields
- covering expanses of water to reduce evaporation
- storage of water underground to reduce evaporation loss.

Inefficient use of water can lead to:
- salinisation (the build-up of toxic salts in the soil)
- waterlogging (which produces cold, oxygen-deficient conditions in a soil, making it useless for farming).

Managing water supplies in Chad

Chad is a land-locked country in north central Africa. It has been independent since 1960, but it has not been at peace. There are three distinct zones in Chad:

- the tropical, cotton-producing south (the most prosperous region in Chad)
- the central semi-arid Sahelian belt
- the northern desert and the Tibesti Mountains.

Oil deposits have recently been discovered in the south. This may bring economic prosperity to the country or it could keep the warring factions at war for even longer as they battle over the new-found riches.

Chad is a hot, dry country.

- The northern half has temperatures between 10 and 20°C from November to April, and less than 250 mm of rain.
- By contrast the southern half experiences temperatures of between 20 and 29°C, and less than 250 mm of rain.
- During winter, the Harmattan, a hot, dry wind, blows from the Sahara raising daytime temperatures in the south.
- Between May and October much of the northern half has temperatures over 30°C whereas the south has temperatures between 20 and 30°C. Rainfall at this time in the north is low (< 250 mm) but in the south it is higher (> 500 mm).
- The Tibesti Mountains contain reserves of groundwater, which could be used for irrigation.

Options for water development in Chad
- Long-distance transfers of water from wet areas
- Inter-basin transfers
- New dams
- Desalinisation
- Develop groundwater supplies

- Re-use effluent (water used for sewage treatment)
- Build earthen dams to catch and hold back water.

Management options
- Use meters in people's homes
- Repair leaking pipes
- Apply new technology, such as desalinisation.

Population growth and economic growth is increasing the demand for water and it is being used up at a faster rate than it is being renewed. There are, however, means of improving the situation. These include:

- lower subsidies
- use of dryland farming techniques
- less water wastage
- more efficient pipes
- better irrigation methods
- desalinisation of sea water
- less government control of water resources.

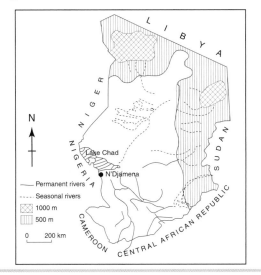

Climatic change

Pages 90 to 91 ask:
- What is climatic change?
- What are its implications for the environment and people?

What is climatic change?

Climate and weather vary at a variety of scales – daily, seasonally, annually, by decades, over centuries and millennia.

Global warming

- **Global warming**: the increase in temperatures around the world that has been noticed over the last 50 years or so.
- The **greenhouse effect**: the process by which certain gases – water vapour, carbon dioxide, methane, and chlorofluorocarbons (CFCs) – allow short-wave radiation from the sun to pass through and heat up the earth, but trap an increasing proportion of long-wave radiation from the earth. This radiation leads to a warming of the atmosphere.
- The **enhanced greenhouse effect**: the increasing amount of greenhouse gases in the atmosphere as a result of human activities, and their impact on atmospheric systems, including global warming.

One concern about global warming is the build-up of greenhouse gases. **Carbon dioxide** (CO_2) levels have risen from about 315 ppm in 1950 to 355 ppm, and are expected to reach 600 ppm by 2050. The increase is due to human activities – burning fossil fuels (coal, oil, and natural gas) and deforestation.

Methane is the second largest contributor to global warming, and is increasing at a rate of 1% per annum. It is estimated that cattle convert up to 10% of the food they eat into methane, and emit 100 million tonnes of methane into the atmosphere each year. Natural wetland and paddy fields are another important source – paddy fields emit up to 150 million tonnes of methane annually. **Chlorofluorocarbons** (CFCs) are synthetic chemicals that destroy ozone, and absorb long-wave radiation. CFCs are increasing at a rate of 6% per annum, and are up to 10 000 times more efficient at trapping heat than CO_2.

The effects of global warming are mixed:

- sea-levels will rise, causing flooding in low-lying areas
- an increase in storm activity
- changes in agricultural patterns
- reduced rainfall over the USA, southern Europe and Russia
- extinction of wildlife.

Causes and consequences of global warming

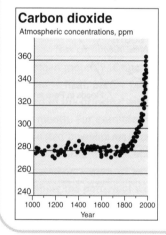

Carbon dioxide
Atmospheric concentrations, ppm

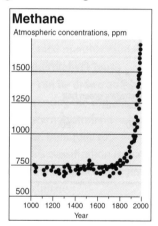

Methane
Atmospheric concentrations, ppm

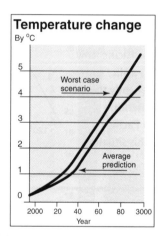

Temperature change
By °C

Worst case scenario

Average prediction

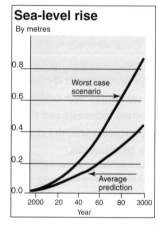

Sea-level rise
By metres

Worst case scenario

Average prediction

Reducing the greenhouse effect

The energy sector

- introduce a carbon tax on electricity generation
- introduce a higher carbon dioxide tax and retain the existing energy tax on non-energy-intensive industry
- introduce an energy tax on combined heat and power
- introduce measures to save electricity (including standards for domestic appliances)

The transport sector

- new rules and taxes on company cars (to reduce long-distance travel)
- expand public transport systems
- set carbon dioxide emission limits on light vehicles
- further develop environmental classification systems for vehicles and fuels
- reduce average speeds on roads
- subject all transport plans and infrastructure investments to environmental impact assessments
- experiment with the introduction of electric vehicles

Other greenhouse gases

- reduce agricultural use of nitrogen fertilisers
- expand methane extraction from waste tips
- reduce process emissions of fluorocarbons from aluminium smelters, and ban their use as chemicals; reduce use of hydrofluorocarbons

The implications of climate change

The effects of global warming on Britain's natural, social, and economic environments are mixed.

```
                                  Long-term ─────────── Temperature, wind, pressure,
                                  change               precipitation, humidity
                     ┌── Climate ──┤
                     │            └── Extreme events ── Storms, drought, fire, erosion, landslides,
Global ──────────────┤                                 sedimentation, avalanches, pests and diseases
warming              │
                     │                                  ┌── Coastal erosion, flooding, salination
                     └── Sea-level rise (through thermal ├── River flooding, bank erosion
                         expansion and ice melt) ────────┤
                                                         └── Waves
Consequences of the                                         Tsunami
greenhouse effect
```

What would be a significant climate change for the UK?

If there is an increase in temperature of 0.5°C, the following can be expected ...	If there is an increase in temperature of 1.5°C, the following can be expected ...
• Summer and winter precipitation increases in the north-west by 2–3%. • Summer precipitation decreases in the south-east by 2–3%. • This implies that annual runoff in the southern UK decreases by 5%. • The frequency of the 1995-type summer (drought) increases from 1:90 to 1:25. • Disappearance of a few niche species. • Increase in demand for irrigation water by 21% over the Increase without climate change, and in domestic demand by an additional 2%.	• Summer and winter precipitation increases in the north-west by about 7%. • Summer precipitation decreases in the south-east by 7–8%. • Annual runoff in the southern UK decreases 15%. • Frequency of 1995-type summer increases from 1:90 to 1:3. • Further disappearance from the British Isles of several species. • Increase in demand for irrigation water by 21% over the increase without climate change, and in domestic demand by an additional 7%.

Policies to combat climate change

Emissions of the main anthropogenic greenhouse gas, CO_2, are influenced by:

• the size of the human population
• the amount of energy used per person
• the level of emissions resulting from that use of energy.

A variety of technical options which could reduce emissions, especially from use of energy, are also available. Reducing CO_2 emissions can be achieved through:

• improved energy efficiency
• fuel switching
• use of renewable energy sources
• nuclear power
• capture and storage of CO_2.

These options are most easily applicable to stationary plant. Another class of measure involves increasing the rate at which natural sinks take up CO_2 from the atmosphere, for example by increasing the amount of forests.

International policy to protect climate

In 1988 the Intergovernmental Panel on Climate Change (IPCC) was established by UNEP and the World Meteorological Organisation.

The Kyoto Protocol (1997) was an addition to the **Rio Convention**. It gave all MEDCs legally binding targets to cut emissions from the 1990 level by 2008–2012. The EU agreed to cut emissions by 8%, Japan 7%, and the USA by 6%. Some countries found it easier to make cuts than others.

There are three main ways for countries to keep to the Kyoto target without cutting domestic emissions:

• plant forests to absorb carbon or change agricultural practices, e.g. keep fewer cattle
• install clean technology in other countries and claim carbon credited for themselves
• buy carbon credits from countries such as Russia where

traditional heavy industries have declined and the national carbon limits are underused.

Even if greenhouse gas production is cut by between 60% and 80%, there is still enough greenhouse gas in the atmosphere to raise temperatures by 5°C. The Kyoto Agreement was only meant to be the beginning of a long-term process, not the end of one.

Although the rest of the world could proceed without the USA, the USA emits about 25% of the world's greenhouse gases. So without the USA, and LEDCs such as China and India, the reduction of carbon emissions would be seriously hampered. According to the Kyoto rules, 55 countries must ratify the agreement to make it legally binding worldwide, and 55% of the emissions must come from MEDCs. If the EU, Eastern Europe, Japan, and Russia agree they could just make up 55% of the MEDC's emissions.

Global ecosystems

Pages 92 to 95 introduce biomes.
- What factors are responsible for the pattern of global biomes?
- What is the importance of global ecosystems?
- What are the major threats to their survival?

On a global scale the main factor affecting the distribution of biomes is climate. Variations in climate are closely related to changes in biomes. Primary productivity (the amount of energy produced by plants) is also closely related to climate, although there are other factors such as age of plant, health of plant, availability of nutrients, density of vegetation, and soil type.

World distribution of vegetation types

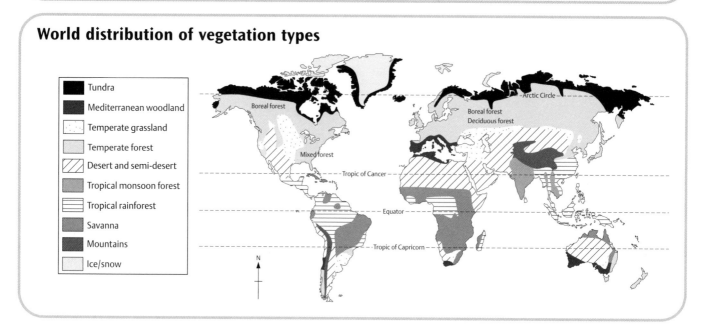

Tundra
Mediterranean woodland
Temperate grassland
Temperate forest
Desert and semi-desert
Tropical monsoon forest
Tropical rainforest
Savanna
Mountains
Ice/snow

Climate and vegetation

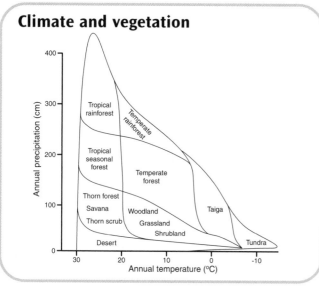

Effect of climate on soils

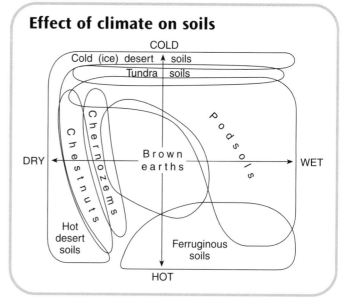

Productivity and biomass

Ecosystem	Mean NP (kg/m²/yr)	Mean biomass (kg/m²)
Tropical rainforest	2.2	45
Tropical deciduous forest	1.6	35
Tropical scrub	0.37	3
Savanna	0.9	4
Mediterranean sclerophyll	0.5	6
Desert	0.003	0.002
Temperate grassland	0.6	1.6
Temperate forest	1.2	32.5
Boreal forest	0.8	20
Tundra and mountain	0.14	0.6
Open ocean	0.12	0.003
Continental shelf	0.36	0.001
Estuaries	1.5	1

The oceans as food sources

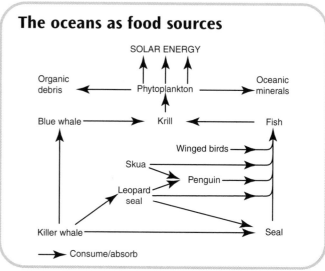

The influence of human activities on ecosystems

There are very few ecosystems that are unaffected by human activities. This includes **direct** modifications such as in the development of farming, and the conversion of natural environments to built ones; and **indirect** effects through human-induced climate change, for example. Such changes are a major concern, since natural biomes provide many advantages.

Australia: changes to major ecosystems, 1788 to 1995

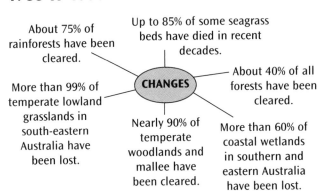

About 75% of rainforests have been cleared.

Up to 85% of some seagrass beds have died in recent decades.

More than 99% of temperate lowland grasslands in south-eastern Australia have been lost.

CHANGES

About 40% of all forests have been cleared.

Nearly 90% of temperate woodlands and mallee have been cleared.

More than 60% of coastal wetlands in southern and eastern Australia have been lost.

Australia has the world's worst record of mammal extinctions: 10 out of 144 marsupial species and 8 out of 53 native rodent species have become extinct over the past 200 years.

The current status of land animals and plants that are extinct, endangered or vulnerable is:

- 5% of higher plants
- 23% of mammals
- 9% of birds
- 7% of reptiles
- 16% of amphibians
- 9% of freshwater fish

In addition, many species have been introduced from other places and are creating much damage. These include rabbits (approximately 200 million), foxes (5 million), cats (12 million), goats, Buffel grass, Rubber vine, Para grass, the giant sensitive plant Siam weed, and the fungus *Phytophthora cinnamoni,* which is a pathogen threatening entire native plant communities in some areas of southern Australia. In addition at least 55 species of marine fish and invertebrates, plus several seaweeds, have been introduced, either intentionally for aquaculture, or accidentally in ships' ballast water or encrusted on their hulls. These are damaging marine and coastal environments.

The eco-compass

The eco-compass developed by Dow Europe is a useful tool for assessing the environmental impact of a product. The assessment is made by constructing a series of concentric hexagons, with each corner representing a different environmental dimension. These are:

- service extension (e.g. making products last longer)
- revalorisation (re-manufacturing, re-use and recycling possibilities)
- resource conservation (renewability of materials used)
- energy (consumed per unit of production)
- material intensity (weight of resources used per unit of production)
- health and environment (risks to people and ecosystems).

The concentric hexagons represent scores of 0–5, starting with 0 at the centre and 5 at the perimeter. All uses of the eco-compass must start with a baseline product, which is given a score of 2 on all six dimensions. The product to be compared is then evaluated on a factor basis for each dimension. For example, if the manufacture of the baseline product uses 100 kWh of energy per unit of production, and

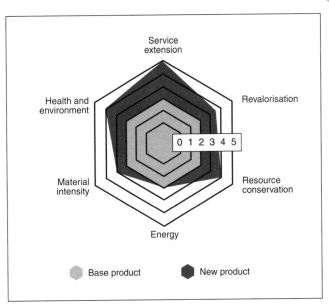

the new product only uses 25 kWh, the new product scores a factor of 4. When scores are plotted for all six dimensions, the eco-compass takes on a new shape, making it easy to compare its environmental performance with that of the baseline.

The importance of ecosystems

Ecosystems are important environmentally, hydrologically, and economically. Human impacts, such as population growth, expansion of farmland, pollution, commercial exploitation, and tourism are having a serious effect on many ecosystems.

The value of wetlands

Functions	Products	Attributes
Flood control	Fisheries	Biological diversity
Sediment accretion and deposition	Game	Culture and heritage
Groundwater recharge and discharge	Forage	
Water purification	Timber	
Storage of organic matter	Water	
Food-chain support/cycling		
Water transport		
Tourism/recreation		

The value of tropical rainforests

Industrial uses	Ecological uses	Subsistence uses
Charcoal	Watershed protection	Fuelwood and charcoal
Sawn logs	Flood and landslide protection	Fodder for agriculture
Gums, resins and oils		Building poles
Pulpwood	Soil erosion control	Pit sawing and sawmilling
Plywood and veneer	Climate regulation	Weaving materials and dyes
Industrial chemicals	e.g. CO_2 and O_2 levels	Rearing silkworms and beekeeping
Medicines		
Genes for crops		Special woods and ashes
Tourism		Fruit and nuts

The cost of environmental inaction in Nigeria

Governments and private sectors have often avoided taking new environmental protection measures because of concern about the costs. This has overshadowed the equally important consideration of the mounting economic, social, and ecological costs of not acting. A recent World Bank study provides a stark assessment of the risks and enormous costs if no remedial action is taken – the long-term losses to Nigeria from environmental degradation have been estimated to be around US$5 000 million annually.

Rapid deforestation

Rates of deforestation in Costa Rica accelerated rapidly during the 20th century. With the eradication of this diverse ecosystem comes the loss of many natural habitats.

Annual costs of inaction (US$ million/year)

Soil degradation	3000
Water contamination	1000
Deforestation	750
Coastal erosion	150
Gully erosion	100
Fishery losses	50
Water hyacinth	50
Wildlife losses	10
Total	**5110**

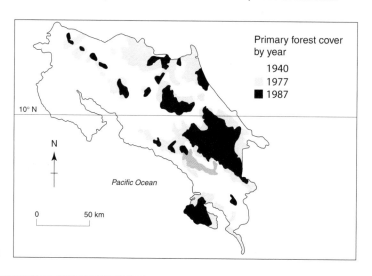

Deforestation in Costa Rica

Threats to ecosystem survival

The world's riches – biodiversity

It is estimated that there are up to 30 million species on earth. However, only 1.4 million species have yet been identified.

- The tropics are the richest area for biodiversity. Tropical forests contain over 50% of the world's species in just 7% of the world's land. They account for 80% of the world's insects and 90% of primates.
- Coral reefs are another ecological hot spot, and are experiencing severe pressures from modern development.
- Oceanic islands are particularly rich in **endemics** (indigenous species not found anywhere else), as their flora and fauna has evolved in isolation from neighbouring land masses. Many of these species have a very precise **ecological niche,** i.e. their position in the ecosystem. Many of these are very specialised and therefore vulnerable to environmental stress and change.
- Wetlands are also very diverse. Lakes, mangroves, and fens are important sources of biodiversity. For example, the Sundarbans mangrove swamps in Bangladesh are the last remaining habitat of the Bengal tiger: protecting one species can save others: protecting the tiger's habitat in India has saved over 300 bird species, 55 mammal species, and 36 reptile species.

Biodiversity means biological diversity. It is the variety of all forms of life on earth – plants, animals, and micro-organisms. It refers to species (species diversity), variations within species (genetic diversity), interdependence within species (ecosystem diversity), and habitat diversity. **Hot spots** refer to small-scale regions that have a high biodiversity or an important ecological value – the Galapagos is a good example of an environmental hot spot on account of its unique species diversity. In contrast, an **ecoregion** is a larger-scale ecosystem, such as a tropical rainforest. It, too, may be very diverse.

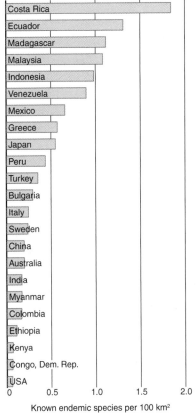

Endemic species in selected countries

The threats

- One of the main threats to biodiversity is **deforestation** (see page 97). Tropical forests are being destroyed at a rate of over 11 million ha/year. This is due to shifting cultivation (largest proportion), commercial logging, cattle ranching, plantation farming, and road clearance.
- In Europe, wetland **drainage** is a major threat to biodiversity. In the USA, less than 50% of the wetlands that existed in 1600 still exist.
- **Pollution** of streams and lakes by domestic, industrial, and agricultural contaminants is an increasing problem.
- **Over-exploitation** of fish stocks has depleted many marine species (see page 102).
- **Trade** in endangered species is also a serious threat. Up to 10 million cacti are imported into the USA every year. In the UK, native orchids have now become very rare.
- **Exotic introductions** have destroyed many island communities. Over 90% of known extinctions of birds since 1600 have been on islands.
- **Modern agricultural methods** replace wild species with relatively uniform species. Areas of greatest crop diversity are in developing countries where the pressure on the remaining habitat is greatest. Reduced diversity may eliminate options to use untapped resources for agriculture, industry, and medicine. Currently less than 5% of the world's rainforests are protected.

The value of biodiversity

- The commercial value of medicines based on natural products is over US$ 20 billion a year. The economic value of good health could be as high as US$ 1800 billion a year!
- Over 60% of the world's population depends on traditional medicines and most of these are derived from plants, e.g. quinine is used to fight malaria, and digitalis from foxglove is used to treat heart disorders.

The conversion of wilderness to human use costs $250 billion annually. Whilst it would cost $45 billion to effectively protect threatened areas of temperate and tropical forest, mangrove and coral reef, in return these global reserves would supply people with at least $4400 billion in goods and services, such as carbon recycling, flood prevention, erosion control, pollination of crops, food, shelter, and raw materials for medicines and industry.

Major forest types

*Pages 96 to 102 examine global ecological issues and the management of threats.
Pages 96 and 97 ask:*
* *Why has the degradation of the world's forests become such a global issue?*
* *Why are forest biomes so difficult to conserve?*

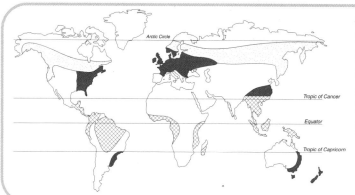

Both tropical rainforests and deciduous forests have become increasingly scattered and fragmented. The latter have been replaced by farming more than the other biomes. Coniferous forests are found largely in continuous stands at high latitudes and high altitudes. They have not been cut down as much for farming, since the farming potential of their environment is limited.

☐ Coniferous forest
■ Temperate forest
▨ Tropical rainforest

The world's forest regions

Vegetation in . . .

A Tropical rainforest

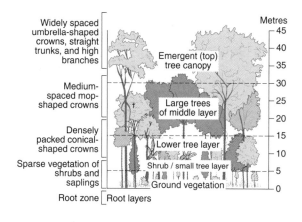

B Coniferous forest

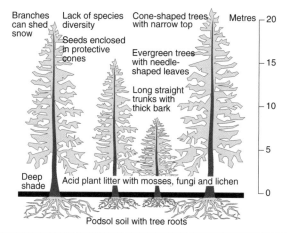

Nutrient cycles

The nutrient cycle in the tropical rainforest is easily disrupted. Despite some of the world's most luxuriant vegetation, they are found on some of the world's least fertile soils. This paradox is explained by the closed nature of the nutrient cycle. Once the vegetation is removed, nutrients are quickly removed from the system, creating infertile conditions and even deserts.

Nutrient cycles in deciduous forests have been studied intensively. Leaching can be quite high although this is balanced by relatively fast rates of weathering.

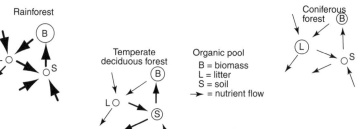

Organic pool
B = biomass
L = litter
S = soil
→ = nutrient flow

Energy flow along a food web

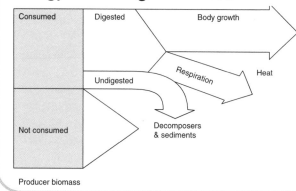

The energy flow is more complex in those ecosystems with most layers and species. Even in a moderately complex biome, energy flows are highly complex.

Issues related to forests (1)

Deforestation of the tropical rainforest

There are a large number of effects of deforestation including:

- disruption to the circulation and storage of nutrients
- surface erosion and compaction of soils
- sandification
- increased flood levels and sediment content of rivers
- climatic change
- loss of biodiversity.

Deforestation disrupts the closed system of **nutrient cycling** within tropical rainforests. Inorganic elements are released through burning and are quickly flushed out of the system by the high-intensity rains.

Soil erosion is also associated with deforestation. As a result of soil compaction, there is a decrease in infiltration, an increase in overland runoff, and surface erosion.

Sandification is a process of selective erosion. Raindrop impact washes away the finer particles of clay and humus, leaving behind the coarser and heavier sand. In Santarem, Rondonia in Brazil, evidence of sandification dates back to the 1890s.

As a result of the intense surface runoff and soil erosion, rivers have a higher **flood peak** and a shorter time lag. However, in the dry season river levels are lower, the rivers have greater turbidity (murkiness due to more sediment), an increased bed load, and carry more silt and clay in suspension.

Other changes relate to **climate**. As deforestation progresses, there is a reduction of water that is re-evaporated from the vegetation, so the recycling of water inevitably diminishes. Evapotranspiration rates from savanna grasslands are estimated to be only about one-third of that of the tropical rainforest. This mean annual rainfall is reduced, and the seasonality of rainfall increases.

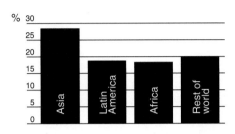

Clearance of the world's tropical rainforests, 1960–90

Causes of deforestation in Brazil

There are five main causes of deforestation in Brazil:

- **agricultural colonisation** by landless migrants and speculative developers along highways and agricultural growth areas
- conversion of the forest to cattle pastures, especially in eastern and south-eastern Para and northern Mato Grosso
- **mining**, for example the Greater Carajas Project in south-eastern Amazonia, which includes a 900 km railway and extensive deforestation to provide charcoal to smelt the iron ore; another threat from mining are the small-scale informal gold mines, *garimpeiros*, which cause localised deforestation and contaminate water supplies
- large-scale **hydroelectric power schemes**, such as the Tucurui Dam on the Tocantins River
- **forestry** in Para, Amazonas and northern Mato Grosso.

Deforestation in Brazil shows five main trends:

1 It is a recent phenomenon.
2 It has partly been promoted by government policies.
3 There is a wide range of causes of deforestation.
4 Deforestation includes new areas of deforestation as well as the extension of previously deforested areas.
5 Land speculation and the granting of land titles to those who 'occupy' parts of the rainforest is a major cause of deforestation.

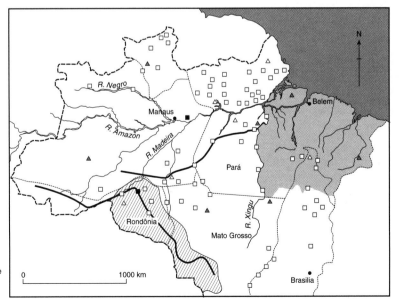

Economic development and deforestation in the Brazilian rainforest

Issues related to forests (2)

There are a number of examples of how forests can be managed. These include a mix of:
- conservation
- reforestation
- forest management
- debt for nature (i.e. reduce a country's debt if they preserve their forests)
- sustainable agroforestry.

Forest biomes are difficult to conserve on account of their:
- fragility
- the specialisation of many of the species
- the lack of speed with which they can adapt to change
- the slow build-up of pollutants and toxins in trees
- the pressures they are put under for development purposes.

Preserving forests and indigenous people

Case study: sustainable agroforestry in Santa Rosa, Mexico

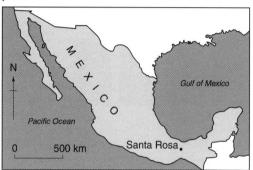

The Popoluca Indians of Santa Rosa, Mexico practise a form of agriculture that resembles shifting cultivation, known as the **milpa system**. This is a labour-intensive form of agriculture, using **fallow**. It is a diverse form of **polyculture** with over 200 species cultivated, including maize, beans, and coffee.

The Popolucas have developed a system that mimics the natural rainforest. The variety of a natural rainforest is reflected by diversity of shifting cultivation. For example, lemon trees, peppervine, and spearmint are **heliophytes** (light seeking), and prefer open conditions not shade. By contrast, coffee is a **sciophyte** (prefers shade), while the mango tree requires damp conditions.

The close associations that are found in natural conditions are also seen in the Popolucas' farming system. For example, maize and beans go well together, as maize extracts nutrients from the soil whereas beans return them. Tree trunks and small trees are left in the soil because they are useful for many purposes, such as returning nutrients to the soil and preventing soil erosion. They are also used as a source of material for housing, hunting spears, and for medicines.

The Popolucas display a vast store of ecological knowledge and management:
- 244 species of plant are used in the farming system
- Animals include chickens, pigs, and turkeys. These are used as a source of food, for barter and exchange for money, and their waste is used as manure.
- Rivers and lakes are used for fishing and catching turtles.
- It is not therefore entirely a subsistence lifestyle, since wood, fruit, turtles, and other animals are traded for some seeds, mainly maize.

Pressures on the Popolucas

About 90% of Mexico's rainforest has been cut down in recent decades, largely for new forms of agriculture. This is partly a response to Mexico's huge international debt and attempts by the government to increase agricultural exports and reduce its imports. The main new forms of farming are:
- **cattle ranching** for export
- **plantations** of cash crops, such as tobacco.

However, these new methods are not necessarily best suited to the physical and economic environment:
- they are very labour intensive
- inputs are expensive
- costs are rising rapidly.

Sustainable development of the rainforest requires the management and use of the natural structure and diversity, namely local species, local knowledge and skills rather than the type of farming developed elsewhere and then imported.

A comparison between the milpa system and the new forms of agriculture

	Milpa system	Tobacco plantation or ranching
Net primary production	High, stable	Declining
Work (labour)	High	High and increasing
Inputs	Few (clearing and seeding)	Very high: 2.5–3 tonnes fertiliser/ha/pa
Crops	Polyculture (244 species used)	Monoculture (risk of disease, poor yield, loss of demand and/or overproduction)
Yield (compared with inputs)	200%	140% if lucky
Reliability of farming system	Quite stable	High-risk operation
Economic organisation	Mainly subsistence	Commercial
Money	None/little	More
Carrying capacity	Several families/4ha	> 1 family on a plantation (200 ha)
Livestock	–	Ranching: 1 ha of good land = 1 cow. 20 ha of poor land = 1 cow

Major grassland types

Pages 99 to 100 ask:
- *What are the pressures which lead to the deterioration and desertification of the world's grasslands?*
- *Why do grasslands prove difficult to manage?*

Savannas are areas of tropical grasslands. They are characterised by a continuous cover of grasses, although a variety of other plant types may also be present. Savannas cover about one-quarter of the world's land surface and are found between the tropical rainforests and the world's great deserts.

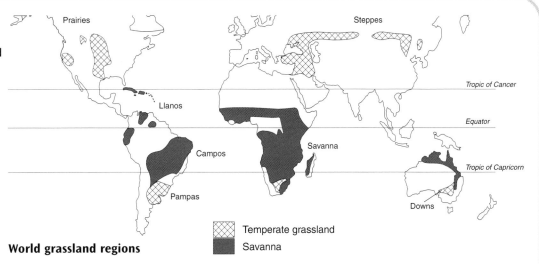

World grassland regions

Temperate grassland
Savanna

There are many different types of savanna depending on moisture availability. Typical species in Africa include the acacia, palm and baobab trees, and elephant grass, which can grow to a height of over 5 m. Trees grow to a height of about 12 m and are characterised by flattened crowns and strong roots. Savannas are productive ecosystems on account of the heat availability, although the seasonal lack of moisture reduces productivity.

Nutrient cycle

1 The biomass store is less than that of the tropical rainforest because there is a shorter growing season.
2 The litter store is small because the grass if often destroyed by fire. This means that the soil store is relatively large.

The savanna nutrient cycle differs from the tropical rainforest nutrient cycle as a result of the combined effects of a seasonal drought and the occurrence of fire. Consequently there is:

- a lower nutrient availability
- a reduced biomass store
- a small litter store
- a relatively large soil store.

Vegetation in savannas is both **xerophytic** and **pyrophytic**.
- NPP is 600 g/m²/yr.
- Biomass is low – 1.6 kg/m – due to the lack of woody species.

The nutrient cycle is affected by:
- climate (drought)
- fire
- deeply matted root system
- the grassland vegetation.

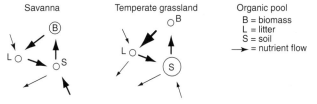

Savanna   Temperate grassland   Organic pool
B = biomass
L = litter
S = soil
→ = nutrient flow

Savanna and temperate grassland nutrient cycles

The area of the boxes is proportional to the calorific value of the vegetation per unit area (1 cal = 4.2J). *Forbs* are herbaceous plants other than grasses. The importance of burning in the system can be gauged by comparing the production box (P) with the total burnt box (B) and the total remaining in the biological system box (R).

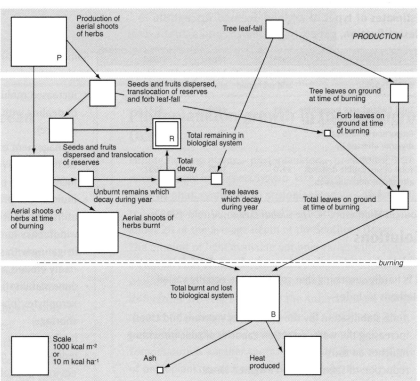

Energy flow to show the effects of burning on the savanna of Nigeria

Pressures on marine ecosystems

Part of the value of coastal ecosystems lies in their **biodiversity** but part also results from the way in which these ecosystems offer opportunities for **sustainable development**, **coastal protection**, and **economic gain**. It is, therefore, important to safeguard coastal ecosystems from the many pressures, e.g. exploitation of resources, and pollution, that threaten them.

Pressures on coral reefs

Coral reefs are among the most tourist-damaged coastal environments (see page 104). Nearly two-thirds of the world's coral reefs are currently at risk from human activity. Destruction takes many forms:

- construction of roads increases runoff which can carry sediment from land-clearing areas, high levels of nutrients from agricultural areas, as well as many pollutants such as petroleum products or insecticides
- large sections of coral reefs are destroyed by boats dropping anchors or grounding; fuel leakage is also damaging
- demand for souvenirs increases commercial exploitation of reefs.

Coral reefs are often thought of as 'the rainforests of the sea' on account of the huge number of species they contain, and their vulnerability to destruction. Occupying less than 0.25% of the marine environment, they nevertheless shelter more than 25% of all known fish species.

The Galapagos Islands

The Galapagos Islands are famed for their rich biodiversity and many unique species, e.g. iguanas, penguins, and the palo alto tree. The native species of the islands have evolved over 3 million years in the absence of competing species and predators; 75% of the land birds and 97% of the reptiles are unique to the Galapagos.

The Galapagos Islands have their own unique climate. Differences in altitude and wind patterns have created four main ecosystems over the years. Arid lowlands of open cactus forest give way to subtropical forest. At higher elevations, moist dense forest shifts to treeless upland areas covered with ferns and grasses.

In 1959 Ecuador declared all of the Galapagos a National Park, except for land already colonised by that date. Today 97% of the archipelago is National Park land, and only 3% is open to humans.

Tourism

Until the mid-1980s regulations on tourism in the Galapagos worked well, but with increasing numbers of new tourist developments these regulations have proved ineffective. Ironically, it is the wilder, more beautiful parts of the islands that are threatened. Where there is tourism there is at least some control. But some of the tourist developments are having an impact on the islands' biodiversity. For example, at Puerto Villamil an airport is being built close to a nesting ground of flamingos.

The government is therefore working to:

- control emigration to the islands
- impose a quarantine on plants and animals
- set up more efficient policing with a new radar network and patrol boats for the archipelago
- maintain tighter rules on tourist development.

The Galapagos National Park N

- **Intensive use zones**
  There are about 25 of these exceptional tourist zones within the Galapagos National Park. The plan recommends that a limited number of people be authorised to disembark at these sites. Some areas are fragile, and control is important.

- **Extensive use zones**
  There are about 16 of these zones, which are not so interesting as the intensive use zones. No large groups allowed.

- **Primitive use zones**
  Most of the land surface of the National Park. Sometimes affected by presence of introduced species, but still ecologically unique. A special permit is required.

- **Primitive scientific zones**
  Kept for scientific research, e.g. Fernandia. No possible access to visitors with no specialised interest.

- **Special use zones**
  Adjacent to colonised areas. These zones may be exploited by local people e.g. for wood, but activity is strictly controlled.

- **Settlement areas**

People as decision makers

Pages 103 to 104 discuss global eco-futures.
- *How are individuals and organisations playing an increasing part in ecosystem management?*
- *What is the future for global ecosystems?*

Ecosystem management – the main players

There are many active players in the work of ecosystem management and conservation. These include:

- individuals (such as the late Gerald Durrell and the Durrell Trust for Conservation)
- groups (such as Greenpeace and the World Wide Fund for Nature)
- public servants, politicians and scientists (such as Diane Fosse, made famous by the film 'Gorillas in the Mist').

In most cases there is a conflict between the need for economic development and the need for environmental conservation or management. Diane Fosse argued for the protection of the mountain habitats in Rwanda and Burundi that were home to the great silverback gorillas. On the other hand, population growth, civil conflict, and the illegal trade in forest products lead to a decline in forest cover and a reduction in the gorillas' habitat.

There is an urgent need for strategic thinking and planning, especially in some of the world's most valuable biomes, such as coral reefs. This needs to be done in a sustainable way, with the cooperation of the indigenous people.

The role of Greenpeace

Greenpeace is an international environmental organisation founded in Vancouver, Canada in 1971. Its confrontational approach has secured it a high public profile, and helped develop a strong support for the organisation. It has tackled many issues such as waste disposal, deforestation, nuclear power, harvesting of seal cubs, and industrial pollution. Greenpeace's goal is 'to ensure the continuing ability of the earth to nurture life in all its diversity'.

Worldwide Fund for Nature (WWF)

Formerly the World Wildlife Fund, the WWF was initially concerned with the protection of endangered species, but now includes all aspects of nature conservation, including landscapes (the environments in which species live). It has over 5 million supporters globally, and is increasingly concerned with the fight against environmental destruction.

Managing the Korup National Park

The Korup National Park was created in 1986 by the government of Cameroon, with the support of the WWF. Under Cameroon law, human activity in the park is limited to tourism, research, and recreation. The project is designed to 'protect and manage the National Park and integrate it into the local economy and regional development plans'.

One example of sustainable development in Korup is that of **community forests**. These are large areas of forest in which villagers hold and manage part of the communal forest for a long period of time. The project is reviewed regularly by the government and the WWF to ensure that the villagers are using the forest in a sustainable way. Other projects have included over 30 natural resources, management committees, more than 40 village infrastructural developments and over 70 income-generating and credit activities (such as sustainable forms of agroforestry).

Management of Korup is important – it has many unique species:
- over 400 species of trees
- 425 species of birds
- 120 species of fish
- 100 mammal species
- more than 60 species are found only in Korup
- 170 species are considered to be endangered or vulnerable.

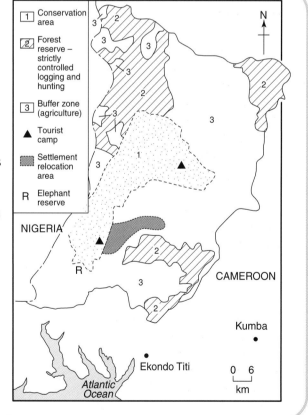

The future of global ecosystems

The state of the environment

According to the United Nations Environment Programme (UNEP) *Global Environment Outlook, 2000,* there are a number of issues facing the earth, which will have a direct or indirect impact on global ecosystems. These include:

- climate change
- ozone depletion
- nitrate pollution
- chemical pollution
- natural disasters
- El Niño (see page 89)
- degradation of forests (see pages 97–8) and grasslands (see pages 99–100)
- declining water availability and water quality
- degradation of coastal and marine areas (see pages 101–2).

Ecosystems at risk

Forests, woodlands, and grasslands continue to be **degraded**. Marginal lands become deserts and natural ecosystems are reduced or fragmented, which threatens biodiversity. Climate change may increase soil erosion, which may decrease food production. **Deforestation** of the tropical rainforest continues to be rapid (see page 97) – between 1990 and 1995 over 16% of the rainforest was lost, and the quality of the remaining forest is threatened by a range of pressures including acidification, fuelwood and water abstraction, the introduction of exotic species, and fire. Other ecosystems, notably coral reefs, are equally vulnerable.

Trends likely to worsen

In coastal areas fisheries have been mismanaged. Coastal land suffers from poorly planned and regulated urbanisation, industrialisation, aquaculture, tourism, port development and flood control (see page 102). Resource exploitation, changes to habitat, and disruption of ecosystems are more serious threats to many marine and coastal areas than pollution.

The deliberate and accidental introduction of species is also increasing. Through competition and pathogenic impacts (disease and mortality), many indigenous (native) species are threatened.

Strategic planning in the Caribbean

Nearly all countries in the Caribbean have threatened ecosystems, and most have now developed plans to protect these environments. Biodiversity strategies have been developed in ten countries, and land use planning has been introduced to limit the damage on vulnerable locations. Environmental information is increasingly used in decision making for sustainable development in Caribbean countries. Government policy is to establish environmental management institutions. NGOs are also increasingly involved in data collection and public education. In St Lucia, for example, the National Trust now incorporates scientific data in the management of its National Parks, such as Barre de Isle rainforest.

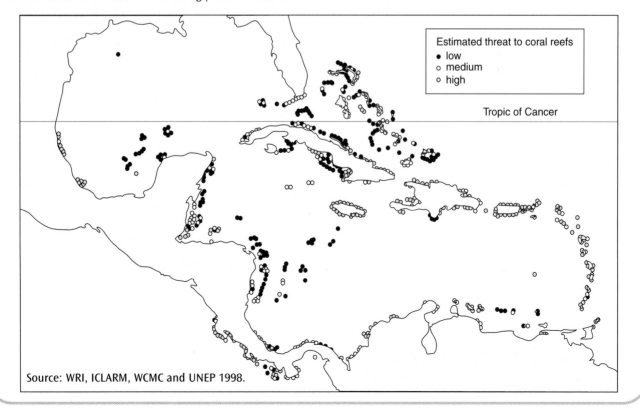

Source: WRI, ICLARM, WCMC and UNEP 1998.

The future of the living planet

The **Living Planet Report** is WWF's annual update on the state of the world's ecosystems – as measured by the Living Planet Index – and the human pressures on them through the consumption of renewable natural resources – as measured by the Ecological Footprint. There is a cause-effect linkage between the two measures.

The **Living Planet Index** (**LPI**) is the average of three ecosystem-based indices and is derived from trends over the past 30 years in populations of hundreds of species of birds, mammals, reptiles, amphibians, and fish.

Between 1970 and 2000:

- the Index declined by about 35%
- the forest species population index declined by about 15%
- the marine species population index declined by about 35%
- the freshwater species population index declined by about 55%.

The world is currently undergoing a very rapid loss of biodiversity, comparable with the great mass extinction events that have previously occurred only five or six times in the earth's history.

The Living Planet Index, 1970–99

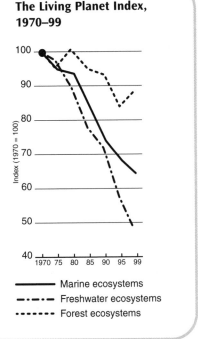

— Marine ecosystems
–·–·– Freshwater ecosystems
········ Forest ecosystems

Ecological footprint

The ecological footprint (EF) is a measure of the consumption of renewable natural resources by a population. A population's EF is the total area of productive land or sea required to produce all the resources it consumes.

This planet has about 11.4 billion ha of productive land – about one-quarter of its surface area. Divided between the global population of 6 billion people, this total equates to just 1.9 ha per person. In 1999, footprints were estimated to be as follows:

- less than 1.4 ha per person for the average African or Asian consumer
- about 5.0 ha for a Western European
- about 9.6 ha for a North American
- 2.3 ha per person for the world average consumer, or 20% above the earth's capacity. In other words, humanity now exceeds the planet's capacity to sustain its consumption of renewable resources.

Furthermore, future projections show that humanity's footprint is likely to grow to about 180–220% of the earth's biological capacity by the year 2050. This is an unsustainable situation.

If we are to return to a sustainable development pathway, four fundamental changes are necessary.

1 It is necessary to improve the resource-efficiency with which goods and services are produced.
2 We must consume resources more efficiently, and redress the disparity in consumption between high-income and low-income countries.
3 Population growth must be controlled through promoting universal education and health care.
4 It is imperative that we protect, manage, and restore natural ecosystems in order to conserve biodiversity and maintain ecological services, and so conserve and enhance the planet's biological productivity, for the benefit of present and future generations.

USA

The Netherlands

India

Some ecological footprints

Population change

Pages 106 to 107 look at the dynamics of population change.
- *What are the components of population change?*
- *How is population change measured and portrayed?*
- *How and why do rates of population change very spatially and over time?*

The components of population change

Population change results from differences in the **birth rate** and the **death rate** (known as **natural increase** or **decrease**) and **migration**. Worldwide variations in the birth rate are greater than variations in the death rate. Hence it is the birth rate that is more likely

to cause differences in population growth. In some places migration has an added impact on population growth. The main flow of migrants is from poorer countries to richer ones, often based on former colonial ties as well as close proximity.

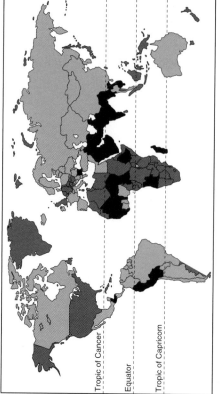

Model of population change

Deaths per 1000 population
- Over 22.0
- 11.0–21.9
- 7.5–10.9
- 2.0–7.4
- No data available

Tropic of Cancer

Equator

Tropic of Capricorn

World death rates

Births per 1000 population
- Over 44.0
- 28.5–43.9
- 18.0–28.4
- 10.0–17.9
- No data available

Tropic of Cancer

Equator

Tropic of Capricorn

World average 28.4

Measurements of birth

Crude birth rate (CBR)

$$\frac{\text{Total no. of births}}{\text{Total population}} \times 1000 = \text{CBR}$$

Mauritius 2001 $= \dfrac{19\ 600}{1\ 189\ 000} = 16.5‰$

The CBR is easy to calculate and the data are readily available. However, it does not take into account the age and sex structure of the population. By contrast, the **standardised birth rate** gives a birth rate for a region on the basis that its age composition is the same as that of the whole country.

The **total fertility rate** is the average number of births per 1000 women of child-bearing age. In the Mauritius in 2001 it was 2.01. It is the completed family size if fertility rates remain constant.

The **general fertility rate** is the number of births per 1000 women aged 15–49 years. This can be shown in the following formula:

General fertility rate =
$$\frac{\text{No. of births}}{\text{Women in 15–49 year age range}} \times 1000$$

Measurements of mortality

Crude death rate (CDR)

$$\frac{\text{Total no. of deaths}}{\text{Total population}} \times 1000 = \text{CDR}$$

The CDR is a poor indicator of mortality trends. Populations with a large number of old people, as in most MEDCs, will have a higher CDR than countries with more youthful populations – compare Denmark 11‰ and Mexico 5‰. Consequently, to compare mortality rates we use the

standardised mortality rate (SMR) or age-specific mortality rate (ASMR), such as the **infant mortality rate** (IMR).

Infant mortality rate (IMR) =
$$\frac{\text{Total no. of deaths of children} < 1\ \text{year old}}{\text{Total no. of live births}} \times 1000$$

Life expectancy (E_0) = average number of years that a person can be expected to live, given that demographic factors remain unchanged.

Counting people

A **census** is an official population count. In Britain, the Office of Population Censuses and Surveys (OPCS) has carried out a census every ten years since 1801 (with the exception of 1941 when the country was at war). The census not only counts the size of the population but it collects other information on a range of economic and social variables such as:

- family income
- occupation (jobs)
- ownership or rental of house
- long-term illness
- overcrowding
- ethnicity
- car ownership.

Sample areas to study changes at small scale

Most AS/A2 questions show information at a **county** or **regional** level. By contrast, most geographical enquiries look at information at the **ward** level or even at **enumeration districts**.

- A **ward** is an administrative division of a town.
- **Enumeration districts** are the smallest areas for which census data are available. They contain a handful of streets and have a population of about 500 people.
- A **district** is much larger, and may comprise a city or a large rural population.

Role of census in planning

The information contained in the census is important for a number of reasons:

- It allows comparisons to be made.
- It allows us to plan for the future – variations in the birth rate, for example, will affect the number of schools that are needed in an area, while an ageing population creates demands for nursing homes, extra health care, and pensions.

At a national level, taking a census allows planners to:

- project forward demographic trends from the past
- project future demands for employment
- suggest likely natural change and migration change – or the need for replacement migrant labour
- plan services such as schools and health care
- provide sufficient housing
- work out how all this will be paid for (taxes).

At a local or regional level a census is important because it enables planners to:

- plan for the future with respect to services and utilities such as water, gas, and electricity
- develop plans for new housing developments
- locate areas of multiple deprivation and develop policies to tackle deprivation efficiently.

The UK's 2001 census

First results of the 2001 census suggest a slowing growth rate and increasing reliance on immigrants to maintain the size of the workforce.

For the first time there were more over-60s (21% of the population) than children under 16 (20%). And there were 1.1 million people aged over 85.

The fastest growing region was the South West of England which has gained 12.5% (347 100 people) in 20 years, followed by the East (11% or 534 000) and the South East (10.4% or 755 100). The population of Scotland fell by 2% over the same period and there were reductions in the North East and North West of England.

Among cities, Manchester was the biggest loser in England and Wales, with a decline of 15.1% since 1981, while the fastest growing area was Milton Keynes, up by 64.4%.

The census overall response rate was 94%, although it was much lower in some areas. Inner London recorded only 78%, with Kensington and Chelsea lowest at 64%.

- The UK population of 58.8 million consisted of 49.1 million in England, 2.9 million in Wales, 5 million in Scotland and 1.7 million in Northern Ireland.

- The North East had the greatest loss, down 5% to 2 515 479. The North West lost 3% (6 728 800).
- Christchurch, Dorset had the most people of retirement age (33.1%).
- Eastbourne had the fewest men (87 per 100 women), and Richmondshire, North Yorkshire, had the most men (107 per 100 women).

Most densely populated (persons per km²)	Least densely populated (persons per km²)
1. Kensington and Chelsea 13 244	1. Highland 8
2. Islington 11 719	2. Western Isles 9
3. Hammersmith and Fulham 10 328	3. Argyll & Bute 13
Highest % of persons aged 85 and over	**Highest % of persons aged under 16**
1. Worthing 4.6%	1. Derry 26.8%
2. Rother 4.6%	2. Newry & Mourne 26.6%
3. Eastbourne 4.4%	3. Newham 26.2%

Demographic transition over time

The **Demographic Transition Model (DTM)** describes how birth rates and death rates change over time. It was developed from a study of changes in birth rates and death rates in England and Wales, and Sweden. It is usually divided into four stages, and, increasingly, a fifth stage. It is a useful diagram as it displays visually complex patterns of changes in birth rate, death rate, **natural increase**, **natural decrease** (the decrease in population when death rates exceed birth rates), and **population growth rates**.

Stages in the DTM

Stage 1 High stationary (birth rates typically 30–40‰, death rates 30–40‰)
- Birth rates and death rates are high and variable.
- Population growth fluctuates.
- There are no countries now at this stage.
- The UK was at this stage until about 1750.

Stage 2 Early expanding (birth rates typically 30–40‰, death rates 20‰)
- The birth rate remains high but the death rate comes down rapidly.
- Population growth is rapid.
- Countries such as Afghanistan, Sudan, and Libya are at this stage.
- The UK passed through this stage by 1850.

Stage 3 Late expanding (birth rates typically 20–25‰, death rates 10–15‰)
- The birth rate drops and the death rate remains low.
- Population growth continues but at a slower rate.
- Brazil and Argentina are at this stage.
- The UK passed through this stage in about 1950.

Stage 4 Low and variable (birth rates typically 10–15‰, death rates 10–15‰)
- Birth rates and death rates are low and variable.
- Population growth fluctuates.
- The UK and most developed countries are now at this stage.

Stage 5 Low and declining (birth rates typically 8–10‰, death rates 10–12‰)
- The birth rate is lower than the death rate.
- The death rate increases due to the ageing of the population.
- The population declines.
- Sweden and Japan typify this stage.

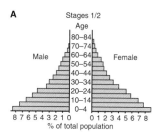

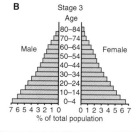

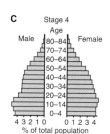

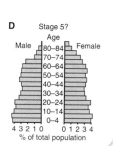

Demographic transition in the UK

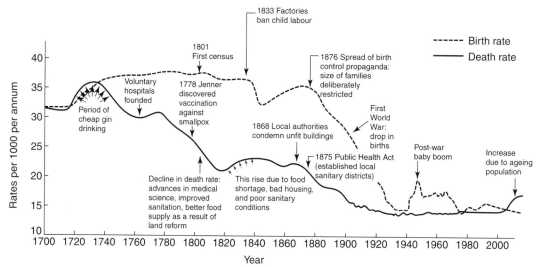

World population growth

Pages 111 to 115 look at the implications of population change.
- What are the global challenges posed by population change?
- What are the national challenges posed by population change?
- How do decision makers seek to manage population change?

Exponential growth

The world's population is growing very rapidly. It doubled between 1650 and 1850, between 1850 and 1920, and again between 1920 and 1970. It is thus taking less time for the population to double. This growth creates:

- great pressures on governments to provide for their people
- increased pressure on the environment for resources such as water
- increased risk of famine and malnutrition
- greater differences between the richer countries and the poorer countries.

Up to 95% of population growth is taking place in LEDCs. Accelerating growth is known as **exponential growth**. The world's population reached 6 billion people in 1999 and is expected to **stabilise** at between 9 and 12 billion in 2050.

The rise of world population

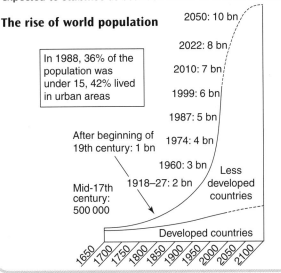

In 1988, 36% of the population was under 15, 42% lived in urban areas

2050: 10 bn
2022: 8 bn
2010: 7 bn
1999: 6 bn
1987: 5 bn
1974: 4 bn
1960: 3 bn
1918–27: 2 bn
After beginning of 19th century: 1 bn
Mid-17th century: 500 000
Less developed countries
Developed countries
1650 1700 1750 1800 1850 1900 1950 2000 2050 2100

Demographic change and global trends

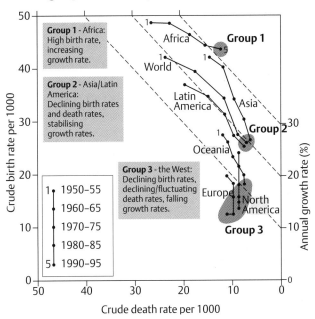

Group 1 - Africa: High birth rate, increasing growth rate.

Group 2 - Asia/Latin America: Declining birth rates and death rates, stabilising growth rates.

Group 3 - the West: Declining birth rates, declining/fluctuating death rates, falling growth rates.

1 1950–55
1960–65
1970–75
1980–85
5 1990–95

Annual growth rate is found by subtracting the crude death rate (‰) from the crude birth rate (‰) and is then expressed as a percentage (%).

Highest growth rates are found in Africa, whilst lowest growth rates are in North America and Europe.

National scale – growth in Pakistan

In 1998 Pakistan had its first population census in almost 17 years. This provided the country's planners with vital statistics on family sizes, literacy levels, occupations, and standards of living. Since 1981 Pakistan's population data has become increasingly unreliable as the country has experienced a deluge of refugees from neighbouring countries.

Pakistan has the fastest population growth among Asian countries. By 2050 it will rise from being the world's seventh most populous country to the third largest in total population. The main reason for this rapid growth is the low status of women:

- only about 20% of Pakistan's girls can read and write (compared with about 40% of boys)
- on average Pakistani women have 5.9 children (compared with 3.4 for Indian women)
- Pakistan has a high infant mortality rate (90%), mostly related to low standards of living (poor access to water, lack of hygiene and sanitation, unreliable food resources, and overcrowding
- Pakistan has one of the highest maternal mortality rates in the world. Up to 600 women die for every 100 000 children born.

Pakistan has among the lowest proportions of women to men – just 93:100. One reason is the high death rate among girls – many of whom are malnourished and have limited access to health care.

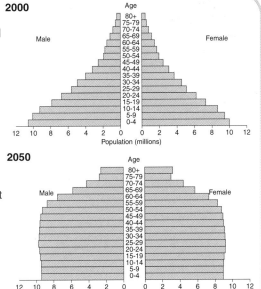

Source: US Census Bureau, International Data Base

Population and resources

Optimum population, overpopulation, and underpopulation

Overpopulation occurs when there are too many people relative to the resources and technology available locally to maintain an adequate standard of living. Bangladesh and Somalia are overpopulated as they have insufficient food and materials. They suffer from natural disasters such as drought and famine and are characterised by low incomes, poverty, poor living conditions, and a high level of emigration.

Underpopulation occurs when there are more resources in an area – e.g. energy and minerals – than can be used by the people living there. Canada could theoretically double its population and still maintain its standard of living.

Optimum population, now known as the **sustainable population,** is the number of people who, when working with all the available resources, will produce the highest per capita economic return. It is the highest standard of living and quality of life. If the size of the population increases or decreases from the optimum, the standard of living will fall.

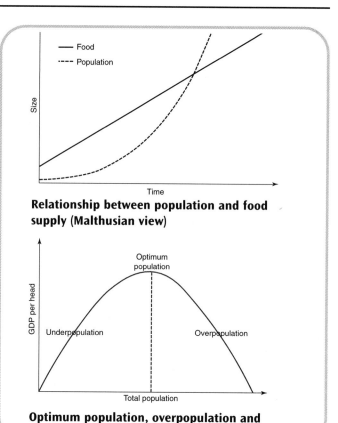

Relationship between population and food supply (Malthusian view)

Optimum population, overpopulation and underpopulation

Malthus

In 1798 the Reverend Thomas Malthus produced his *Essays on the Principle of Population Growth*. He believed that there was a finite optimum population size in relation to food supply, and that any increase in population beyond this point would lead to a decline in the standard of living, and to 'war, famine, and disease'. His theory was based on two principles:

1 In the absence of checks, population would grow at a geometric or exponential rate, e.g. 1, 2, 4, 8, 16 . . . etc. and could double every 25 years.

2 Food supply at best only increases at an arithmetic rate, e.g. 1, 2, 3, 4, 5 . . . . etc.

Malthus suggested preventive and positive checks as two main ways by which population would be curbed once this ceiling had been reached. Preventive checks include abstinence from marriage, or a delay in the time of marriage, or abstinence from sex within marriage. Positive checks such as lack of food, disease, and war directly affected mortality rates.

The Limits to Growth Model

This study examined the five basic factors that determine and therefore ultimately limit growth on the planet: population, agricultural production, natural resources, industrial production, and pollution.

Many of these factors were observed to grow at an exponential rate. Food induces output and population grows exponentially until the rapidly diminishing resource base forces a slowdown in industrial growth. Because of natural delays in the system, both population and pollution continue to increase for some time after the peak of industrialisation. Population growth is finally halted by a rise in the death rate due to decreased food, water, and medical services.

The team concluded that if the trends continued, the limits to growth would be reached by about 2070.

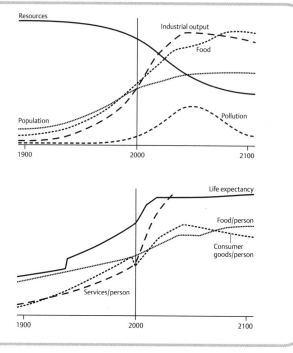

Sustainable limits to growth

Coping with population growth

Population growth can cause many problems. These include the provision of housing, work, services, food supply and so on. The term **carrying capacity** refers to the number of people that an environment can support. There are several ways by which it is possible to support more people on earth.

Carrying capacity

The concept of a **population ceiling** is of a saturation level where population is equal to the carrying capacity of the local environment. There are three models, set out below:

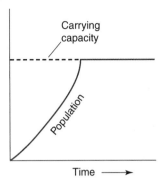

Model 1: The rate of population increase may be unchecked until the ceiling (carrying capacity) is reached, at which point the increase drops to zero.

This highly unlikely situation is not supported by evidence from either human or animal populations.

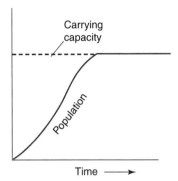

Model 2: The population increase begins to taper off as the carrying capacity is approached, and then levels off when the ceiling is reached.

Populations that are large in size, have long lives and low fertility rates, conform to this S-curve pattern.

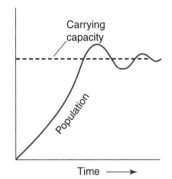

Model 3: The rapid rise in population exceeds the carrying capacity, resulting in a sudden check, e.g. famine, birth control. After this the population recovers and fluctuates, eventually settling down at the carrying capacity.

This J-shaped curve is more applicable to populations that are small in number, have short lives and high fertility rates.

Increasing the carrying capacity

A different view to that of Malthus is that of **Esther Boserup**. She believed that people have the resources of knowledge and technology to increase food production and when a need arises someone will find a solution.

Boserup suggests that in a pre-industrial society, an increase in population stimulated a change in agricultural techniques so that more food could be produced. Population growth has thus enabled agricultural development to occur.

Boserup assumed that people knew of the technologies required by more intensive systems and used them when the population grew. If knowledge were not available then the agricultural system would regulate the population size in a given area.

Since Malthus's time there have been many ways in which people have increased food production. These include:

- draining marshlands
- extensification
- intensification
- reclaiming land from the sea
- cross-breeding of cattle
- developing high-yielding varieties of plants
- terracing on steep slopes
- growing crops in greenhouses
- using more sophisticated irrigation techniques
- making new foods such as soya
- using artificial fertilisers and pesticides
- farming native species of crops and animals
- fish farming.

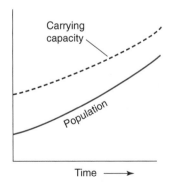

Changing age structures

Ageing population in Japan

There has been a great change in the age structure of Japan's population since 1945. This is largely due to a decrease in the birth rate and death rate. The number of elderly people who are living alone increased from 0.8 million in 1975 to over 2.5 million in 2000. Ageing in Japan is much more rapid than in other countries, although a number of European countries, such as Italy and Greece, are not far behind. The percentage of young has gradually declined since 1975. By 1995 they accounted for about 16% of the population.

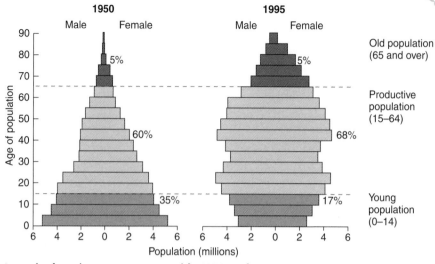

Japan's changing age–sex pyramid, 1950 and 1995

The rapid ageing of the population is placing a huge burden on pension funds and social welfare programmes, especially health care. By 2020 over 25% of the Japanese population will be over the age of 65. At present under 15% of the population are aged over 65. There are a number of problems, including:

- inadequate nursing facilities
- depletion of labour force
- deterioration of the economy
- trade deficit
- migration of Japanese industry to overseas

- the cost of funding pensions and health care
- falling demand for schools and teachers
- new jobs needed for the elderly
- an increase in the burden on the working population to serve the dependent population
- reduced demand for goods from the smaller working population.
- ageing population is now a worldwide problem, especially in MEDCs.

Gender imbalances

There are significant gender imbalances in MEDCs and in LEDCs. Among MEDCs this is mostly among the elderly, whereas in LEDCs there is an important gender imbalance among the very young. In MEDCs women tend to outlive men, for a number of reasons, for example a shorter working life coupled with less 'self-destructive' activities such as heavy smoking or heavy drinking.

In many LEDCs, for example China and India, sex-selective abortions and female infanticide have led to a distorted gender balance in favour of boys. In countries where draconian family planning measures exist, couples may elect to abort their baby when they find it is a girl. Surveys in India have shown that in some clinics, out of 7000 abortions only one was of a boy. The development of lone child families, where the child is a boy, has been coined the 'little emperor syndrome', since the child may well be very spoilt.

Age–sex pyramids for China: 1953, 1964 and 1982

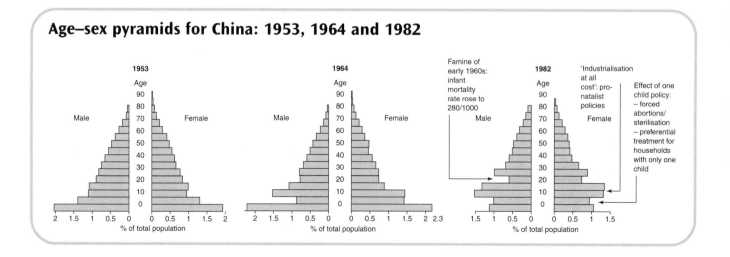

The impact of AIDS

AIDS

The impact of the AIDS epidemic is being increasingly felt in many countries across the world. It has a profound impact on growth, income, and poverty. The annual per capita growth in half the countries of sub-Saharan Africa is falling by 0.5–1.2% as a direct result of AIDS. By 2010, per capita GDP in some of the hardest-hit countries may have dropped by 8%. Heavily affected countries could lose more than 20% of GDP by 2020. Companies of all types face higher costs in training, insurance, benefits, absenteeism, and illness.

One-quarter of households in Botswana, where adult HIV prevalence is over 35%, can expect to lose an income earner within the next 10 years. A rapid increase in the number of very poor and destitute families is anticipated.

Households with an HIV/AIDS patient spend, on average, 20 times more on health care annually than households without an AIDS patient.

According to the FAO, 7 million farmworkers have died from AIDS-related causes since 1985, and 16 million more are expected to die by 2020. Agricultural output cannot be sustained in such circumstances. The prospect of widespread food shortages and hunger is real. Some 20% of rural families in Burkina Faso are estimated to have reduced their agricultural work or even abandoned their farms because of AIDS. Rural households in Thailand are seeing their agricultural output shrink by half. In 15% of these instances, children are removed from school to take care of family members who are ill, and to regain lost income.

Families often remove girls from school to care for sick relatives or to assume other family responsibilities, jeopardising the girls' education and future prospects. In Swaziland, school enrolment is reported to have fallen by 36% due to AIDS, with girls being most affected.

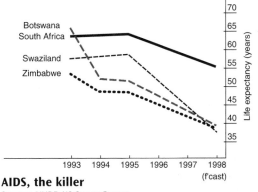

AIDS, the killer
Sources: UNDP, US Census Bureau

Development and stability threatened

Meanwhile, the epidemic is claiming huge numbers of teachers, doctors, extension workers and other human resources. Teachers and students are dying or leaving school, reducing both the quality and efficiency of educational systems. In 1999 alone, an estimated 860 000 children lost their teachers to AIDS in sub-Saharan Africa.

Coping with crisis

In the worst-affected countries, there is already a steep drop in life expectancy, most drastically in sub-Saharan Africa, where four countries (Botswana, Malawi, Mozambique, and Swaziland) now have a life expectancy of less than 40 years.

As more infants are born HIV-positive in badly affected countries, child mortality rates are also rising. In the Bahamas, it is estimated that some 60% of deaths among children under the age of 5 are due to AIDS, while in Zimbabwe the figure is 70%.

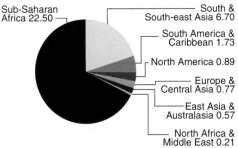

People estimated to be living with HIV/AIDS at end 1998 (millions)
Sources: UNAIDS, WHO

How to fight the virus

Two success stories show that the hurdles to prevention are not impossibly high.

Uganda

Uganda shows that there is hope even for countries that are poor and barely literate. President Yoweri Museveni recognised the threat shortly after becoming president in 1986, and deluged the country with anti-AIDS warnings. Every government department took the problem seriously, and implemented its own plan to fight the virus. The government gave free rein to scores of non-governmental organisations (NGOs), such as the Straight Talk Foundation, to do whatever it took to educate people about risky sex.The climate of free debate has led Ugandans to delay their sexual activity, to have fewer partners, and to use more condoms.

Senegal

Senegal shows how to stop the disease from taking off in the first place. In Senegal's brothels, which had been regulated since the early 1970s, condom use was firmly encouraged. The country's blood supply was screened early and effectively. Vigorous education resulted in 95% of Senegalese adults knowing how to avoid the virus.

Managing population change

There are a number of ways in which governments attempt to control population numbers. There are contrasting strategies depending on whether the country wishes to increase its population size (**pronatalist**) or whether it wants to limit it (**antinatalist**).

Family planning in developing countries

Family planning refers to attempts to limit family size. Family planning methods include contraceptives such as the pill and condoms, as well as drastic methods such as forced sterilisation, abortion, and infanticide.

Population growth and the status of women

In many societies, high rates of population growth are associated with a low status of women in society. Reasons for this include:

- a wife continues to bear children to prove her continued fertility, and to prevent the husband from marrying another wife
- wives in polygamous families compete with each other to produce the largest number of children
- children provide labour for fetching firewood and water and for farming activities
- children are an investment as they provide security in their parents' old age
- in large families there are likely to be not only rogues and robbers but also professionals such as doctors, lawyers, engineers, etc.
- women have no say in determining the size of the family.

China

China operates the world's most severe and controversial family planning programme. In 1979 the 'one child' policy was imposed. The impact was drastic. The birth rate fell from 33 per 1000 in 1970 to 17 in 1979.

In urban areas most families have only one child, and the growing middle classes do not discriminate against daughters as much. However, the countryside remains traditionally focused on male heirs. But the policy is being relaxed. In most provincial rural areas, couples can have two children without penalties. Increasingly, rich farmers are able and willing to pay fines or bribes in order to get permission to have more children.

The sex ratio at birth in China is around 118 boys to 100 girls, compared with the natural rate of 106:100. Selective abortion is a major cause, but many baby girls are probably not registered.

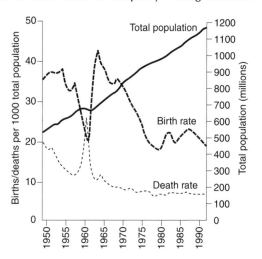

Changes in China's population, birth and death rates, 1949 to 1990s

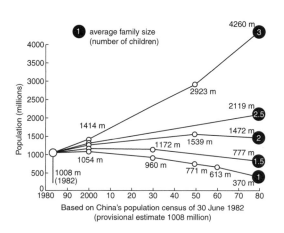

Five possible options for China's future population

Singapore

Between the 1960s and 1970s the Singapore government pursued an antinatalist policy. However, as the economy prospered and the population growth rate fell, it adopted a pronatalist policy.

Despite incentives such as the 'love cruises' arranged to help couples meet, the Singapore government found it difficult to raise population growth. Although the number of marriages increased the birth rate did not.

The government has now realised that by increasing the status of women, and having more working women, women themselves do not want to have as many children as previous generations but want to enjoy for themselves their newly-earned occupational status and material possessions.

Migration

Pages 117 to 120 discuss the global challenge of migration.
- What are the causes of international migration?
- What are the impacts of international migration?
- What are the key issues posed by international migration?

Migration is the permanent change of residence with a complete change of community affiliations. Thus it does not include commuting (a daily movement to work), seasonal movements, or moving house in the same city.

Patterns of migration according to Ravenstein

Findings	Explanation
Most migrants proceed over a short distance.	Due to limited technology/transport and poor communications, people know more about local opportunities.
Migration occurs in a series of steps or stages.	Typically from rural area to small town, to large town, to city – i.e. once in an urban area they become 'locked in' to the urban hierarchy.
As well as movement to large cities there is movement away from them (dispersal).	The rich move away from the urban areas and commute from nearby villages and small towns.
Urban dwellers are less migratory than rural dwellers.	There are fewer opportunities in rural areas.
Women are more migratory than men over short distances.	This is especially true for marriage, and in societies where the status of women is low.
Migration increases with advances in technology.	For example, transport, communications, and the spread of information.

Migration according to Lee

Lee (1966) described migration in terms of **push** and **pull** factors.

- Push factors are the negative features that cause a person to move away from a place (e.g. unemployment, low wages, and natural hazards).
- Pull factors are the attractions (whether real or just imagined) that exist at another place (e.g. better wages, more jobs, and good schools).

All of these models are simplifications, and they contain hidden assumptions that may be unrealistic. For example:

- Are all people free to migrate?
- Do all people have the skills, education, and qualifications that allow them to move?
- Are there barriers to migration, such as race, class, and so on?

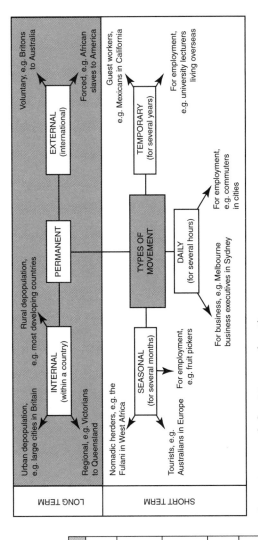

Origin

Intervening obstacles

Destination

- Disadvantages
+ Advantages
○ Other unimportant, less vital, variable factors
⋏⋏ Obstacles and opportunities, e.g. distance, cost, employment

More attractions = more migration

More obstacles and opportunities = less migration

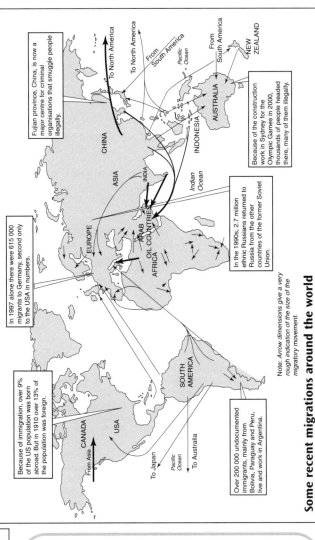

LONG TERM	Urban depopulation, e.g. large cities in Britain
	Regional, e.g. Victorians to Queensland
SHORT TERM	Nomadic herders, e.g. the Fulani in West Africa
	Tourists, e.g. Australians in Europe

INTERNAL (within a country)

Rural depopulation, e.g. most developing countries

PERMANENT

EXTERNAL (international)

Voluntary, e.g. Britons to Australia

Forced, e.g. African slaves to America

Guest workers, e.g. Mexicans in California

TEMPORARY (for several years)

For employment, e.g. university lecturers living overseas

TYPES OF MOVEMENT

SEASONAL (for several months)

For employment, e.g. fruit pickers

DAILY (for several hours)

For business, e.g. Melbourne business executives in Sydney

For employment, e.g. commuters in cities

Long-term and short-term migrations

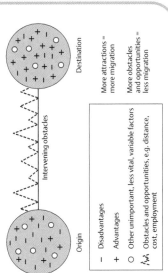

In 1997 alone there were 615 000 migrants to Germany, second only to the USA in numbers.

Fujian province, China, is now a major centre for criminal organisations that smuggle people illegally.

Because of the construction work in Sydney for the Olympic Games in 2000, thousands of people headed there, many of them illegally.

In the 1990s, 2.7 million ethnic Russians returned to Russia from the other countries of the former Soviet Union.

Because of immigration, over 9% of the US population was born abroad. But in 1910 over 13% of the population was foreign.

Over 200 000 undocumented immigrants, mainly from Bolivia, Paraguay and Peru, live and work in Argentina.

Note: Arrow dimensions give a very rough indication of the size of the migratory movement.

To North America

From South America

From South America

AUSTRALIA

NEW ZEALAND

CHINA

ASIA

INDIA

ARAB OIL COUNTRIES

INDONESIA

Indian Ocean

EUROPE

AFRICA

SOUTH AMERICA

USA

CANADA

From Asia

To Japan

Pacific Ocean

Pacific Ocean

To Australia

Some recent migrations around the world

The impact of international migration

International migrations can have a range of positive and negative impacts on both the source area and the destination.

Source area

Positive impacts
- Population pressure reduced, e.g. Ireland during the 1950s and 1960s
- Remittances sent home, e.g. labour migrants from Malawi and Lesotho in South Africa

Negative impacts
- Removal of younger, more educated people, e.g. Indian software experts to the USA
- Decline in local market/pulling power, e.g. southern Italy
- Reduced workforce, e.g. Swaziland migrants moving to South Africa
- Reduced purchasing power (smaller market), e.g. rural Ireland in the 1950s and 1960s
- Closure of local services such as schools, hospitals etc, e.g. following expulsion of Ugandan Asians to UK in 1973

Destinations

Positive impacts
- Population growth, e.g. Turks to West Germany in the 1970s and Portuguese to Switzerland
- Larger workforce, e.g. USA
- Increased demand for housing, e.g. Silicon Valley, California
- Increased demand for services, e.g. M4 Corridor, UK
- Attracts new industry and investment
- New skilled, young workforce, e.g. Italians in Bedford in the 1950s
- Multicultural enrichment, e.g. Toronto, Canada

Negative impacts
- Can lead to racism and segregation, e.g. Los Angeles
- Cultural disharmony, e.g. Bradford and Oldham, UK
- Overcrowding, ghettoisation, e.g. blacks in New York
- Spread of diseases, e.g. flu to Amazonian tribes or those of Easter Island

	Benefits		Costs	
	Individual	for the country	Individual	for the country
Emigrant countries	1 Increasing earning and employment opportunities 2* Training (human capital) 3* Exposure to new culture, etc.	1* Increased human capital with return migrants 2 Foreign exchange for investment via migrant remittances 3 Increased output per head due to flow of unemployed and underemployed labour 4 Reduced pressure on public capital stock	1 Transport costs 2 Adjustment costs abroad 3 Separation from relatives and friends	1 Loss of social investment in education 2 Loss of 'cream' of domestic labour force 3* Social tensions due to raised expectations of return migrants 4* Remittances generate inflation by easing pressure on financing public sector deficits
Immigrant countries	1(*) Cultural exposure, etc.	1 Permits growth with lower inflation 2 Increased labour force mobility and lower unit labour costs 3 Rise in output per head for indigenous workers	1 Greater labour market competition in certain sectors	1* Dependence on foreign labour in particular occupations 2 Increased demands on the public capital stock 3* Social tension with concentration of migrants in urban areas

* indicates uncertain effects. Source: *Economist*, 15 November 1988

US immigration since 1820

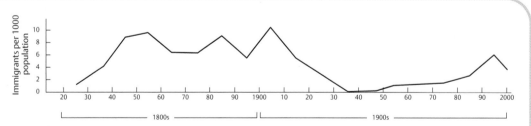

The impact of migration on the US economy

America's economic boom of the 1990s coincided with a large influx of immigrants – more than 13.5 million – accounting for 40% of America's population growth.

The new migrants accounted for more than 50% of the growth of the labour market. This was, in part, due to the ageing of America's population. The migrants helped fill the gap left by the 4.5 million decline in the number of workers aged between 25 and 34. Some 2.8 million foreign workers in that age group joined the economy during the 1990s. Without them, the labour force in that key age group would have declined by 21%.

In contrast, relatively few of the new immigrants were elderly, and male workers outnumbered women more than among native-born Americans

- Although fewer newcomers arrived in the north-east than the west, they accounted for the bulk of the population growth in New York, New Jersey, Connecticut, Massachusetts and Rhode Island
- Without the new arrivals the north-eastern states would have had a much smaller share of the economic boom.
- Up to 9 million of the 13.5 million arrivals were undocumented workers, living in the US illegally.

The world refugee problem

Definitions

- **Refugee** – a person genuinely fleeing from persecution and repression
- **Asylum seeker** – a person who seeks refugee status in another country
- **Illegal immigrant** – a person who enters another country without permission and plans to remain there
- **Economic migrant** – a person seeking opportunities

A refugee is someone who can demonstrate that he/she has fled their usual country of residence for reasons of persecution or fear of persecution.

For refugees there is a lack of civil liberties. The cause is therefore political and the migration has to be across an international border. However, it is difficult even to define persecution, never mind measure it or prove that it has happened.

Refugees are an example of a **forced migration**.

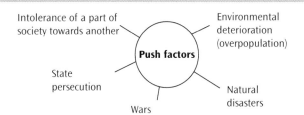

There are between 15 and 30 million refugees worldwide, depending upon the definition. According to the UN High Commission for Refugees (UNHCR), this definition is vital for the distribution of aid.

The growth in the number of refugees since 1971 has been dramatic.

1971	2.5 million
1980	8.2 million
1991	17.5 million
1995	23 million
2000	22 million

Refugees from Afghanistan

The consequence of attacks on the USA in 2001 by Osama bin Laden and the Al Qaeda network was an attack on terrorism by UN forces. The subsequent war in Afghanistan resulted in up to 1.5 million people fleeing the country, in addition to the 5 million refugees who had already left.

Following the events of September 11 2001, refugees headed for Pakistan and Iran, which were already hosts to some 3.5 million Afghan refugees. There were major problems trying to get food to the refugees, due to their huge numbers, and the inaccessibility of the refugee camps. According to the UNHCR, Afghanistan was the 'world's worst humanitarian disaster'. During the winter of 2001/02 up to 7.5 million people were at risk of starvation.

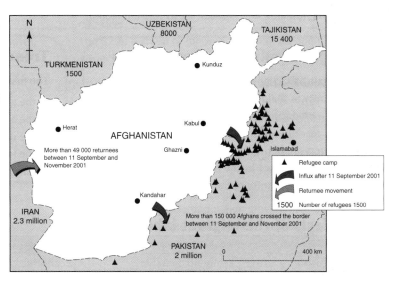

Main nationalities of applicants for UK asylum (2001)

Afghanistan	12	China	3
Somalia	8	Pakistan	3
Iraq	7	Czech Republic	3
Sri Lanka	7	India	4
Turkey	6	Sierra Leone	3
Iran	5	Zimbabwe	3
Romania	5	Other nationalities	27
Yugoslavia	4		

Countries of asylum (2000)

	Applications	Refugee status
UK	75 680	10 185
Germany	117 648	11 446
Netherlands	43 895	1808
Canada	34 252	13 989
USA	91 595	24 000
World total	**983 679**	**191 710**

Costs of asylum seekers at destination

There are increased costs of housing, social services, schooling, welfare payments, policing, and security.

Policy responses

A range of options includes:

- making travel more difficult
- greater policing of known asylum routes
- acceptance of those with skills from which a country could benefit
- fast-track procedures to accommodate genuine asylum seekers
- temporary protection followed by repatriation.

The pattern of economic wealth

A number of characteristics are used to measure levels of development. One of the most widely used indicators is **gross national product (GNP) per capita**.

The North–South divide

Approximately 15% of the world's population live in areas with a high GNP/capita. The map of GNP/capita shows a clear bias towards MEDCs. Western Europe, North America, Japan and Australia come out on top – the highest values are:

- Switzerland (US $36 310)
- Luxembourg (US $42 930)
- Japan (US $34 340).

By contrast, 56% of the world's population live in areas classified as having a low GNP/capita. Moreover, a number of countries have a GNP/capita of less than $250 per year. These are the LEDCs, and include Rwanda, Burundi, Ethiopia, Tanzania, Uganda, Mozambique, Sierra Leone, and Vietnam. Reasons for their stagnation include:

- civil war
- rapid population growth
- paying off previous debt
- a lack of resources
- natural and human hazards (including AIDS).

However, political mismanagement and/or war are major causes of their economic stagnation.

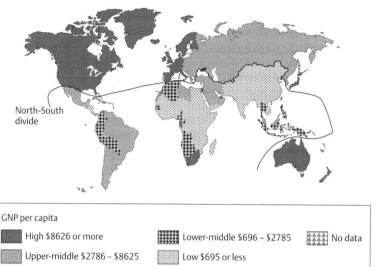

North-South divide

GNP per capita

High $8626 or more · Lower-middle $696 – $2785 · No data
Upper-middle $2786 – $8625 · Low $695 or less

Inequalities in development

Within the South there is also considerable variation. As well as the LEDCs there are some countries which are relatively well off. NICs such as South Korea and Taiwan have quite high levels of GNP/capita. The development of the original Asian 'tigers' is the result of a combination of state-led industrialisation, spontaneous industrialisation, and TNC-led industrialisation.

There are a number of problems in using GNP/capita:

- It does take into account inequalities in income – it only shows a national average.
- It does not show regional variations.
- It does not show ethnic and racial variations in GNP/capita.
- It does not take into account the local cost of living – unlike purchasing power parity (PPP).
- It fails to pick up the social and environmental costs of development.

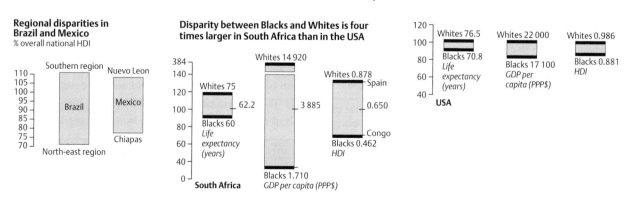

Some regional and racial disparities

Trading blocs – the European Union

A trading bloc is an arrangement among a group of nations to allow free trade between member countries but to impose tariffs (charges) on other countries that may wish to trade with them.

Plans to increase the number of countries in the EU and to extend into Central and Eastern Europe are no longer based on trade alone but increasingly on political grounds. The chances of conflict in an expanded EU are much less than if the same countries are outside of the EU.

The development gap

Global inequalities

The gap between rich and poor people in the world has been increasing for the last two centuries. In 1820, the difference between the richest and poorest country was about 3:1. By 1913 this had risen to 11:1, while by 1950 it had broadened to 35:1. In 1999 the richest country was about 95 times richer than the poorest country. Indeed, Britain's income in 1820 was four times greater than that of Sierra Leone in 1999! Nevertheless, many LEDCs have improved their GNP in recent decades.

- The assets of the world's three richest people are more than the combined GNP of all less developed countries.
- The assets of the world's 200 richest people are more than the combined incomes of 41% of the world's people. By making an annual contribution of just 1% of their wealth, those 200 people could provide access to primary education for every child in the world.
- The gap between the world's richest countries, and the world's poorest countries is widening rapidly.

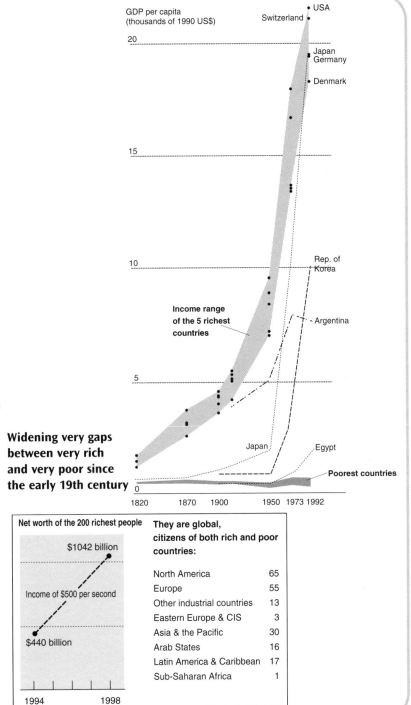

Widening very gaps between very rich and very poor since the early 19th century

Ratio of income of richest 20% of the population to the poorest 20% of the population

1960	30:1
1970	32:1
1980	45:1
1989	59:1
1991	61:1

The world's 200 richest people are getting richer – fast

Net worth of the 200 richest people

$1042 billion

Income of $500 per second

$440 billion

1994   1998

They are global, citizens of both rich and poor countries:

North America	65
Europe	55
Other industrial countries	13
Eastern Europe & CIS	3
Asia & the Pacific	30
Arab States	16
Latin America & Caribbean	17
Sub-Saharan Africa	1

The world's richest and poorest countries, 1820–2002 (GDP per capita, US$)

Richest					
1820		**1900**		**2002**	
UK	1756	UK	4593	Luxembourg	42 930
Netherlands	1561	New Zealand	4320	Bermuda	41 000
Australia	1528	Australia	4299	Switzerland	36 310
Austria	1295	USA	4096	Japan	34 340
Belgium	1291	Belgium	3652	Iceland	34 340
Poorest					
1820		**1900**		**2002**	
Indonesia	614	Myanmar	647	Ethiopia	100
India	531	India	625	Burundi	110
Bangladesh	531	Bangladesh	581	Congo	110
Pakistan	531	Egypt	509	Liberia	130
China	523	Ghana	462	Myanmar	130

Globalisation

The concept of **globalisation** developed in the 1960s after the Canadian academic Marshall McLuhan used the term **global village** to describe the breakdown of spatial barriers around the world. Globalisation refers to a range of processes and impacts that occur at a global scale – usually relating to economic systems, but it can include physical systems (global warming) and socio-cultural systems (fashion, music).

McLuhan argued that the similarities between places were greater than the differences between them, and that much of the world had been caught up in the same economic social and cultural processes. He suggested that economic activities operate at a global scale and that other scales were becoming less important.

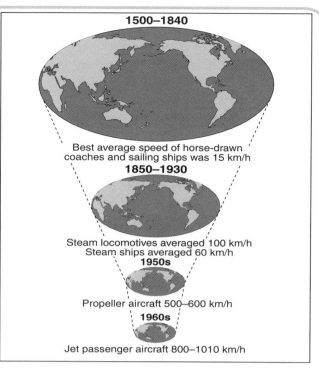

1500–1840
Best average speed of horse-drawn coaches and sailing ships was 15 km/h

1850–1930
Steam locomotives averaged 100 km/h
Steam ships averaged 60 km/h

1950s
Propeller aircraft 500–600 km/h

1960s
Jet passenger aircraft 800–1010 km/h

A shrinking world: the effect of changing transport on time-distance

Why has globalisation occurred?

- Improvements in transport and other forms of communications (such as the internet)
- The desire by multinational enterprises (MNEs) to reach new markets
- The attempt by MNEs to tap cheap sources of labour
- The expansion of economic activity to use resources from a wide range of locations
- The rise of free market economies and the spread of democratic governments
- The role of trading blocs, free trade and the impact of the World Trade Organisation
- The increasing importance of multinational companies (MNCs)
- The growth of the service sector
- The impact of aid

Forms of globalisation

There are three main forms of globalisation:

1 **Economic** – largely caused by the growth of MNCs/TNCs.
2 **Cultural** – the impact of Western culture, art, media, sport, and leisure pursuits on the world.
3 **Political** – the growth of Western democracies and their influence on poor countries, and the decline of centralised economies.

Globalisation versus regionalism

While globalisation of economic activity has certainly occurred, and there is evidence of a new international division of labour, political and cultural values have often created a new feeling of regional identity. Within major trading blocs such as the EU there are very strong nationalist tendencies, such as within Spain and the United Kingdom.

The new international division of labour

The division of labour suggests that, at a crude level of analysis, it is possible to differentiate between two groups:

1 The highly skilled, highly paid decision-making, research and managerial occupations. At a national level, these are concentrated in the economic core regions of the country. At a global scale, these occupations are located in MEDCs.

2 The unskilled poorly-paid assembly occupations. At a national level these 'screwdriver industries' are located in the cheap peripheral parts. Assembly production is located in LEDCs which offer low labour costs.

Distribution of the offices of one MNE – Barclays capital offices

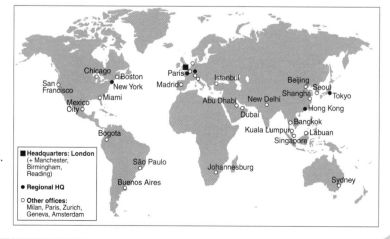

The changing global economy

Pages 125 to 130 examine globalisation and changing economic activity.
- What changes are taking place in the character and location of the global economy?
- Who are the key players in changing the location of economic activity?
- What are the implications of the changes in economic activity?

The changing car industry

The automobile industry was the key manufacturing industry for much of the 20th century. The importance of the industry was not just in its scale, but also in the linked industries it supported:

- about 4 million workers are employed in the core automobile industry
- 10 million work in the manufacture of components and materials
- 6 million are employed in selling and servicing vehicles.

The automobile industry is a global industry, dominated by large transnational organisations. The ten leading producers account for 76% of the world's production. Production takes place in developed and developing countries, although the main automobile companies are from developed countries. Distribution of plants is a response partly to sources of cheap labour, and partly to government attempts to bid for foreign investment.

The concentration of economic activity related to the automobile industry – both the automobile company and its suppliers – means that regions may become very dependent upon vehicle production and therefore very vulnerable during times of recession.

Global shift

Global shift refers to the movement of manufacturing production from traditional areas in MEDCs to certain LEDCs.

Since 1960 the pattern of vehicle production has changed dramatically. More vehicles are being produced, and they are being produced in new locations.

Production is strongly concentrated in three economies – the USA, Western Europe, and Japan. Japan has made the most dramatic growth since 1960, while the USA and the UK have been particularly hit by decline. There are also three smaller but important producers: the former Soviet Union and Eastern Europe; Latin America (notably Mexico, Brazil, and Argentina); and South-east Asia (especially Korea).

Much of the assembly takes place in LEDCs to make use of cheap labour. This is known as the **new international division of labour** – highly-paid skilled and managerial employees in MEDCs, and low-paid, unskilled labour in the LEDCs.

% world share of car production			
	1960	1990	2000
Europe	40.6	40.7	35.0
North America	53.9	22.0	36.0
Asia	1.3	28.0	26.0
Latin America	1.5	3.6	3.4

Volkswagen's global assembly line

Trade

Trade develops as a result of regional economic differences. It serves to balance production and consumption by moving raw materials, goods, and services from regions of supply to regions of demand.

Trade wars

There are a number of trade wars around the world, in industries as diverse as bananas, beef, steel, and cars. To help prevent such frictions, 134 countries agreed on trading rules and joined the World Trade Organisation (WTO) to mediate disputes.

Beef: the USA and the EU

For example, the EU and the USA are embattled over beef. The EU claims that beef from cattle reared using growth hormones deemed safe for human consumption is not safe. While the Americans say there is no health risk, the EU maintains that some of the hormones may cause cancer. Hormones are widely used in US agriculture, with more than 90% of American cattle producers feeding them to their cattle to make them grow faster and bigger.

The USA says this amounts to protectionism, and the World Trade Organisation (WTO) approved an American request to impose sanctions on the European Union in response to its ban on hormone-treated beef. The USA wanted to impose 100% duties against $202 million of imports from the EU – the amount of trade it says it has lost because of the 11-year-old ban.

GM food: USA and the EU

America and Europe are squaring up for another trade war, this time over genetically modified (GM) food. It is predicted that nearly all of the soya grown in America – 24 million hectares – will be genetically modified. At the same time Europe has banned the commercial growth of GM crops. Health concerns are also at the centre of the crops issue, with widespread public concern in Europe. The GM firm Monsanto claims that crops will provide great benefits to farmers, particularly in LEDCs.

Steel: USA and Japan

The USA is also at war with Japan over steel. The devaluation of the Asian currencies led to a flood of cheap steel in world markets. Japanese steel exports to the USA surged by a massive 400%. The American steel industry accused Japanese, Russian, and Brazilian producers of dumping steel on the USA at prices below production costs or home market rates.

The US Commerce Department proposed tariffs as high as 67%. The government reached agreements with Russia and Brazil on voluntary reductions in steel shipments. But Japan dismissed the idea.

The US industry has spent $50 billion on modernisation since 1980 and laid off more than 300 000 employees – almost three-quarters of the workforce. Its productivity of less than four man-hours per tonne of steel is better even than in Germany and Japan.

Brazil and Argentina

It is not just the USA that gets involved in trade wars. In 1999 Brazil suspended all trade talks with Argentina after the latter introduced several hurdles to limit the import of Brazilian products.

The devaluation of Brazil's currency during the global economic crisis has undermined prospects for trade liberalisation. Brazil's products became very cheap and swamped the Argentinian market. Argentina's economy is shrinking, and its industries are being priced out of the market because of the country's strong currency.

In an attempt to protect its industries, Argentina has now set import quotas for Brazilian textiles, minimum prices for steel, and other regulatory hurdles for importing home appliances.

World trade and the banana war

Many LEDCs are highly dependent on the export of one primary product. This makes them vulnerable. This is shown by changes in the world's banana trade.

In the 1990s a trade war developed between the USA and Europe over bananas, and the access that certain African, Caribbean, and Pacific (ACP) countries have to the European market. It is ironic that the USA and Europe fell out over bananas, since neither of them exports bananas and it is a relatively insignificant item in terms of world trade.

Dominica, Grenada, St Lucia, and St Vincent smallholder growers supply up to 66% of the bananas consumed in the UK, although their supplies to Europe as a whole are low. Their governments claim that they cannot compete against cheaper bananas produced in Central America by multinationals. However, there is a knock-on or **multiplier effect**. If banana traders' boats no longer visited the main Caribbean trading ports, trade in avocados and citrus fruits could be damaged, as these products are not exported in large enough quantities on their own to attract boats, but they are a useful supplementary trade.

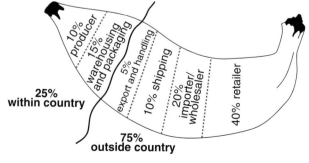

The banana trade – where the profits go

Models of aid

Aid

Aid is any help or assistance given to improve the quality of life of the receiver. It includes money, equipment, goods, staff, and services. Most aid is from MEDCs to LEDCs but aid is also given to the poorer regions in MEDCs. For example, Northern Ireland and Scotland receive much **regional aid** from the EU, and parts of Croatia and Bosnia receive aid from the United Nations.

Aid to LEDCs is often divided into:

- **short-term aid** or **emergency relief**
- **long-term aid**.

Types of aid

- **Bilateral aid**: Aid is given from one country to another. The transfer is generally between countries with political ties. The MEDC often uses such aid to its own advantage, dictating the conditions of the exchange. Bilateral aid accounts for about 75% of all official aid.

Donor

Recipient

- **Multilateral aid**: A number of countries receive aid from more than one country. The amount received may be low and the interest rates are often high.

World Bank or United Nations

- **Charities:** The amounts involved are considerably less than those received through other types of aid, but there are no political ties (charities are **non-government organisations**). Charities are more flexible and have specialist knowledge and skills.

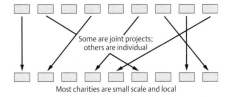

Some are joint projects; others are individual

Most charities are small scale and local

- **Food aid** accounts for about 10% of all bilateral aid.
- **Disaster relief** accounts for about 2% of all bilateral aid.
- **Tied aid** locks the recipient into buying from the donor.
- **Programme aid** supports vital imports when a country can no longer pay for them, while **project aid** is linked to a specific project.

The impact of aid

When aid is effective	When aid is ineffective
• It provides humanitarian relief. • It provides external resources for investment, and finances projects that could not be undertaken with commercial capital. • Project assistance helps expand much needed infrastructure. • Aid contributes to personnel training and builds technical expertise. • Aid can support better economic and social policies.	• Aid might allow countries to postpone improving economic management and mobilisation of domestic resources. • Aid can replace domestic saving, direct foreign investment and commercial capital as the main sources of investment and technology development. • The provision of aid might promote dependency rather than self-reliance. • Some countries have allowed food aid to depress agricultural prices, resulting in greater poverty in rural areas and a dependency on food imports. It has also increased the risk of famine in the future. • Aid is sometimes turned on and off in response to the political and strategic agenda of the donor country, making funds unpredictable, which can result in interruptions in development programmes. • The provision of aid might result in the transfer of inappropriate technologies or the funding of environmentally unsound projects. • Emergency aid does not solve the long-term economic development problems of a country. • Too much aid is tied to the purchase of goods and services from the donor country, which might not be the best or the most economical. • A lot of aid does not reach those who need it.

Tanzania 2001

In 2001 the UK government was involved in a serious disagreement over a £28 million agreement with Tanzania. The UK intended to sell a military air traffic control system to Tanzania, one of the world's poorest countries.

Aid agencies, the World Bank, and aviation experts condemned the plan. According to Oxfam, the sale would wipe out two-thirds of the savings made from debt relief. The same sum of £28 million would pay for basic health care for 3.5 million people – something greatly needed in Tanzania.

The UK government argued that it would allow Tanzania to charge traffic using its air space, and lead to an increase in flights to Tanzania, thereby boosting tourism.

Transnational corporations (TNCs)

A **TNC, multinational corporation (MNC)** or **multinational enterprise (MNE)** is an organisation that has operations in a large number of countries. Generally, research and development, and decision making, are concentrated in the core areas of developed countries, while assembly and production are developing countries and depressed, peripheral regions.

Imperial Chemical Industries (ICI)

ICI was formed in 1926 and has its headquarters in the UK. It employs about 130 000 people worldwide and has sales of about £6500 million each year. ICI is often seen as one of the flagships of British industry, and its fortunes are seen as a barometer of the nation's fortunes.

The corporation is a vast conglomerate that makes almost the complete range of chemicals and chemical-related products including fertilisers, paints, pharmaceuticals, and plastics. Its sales and profits now depend on four main markets: the UK, Western Europe, North America, and Australia and the Far East.

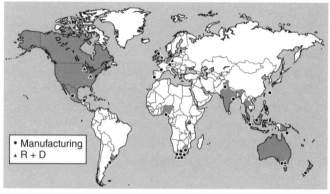

- Manufacturing
- ▲ R + D

ICI Paints Worldwide

TNCs – the balance sheet

TNCs provide a range of **advantages** and **disadvantages** for the host country.

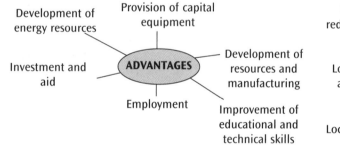

ADVANTAGES
- Development of energy resources
- Provision of capital equipment
- Investment and aid
- Development of resources and manufacturing
- Employment
- Improvement of educational and technical skills

DISADVANTAGES
- Mechanisation reduces the demand for labour
- Cost of manufactured products is beyond the range of people in the host country
- Local labourers are exploited
- Few skilled workers are employed
- Local resources are exported
- A large proportion of the profits goes overseas
- Increased imports, leads to increased national debt

TNC power

The sheer scale of the economic transactions that TNCs make around the world and the effect they have on urban, regional, and national economies gives them tremendous power. Thus TNCs have become planned economies with vast **internal markets.**

- Up to one-third of all trade is made up of internal transfers of TNCs. These transfers produce money for governments via taxes and levies.
- Economic power comes from the **ownership of assets**.
- Over 50 million people are employed by TNCs.
- Although many governments in developing countries own their own resources, TNCs still control the marketing and transport of goods.

TNCs and the world's economic crises

Reduced demand and increased competition creates unfavourable economic conditions. In order to survive and prosper, TNCs have used three main strategies:

- **rationalisation** – a slimming down of the workforce, which involves replacing people with machines
- **reorganisation** – includes improvements in production, administration and marketing, such as an increase in subcontracting of production
- **diversification** – refers to firms that have developed new products.

Inward investment

Inward investment refers to the attraction into an area of foreign capital from another country. Good examples include the Japanese car manufacturers in Britain. Inward investment occurs for a number of reasons:

- to gain a foothold in a new market
- to gain entry into a protected market, such as the European Union
- to exploit sources of cheap labour
- to gain access to raw material sources.

For the national government, inward investment is a good process, as it reduces the amount of investment that the government has to make, although it is very vulnerable to branch plant closures.

Changing patterns of foreign direct investment (FDI)

FDI is changing by economic sector and geographically. Over the last 30 years there has been a decline in FDI in natural resources-based activities (such as mining and plantations) and an increase in FDI in services. Although FDI in primary industries is important it is dwarfed by FDI in manufacturing and services.

Certain manufacturing sectors attract more FDI than others
- technologically advanced sectors, e.g. computers, pharmaceuticals, electronics
- large volume, medium-technology consumer goods industries, e.g. motor vehicles, cars, televisions, refrigerators

- mass-production consumer goods, e.g. cigarettes, soft drinks, breakfast cereals.

FDI in services is likewise concentrated in certain sectors:
- financial services, e.g. banking, insurance, accounting
- trade related, e.g. wholesaling, marketing, distribution
- telecommunications
- business services, e.g. consulting, advertising, hotels, transport
- some consumer activities, e.g. retailing, fast food.

The destination of FDI is largely to MEDCs and NICs. However, the source of FDI is changing. Historically, it came from MEDCs such as the USA, Japan, and the UK. Their dominance has decreased and there is now increasing FDI from other MEDCs as well as from NICs such as Korea, Taiwan, and Singapore.

Inward investment in Telford

Telford was designated a **New Town** in 1968 to accommodate some of the overspill population from Birmingham. In order to restructure the local economy, local planners attempted to attract foreign investment, which would enable the region to diversify its economic base and modernise its industries.

The reasons why so many companies chose Telford include:
- its favourable location with national motorway access via the M54
- its young, skilled population
- a favourable working environment, i.e. a modern infrastructure and three modern industrial estates at Halesfield, Stafford Park, and Hortonwood
- the quality of the built environment
- the surrounding Shropshire countryside.

Up to one in six jobs in Telford are the result of overseas investment. Important sectors include electronics, automotive components, electrical systems and equipment, computers, office equipment, and packaging. Important investors include Fruit of the Loom, Samsung, Maxell, Ricoh, and Nestlé.

Location of Telford

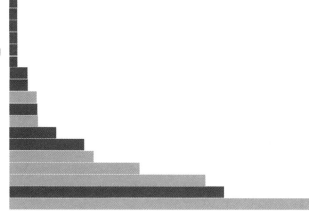

Overseas companies in Telford

Implications of economic change

Industrial change in Scotland

The manufacturing sector contributed a third of Scottish GDP in 1966 but less than one-fifth by the 1990s, while the share of services rose from a half to two-thirds.

The most important production industries include:

- the extraction of oil and oil-processing industries
- chemical-processing industries
- electronics
- high-technology engineering industries.

During the 1980s the output of electronics quadrupled and employment increased by 12%. Electronics and instrument firms are concentrated in Silicon Glen, the area of high-tech industry in central Scotland, centred on Glenrothes (Fife).

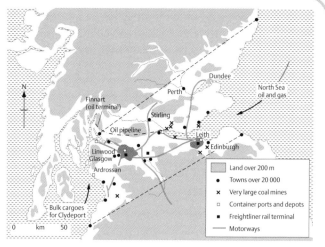

Scotland in the 20th century

Deindustrialisation

The Scottish metal, engineering, and shipbuilding industries all reached their peak early in the 20th century and have been declining ever since. The economic transformation since 1945 has led to periods of high unemployment and high outmigration. The cities of Glasgow, Dundee, and Edinburgh, and the depressed urban areas of Lanarkshire, account for almost 60% of Scotland's unemployed.

Strathclyde is by far the most populous region and contains the main concentration of heavy industries. Since the early 1960s, it has experienced extreme **deindustrialisation**.

Inward investment by foreign companies now accounts for the predominant part of Scotland's electronics industry, and a very important part of the North Sea oil-related activity. The dependence on inward investment is such that the electronics industry is unable to respond spontaneously to market opportunities.

Electronics and Silicon Glen

In 1995–96 almost £1000 million of **inward investment** was committed to Scotland. Three-quarters of this was in electronics. Scotland now produces about 35% of all branded personal computers made in Europe, partly due to the presence of IBM and Compaq. Silicon Glen employs 55 000 people, and in 1994 accounted for 30% of all Scottish manufacturing output.

Much of Scotland's electronics industry consists of assembly plants. TNCs spend very little on research and development in Scotland.

Inward investment into Scotland reached a record high between 1996 and 1997. Some 86 projects with a total value of £3.1 billion were agreed, creating or safeguarding nearly 14 300 jobs. Both are the highest numbers since 'Locate in Scotland', the inward investment agency, was established in 1981.

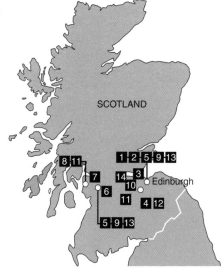

Job losses in Silicon Glen, 2000–01

1 **3Com**, *Edinburgh*: 5200 jobs worldwide

2 **Adobe**, *Edinburgh*: 247 jobs worldwide

3 **Agilent**, *South Queensferry*: 8000 jobs worldwide

4 **Cadence**, *Livingston*

5 **Cap Gemini**, *Edinburgh* and *Glasgow*

6 **Cisco**, *Bellshill*: 5000 jobs worldwide

7 **Compaq**, *Erskine*: 700 Scottish jobs

8 **IBM**, *Greenock*: 1000 jobs worldwide

9 **Microsoft**: *Edinburgh* and *Glasgow*

10 **Motorola**, *Bathgate*: closed with loss of 3100 mobs

11 **National Semiconducor**, *Greenock*: 1000 jobs worldwide

12 **Oracle**, *Edinburgh* and *Glasgow*

13 **Sun Microsystems**, *Linlithgow*: 4000 jobs worldwide

In 2000–01 the downturn in the global economy had a major impact on the branch plants in Silicon Glen:

- NEC at Livingston closed its semiconductor plant, which employed 1250 people
- Motorola closed with the loss of 3100 jobs
- Compaq lost 700 jobs
- In all, in 2001, 12 000 workers in the Scottish electronics industry lost their jobs.

Expanding global economy

Pages 131 to 139 discuss economic futures.
Pages 131 to 132 ask:
- *How might the global economy change in the future?*
- *How might the development gap be addressed?*
- *Can sustainable development be achieved?*

The expanding global economy

Definition

The **global economy** refers to the interdependence of MEDCs and LEDCs in the export and import of goods. MEDCs cannot exist without LEDCs (as they are a source of raw materials and cheap labour), while LEDCs cannot exist without MEDCs (a source of investment and lucrative markets). The key to success is for each to exploit the other as far as possible without damaging its own interests.

Reasons for the global economy

Companies and countries have 'gone global' for a number of reasons. The most important ones are:

- to reach new markets
- to utilise raw materials
- to use sources of cheap labour.

As stated by Vernon's product life cycle, once the home market is saturated, companies need to find new areas where they can sell their goods.

The search for new markets is crucial. This increasingly involves penetration into trading blocs. For example, the EU is a trading bloc of 15 nations (likely to expand to 21 nations in the next decades). It represents a rich market of over 370 million people. For US and Japanese producers it is a market they must reach.

Other markets are also important, especially:

- the emerging markets of South-east Asia
- China and India, on account of their sheer size.

Labour costs

Globalisation aims at a worldwide intra-firm division of labour. In this strategy, activities are established in many sites spread over the world, based on a country's comparative advantages. A manufacturer striving for globalisation aims to secure the supply of its inputs by locating production of these inputs at the most favourable sites. Thus, labour-intensive production of components will be situated in low-wage areas, while the production of high-technology and high-value-added parts will require a skilled or well-educated workforce. A globalisation strategy will promote a spatial division of labour.

The example of Glaxo shows a possible model for the global expansion of a company. It starts from a point where a company begins to export from its home base through locations overseas, and finally makes a decision to rationalise its global location in areas of comparative, competitive, or strategic advantage.

- Export-led development has the advantage of concentrating activities in the home country where labour and sourcing are established.
- Overseas location of branch plants has the advantage of overcoming trade restrictions and accessing cheap labour and new markets.
- Shift of research and development (R&D) and headquarters functions shows a greater commitment to globalisation. Managerial and research decisions shift away from the host country.
- Rationalisation sees the internationalised company concentrating activities in the best locations. Some profitable plants may be closed down or downgraded because their activities are represented elsewhere in lower-cost or more strategic locations.

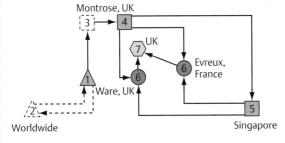

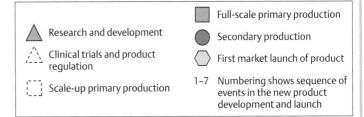

Glaxo and globalisation

India: a third generation NIC

Although India has a reasonably diverse manufacturing base, it has not yet achieved the rapid expansion experienced by countries such as South Korea, Taiwan, Thailand, Malaysia, and China.

Asia – five levels of economic development

Level	Countries	GNP per capita 2000 (US$)
1	MEDCs, e.g. Japan	37 676
2	First generation NICs, e.g. Korea, Taiwan NB Singapore has been reclassified as an MEDC. Hong Kong is now part of China.	9660
3	Second generation NICs, e.g Malaysia, Indonesia, Thailand	3840
4	Third generation NICs, e.g. China, India, Philippines	485
5	LEDCs, e.g. Nepal, Afghanistan, Cambodia	300

Economic development in Asia has followed a filter-down pattern. When Japanese companies first decided to locate abroad for lower-cost labour, they looked to the most developed of their neighbouring countries, notably South Korea and Taiwan. As the economies of the first generation NICs (South Korea, Taiwan, Hong Kong, and Singapore) grew stronger and more diversified, the level of wages increased significantly resulting in:

- Japanese and Western NICs seeking locations in second generation NICs (e.g. Thailand, Malaysia, Indonesia) where wages were still low
- indigenous companies from the first generation NICs moving routine tasks to their low-labour-cost neighbours.

With time, the process repeated itself to include a third generation of NICs whose members include China, the Philippines, and India.

India

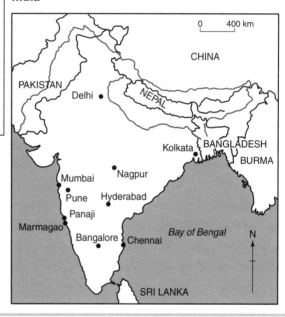

India

India has achieved economic growth by a different route from that of its main Asian economic rivals. This is because:

- the rapid economic growth of the 1990s was due much more to the expansion of the service sector than to manufacturing
- the filter-down of employment to India has been dominated by business links with North America and Europe, with a relatively low level of involvement with Japan and the other dynamic Asian economies.

The slow growth of India's manufacturing sector was partly due to a policy of import substitution (manufacturing its own products rather than importing from other countries), which led to the development of a broad industrial base. The lack of competition contributed to poor product quality and inefficiencies in production. The first liberalisation of India's economy began in 1991. As a result of changes in government policy, foreign direct investment (FDI) rose to over $2 billion a year in 2000. The government aims to increase FDI to $10 billion a year by 2005.

Services are the driving force of India's rise to NIC status.

The software and ICT services sector

India's software and ICT services sector has been at the forefront of the country's economic growth since 1991. Revenues from Indian software exports grew from less than $1 billion in 1996 to $4 billion in 2000. The ICT sector accounts for about 2% of GDP, and is expected to rise to 7% by 2008. Outsourcing (subcontracting) to India occurs because:

- labour costs are considerably lower
- a number of developed countries have significant ICT skills shortages
- India has a large and able English-speaking workforce (it has about 50 million fluent English-speakers).

The early growth of the sector was driven by foreign companies, mainly American. It has only been relatively recently that the number of home-grown companies has significantly increased. Bangalore, Hyderabad, and Madras, in the south, along with the western city of Pune and the capital city Delhi, have emerged as the centres of India's ICT industry. The country's biggest ICT companies, such as Infosys, Wipro and Satyam, have all developed from these dynamic clusters of industry.

After: Guiness, p. 2002

Changing workplaces

New technology is having an impact on people's working lives. More people now work in **services** than in **manufacturing**, and there is the potential for more people to work at home. Many of these are **telecommuters**, who send their work to the office by the internet.

One of the main shifts in the UK over the last 30 years has been the shift from unskilled manufacturing jobs, mostly for men, to semi-skilled service jobs, many of which employ women on a part-time basis. Women are more flexible in their working requirements but are also more likely to be non-unionised and less militant.

Phone factories

There are now some 200 000 people involved in **call centres**, easily outstripping the number employed in steel, coal, and in vehicle manufacture. The so-called 'computer telephonists' are the fastest-growing occupational group in Britain, providing customer services, and sales information.

There are some similarities between the 'dark satanic mills' of the 19th century and the new 'production lines':

- In most such workplaces, operators are expected to take a maximum 10-second break between each call.
- Employees can be routinely dismissed for not meeting their production target without 'reasonable' excuse.
- There is a problem of 'burn-out' associated with the need to repeat endlessly the same basic task many times a day.

In some call centres, staff turnover can be as high as 30% a year.

Many of the big centres are located outside London to take advantage of plentiful relatively skilled staff and lower wages.

Factors affecting the global distribution of call centres

- **Infrastructure** – call centres need a rapid telecommunications network, such as satellites, which most LEDCs cannot afford.

- **Labour** needs to be literate and technically skilled – English is the international business language.
- **Political stability** and **political incentives** – the Irish government has attracted much US investment.
- **Capital** – staff salaries are the largest costs, so there is some transfer from MEDCs to LEDCs, e.g. from the USA to Jamaica.

① Tesco Customer Service Centre	340
② Sky Subscriber	3099
③ London Electricity	585
④ Royal Bank of Scotland (direct banking)	519
⑤ Barclaycall	415
⑥ Littlewoods Home Shopping	519
⑦ Halifax Direct	500
⑧ First Direct	2930
⑨ Freemans services	1001
⑩ CO-OP Bank personal customer services (also Skelmersdale)	754
⑪ Alliance & Leicester Personal Finance	390
⑫ Sitel	771
⑬ Virgin Direct	350
⑭ NatWest Primeline	405
⑮ Prudential retail	268
⑯ Guardian Direct	426

The location of phone factories in the UK

Back office functions in India

India has been described as the 'back office of the world'. This 'office industry' has two sections:

- 'Captive' operations of large Western companies seeking to cut back office costs without outsourcing. For example, GE Capital Services opened India's first international call centre in the mid-1990s, and now employs over 5000 people. Other companies include American Express, British Airways, and Swissair.
- Shorter-term contracts between Western companies and subcontractors in India, e.g. 200 medical transcription companies employ 10 000 transcribers.

Jamaica's call centres

In 1988 the Jamaican government opened a satellite-receiving station at Montego Bay offering digital long-distance low-cost telephone calls and dedicated high-speed data transfer to the USA. Literacy levels are high (96%), English is the first language, and wages are just 25% of those in the USA.

Internet usage worldwide

Region	Regional population (% of world population)	Internet users (% of regional population)
USA	4.7	26.3
OECD* (excluding USA)	14.1	6.9
Latin America and the Caribbean	6.8	0.8
South-east Asia and the Pacific	8.6	0.5
East Asia	22.2	0.4
Eastern Europe and the FSU	5.8	0.4
Arab States	4.5	0.2
Sub-Saharan Africa	9.7	0.1
South Asia	23.5	0.04
World	100.0	2.4

*OECD (Organisation for Economic Cooperation and Development) refers to developed countries

Closing the development gap

Pages 134 to 135 ask:
- How might the development gap be addressed?
- What are the strategies for change?

There are many ways in which the development gap may be addressed. Unfair trading patterns is one of the causes of the development gap. MEDCs account for 75% of the world's exports and over 80% of manufactured exports. The pattern is complicated by flows of foreign direct investment (FDI), and the internal trade within TNCs. Most of the flow of profits is back to MEDCs, while an increasing share of FDI is to NICs. Reform of trade is necessary to protect LEDCs and small countries.

Regulatory bodies

International regulators
e.g. the International Monetary Fund (IMF) and the World Trade Organisation (WTO)

Regional trading blocs
e.g. the European Union (EU) and the North American Free Trade Association (NAFTA)

MAIN REGULATORY BODIES

Coordinating groups of countries
e.g. G8

National governments

Much of the trade and money exchange that takes place is run by stock exchanges and the world's main banks.

For example, Barclays Capital is the investment-banking sector of Barclays Bank. It deals with over £360 billion of investment through its 33 offices located worldwide. Its regional headquarters are located mostly in MEDCs in places such as London, Paris, Frankfurt, New York, and Tokyo. Hong Kong is the exception, although it is an important financial centre, like most of the other cities on the list.

There is widespread criticism that many of the regulatory bodies have limited power, and that when faced with a powerful MEDC or TNC they capitulate.

Fair trade or ethical trade

Fair trade or ethical trade can be defined as trade that attempts to be socially, economically, and environmentally responsible. It is trade in which companies take responsibility for the wider impact of their business. Ethical trading is an attempt to address failings of the global trading system.

Ethical traders: Prudent Exports

Prudent Exports is a pineapple-exporting company in Ghana. It grows as well as exports pineapples, supplying a leading British supermarket. It has introduced better working conditions for its farmers, including longer contracts and better wages. The company has its own farms, buys pineapples from smallholders, and exports directly to European supermarkets. It has also responded to requests to cut back on the use of pesticides and chemical fertilisers. The result has been an increase in productivity and sales.

Implications of fair trade

Some retailers appear to be the driving force behind fair trade as they seek out good practice in their suppliers in terms of:

- health and safety at work
- employment of children
- pay and conditions
- the freedom of association of workers.

Nevertheless, there are conflicts of interest. For many Western consumers, fair trade means banning pesticides or banning the use of child labour. Yet in many LEDCs it is normal for children to help out on farms, just as it was in the UK in the late 19th and early 20th centuries! Most LEDC farmers would prefer to send their children to school, but if the price they receive for their produce is low then they cannot afford to. If Western consumers want to stop child labour on farms, they may have to pay high prices for the food they buy.

Achievements of LEDCs

People in the West tend to forget about the achievements of the developing world. For example:

- Average real incomes in the poor world have more than doubled in the past 40 years despite population growth.
- Under-5 death rates have been cut by 50% or more in every region over the past 40 years.
- Average life expectancy has risen by more than one-third in every region since 1950.
- The percentage of people with access to a safe water supply has risen from about 10% to 60% in rural areas of the developing world since 1975.

Several types of development can help countries to develop, e.g. top-down and bottom-up development.

Strategies for change

Types of development

Top-down development	Bottom-up development
• Usually large-scale • Carried out by governments, international organisations, and 'experts' • Done by people from outside the area • Imposed upon the area or people by outside organisations • Often well funded and can respond quickly to disasters • Local people are not involved in the decision-making process • Emergency relief can be considered top down	• Small-scale • Labour intensive • Involves local communities and local areas • Run by local people for local people • There is limited funding available • Local people are involved in the decision-making process • Common projects include building earthen dams, creating cottage industries

Appropriate development

- Development that is culturally acceptable, technologically understandable, and economically affordable.
- It is for the community, by the community, using the community's own resources.
- It is a type of bottom-up or sustainable form of development.

Non-governmental organisations (NGOs)

- They are mostly charities.
- NGOs normally work with local communities and small groups.
- They also help with emergency relief (short-term disaster relief).

Poor countries' debt

Sub-Saharan Africa (SSA) includes most of the 41 countries classified as *heavily indebted,* and 25 of the 32 countries rated as *severely indebted.* In 1962, SSA owed $3 billion (£1.8 billion). Twenty years later this debt had reached $142 billion. Today it is about $235 billion. The most heavily indebted countries are Nigeria ($35 billion), Côte d'Ivoire ($19 billion), and Sudan ($18 billion).

Many developing countries borrowed heavily in the 1970s and early 1980s, encouraged to do so by Western lenders, including export credit agencies. They soon ran into problems:

- low growth in industrialised economies
- high interest rates between 1975 and 1985
- rise in oil prices
- falling commodity prices.

Dealing with the problem

- Since 1988, the Paris Club of government creditors has approved a series of debt relief initiatives.
- The World Bank has lent more through its concessional lending arm.
- The International Development Agency has given loans for up to 50 years without interest but with a 3%–4% service charge.
- Lending has risen from $424 million in 1980 to $2.9 billion, plus a further $928 million through the African Development Bank.
- The IMF has also introduced a **soft loan facility** which is conditional on wide-ranging economic reforms.

Structural adjustment programmes

Structural adjustment programmes (SAPs) were designed to cut government expenditure, reduce the amount of state intervention in the economy, and promote liberalisation and international trade. SAPs were explicit about the need for international trade.

SAPs consist of four main elements:

1 greater use of a country's resource base
2 policy reforms to increase economic efficiency
3 generation of foreign income through diversification of the economy and increased trade
4 reducing the active role of the state.

These elements were sometimes divided into two main groups:

- **stabilisation measures** – short-term steps to limit any further deterioration of the economy (e.g. wage freeze, reduced subsidies on food, health, and education)
- **adjustment measures** – longer-term policies to boost economic competitiveness (tax reductions, export promotion, downsizing of the civil service, privatisation, and economic liberalisation).

Sustainable development (1)

Pages 136 to 137 ask:
- *Can sustainable development be achieved?*

Handling cross-unit ideas

You should make sure as you are studying Unit 4 that you make linkages wherever possible between the Natural Environment and Population and Economy, because one section of the examination paper, Section C, contains cross-unit questions where questions overarch the whole Global Challenge.

Possible styles of cross-unit question include:

1 Overarching topics such as global warming and its impact on economies and the environment.

2 Overarching concepts such as sustainability in a number of contexts.

3 A range of world issues, for example environmental degradation, then focusing on one or two issues from a wide selection – the trigger resource could be a cartoon or some statistics.

4 A particular geographical problem such as world poverty, which is caused by a number of interacting causes or issues in LEDCs.

5 A particular location (e.g. small island economies, or coastal zones, or a particular continent such as Africa) to explore a number of inter-related issues.

6 Questions that make links across sections, for example climate and biodiversity, population and economy, biodiversity and economy.

Sustainable development is development that 'meets the needs of the present without compromising the ability of future generations to meet their own needs'. It is a process by which:

- human potential (standards of well-being) is improved and there is involvement in decision making
- the environment (the resource base) is managed to supply humanity on a long-term basis

- social justice is implied.

The definition suggests that mankind has degraded the planet and must make amends for future generations.

For some the term 'sustainable development' is a catchphrase of 'beguiling simplicity' which is frequently used, but only as a form of lip service to environmentalists. Others claim that the term 'sustainable' is vague, emotive and ambiguous, as is the term 'development'.

Global tensions

The world is facing a number of interlinked crises that undermine the ability to achieve sustainable development. The United Nations Conference on the Environment and Development (the Earth Summit), held in Rio de Janeiro in 1992, warned that unless there were changes in the ways in which development proceeded, there would be a large increase in the amount of human suffering and environmental damage. The crises encompass social, economic, environmental, and political aspects.

Social and economic tensions

Currently about one-fifth of the world's population live in desperately poor conditions – these are the global 'underclass'. Within the underclass certain groups are more vulnerable than others: in particular, women, children and indigenous people. In an ordinary year, 14 million children under the age of 5 die in LEDCs. During wars, famines, plagues, economic recession, and other disasters the number increases.

Environmental tensions

The environmental crisis is a result of the limited amount of resources that the earth contains and the rate at which they are being destroyed. Moreover, there is a social aspect to the destruction of resources: the 20% of the world's population that live in MEDCs consume 80% of the world's resources, whereas the 80% of the population that live in LEDCs use only 20% of the resources.

The world's environmental crises are increasingly rapid, and cross international boundaries. There is a change in the cause of the crisis: in the early part of the 20th century it was linked to coal-burning industries, and in the 1990s to the phenomenon of mass private car ownership. Since 1900 the world's population has tripled and industrial production has increased 50-fold. Some 80% of industrial production has taken place since 1950.

Political tensions

Political conflict in the form of war, ethnic cleansing, refugee crises, trade wars, and economic sanctions, has increased. In the early 1990s there were conflicts and renewed violence in Somalia, Ethiopia, Sudan, Rwanda, Burundi, Kuwait, Nigeria, Croatia, Bosnia, Serbia, Chechnya, Israel, Sri Lanka, Northern Ireland and Iraq, among others. Since 2000, conflict in Pakistan has worsened and terror attacks in New York and Bali have intensified political tensions (resulting in such conflicts as those in Afghanistan and Iraq). Nowhere appears to be safe from terrorism.

Sustainable development (2)

Working list of indicators of sustainable development

Chapters of Agenda 21	Driving force indicators	State indicators	Response indicators
Category: Social			
Combating poverty	– Unemployment rate	– Poverty gap index	
Demographic dynamics and sustainability	– Population growth rate – Net migration rate	– Population density	
Promoting education, public awareness and training	– Rate of change of school-age population – Primary school enrolment ratio (gross and net) – Adult literacy rate	– Children reaching grade 5 of primary education – School life expectancy – Difference between male and female school enrolment ratios	– GDP spent on education
Protecting and promoting human health		– Basic sanitation: % of population with adequate excreta disposal facilities – Access to safe drinking water – Life expectancy at birth	– Immunisation against infectious childhood diseases – Contraceptive prevalence – Proportion of potentially hazardous chemicals monitored in food
Promoting sustainable human settlement development	– Rate of growth of urban population – Per capita consumption of fossil fuel by motor vehicle transport	– % of population in urban areas – Area and population of urban formal and informal settlements	– Infrastructure expenditure per capita
Category: Economic			
International cooperation to accelerate sustainable development in countries and related domestic policies	– GDP per capita – Net investment share in GDP	– Share of manufactured goods in total merchandise exports	
Changing consumption patterns	– Annual energy consumption	– Proven mineral reserves – Proven fossil fuel energy reserves	
Financial resources and mechanisms	– Total ODA given or received as a percentage of GNP	– Debt/GNP – Debt service/export	– Environmental protection expenditures as % of GDP – Amount of new or additional funding for sustainable development
Category: Environmental			
Protection of the quality and supply of freshwater resources	– Annual withdrawals of ground and surface water – Domestic consumption of water per capita	– Groundwater reserves – Concentration of faecal coliform in fresh water	– Waste-water treatment coverage – Density of hydrological networks
Protection of the oceans, all kinds of seas and coastal areas	– Population growth in coastal areas	– Maximum sustained yield for fisheries	
Managing fragile ecosystems: combating desertification and drought	– Population living below poverty line in dryland areas	– Satellite-derived vegetation index – Land affected by desertification	
Promoting sustainable agriculture and rural development	– Use of agricultural pesticides – Use of fertilisers – Irrigation as % of arable land – Energy use in agriculture	– Arable land per capita – Area affected by salinisation and waterlogging	– Agricultural education
Conservation of biological diversity		– Threatened species as % of total native species	– Protected area as % of total area
Protection of the atmosphere	– Emissions of greenhouse gases, sulphur oxides, nitrogen oxides and ozone-depleting substances	– Ambient concentrations of pollutants in urban areas	– Expenditure on air pollution abatement
Environmentally sound management of solid wastes and sewage-related issues	– Generation of industrial and municipal solid waste – Household waste disposed per capita		– Expenditure on waste management – Waste recycling and reuse
Category: Institutional			
Integrating environment and development in decision making			– Sustainable development strategies – Programme of integrated environmental and economic accounting
Science for sustainable development		– Potential scientists and engineers per million population	– Scientists and engineers engaged in R&D per million population – Expenditure on R&D as % of GDP
Information for decision making		– Main telephone lines per 100 inhabitants – Access to information	– Programmes for national environmental statistics

Sustainable development (3)

Strategic thinking
The World Commission on Environment and Development (WCED)

WCED (1987), chaired by Brundtland, investigated the capacity of the earth to support its population, and the ways in which human activities were affecting the environment. These activities have created crises of environment, development, security, and energy. Key aspects of the Commission were:

- the achievement of basic needs for all people, especially the global underclass
- limits to growth are technical, cultural, and social.

Brundtland suggested seven major proposals for a strategy for sustainable development:

1	revive economic growth
2	change the quality of growth
3	meet basic needs of food, water, employment, energy, and sanitation
4	stabilise population growth
5	conserve and enhance resources
6	adapt technology to manage risk
7	put environment into economics.

The Brundtland Commission reported to the United Nations General Assembly, which in turn requested a five-year progress report. This became the Rio conference, the largest environmental conference ever.

Managing global ecosystems
United Nations Conference on Environment and Development, 1992 (UNCED)

The outcomes of Rio were:

- convention on biodiversity
- framework convention on climatic change
- principles of forest management
- Agenda 21
- the Rio Declaration on Environment and Development.

Local developments
Role of local Agenda 21

As a result of the Earth Summit, national governments are obliged to formulate national plans or strategies for sustainable development – **Agenda 21**. It is *people* who do development, not governments, and therefore sustainable development is a local activity. All people, however poor, have some ability, however constrained, to change what they do, in small ways.

Local authorities are beginning to translate the global sustainability agenda into local action. Just as global sustainability cannot exist without national sustainable policies, national Agenda 21 is incomplete without local Agenda 21.

Local authorities have a number of roles in sustainable development:

- as a consumer of resources
- as a force for change in the marketplace
- as a role model for other organisations
- as providers of information
- as providers of services
- as planners
- as local governments and decision makers.

Concepts

Green growth refers to developments that are environmentally friendly and sustainable, e.g. renewable forms of energy, low-technology agriculture and sustainable water management. It implies the use of the environment to improve standards of living for local people. Ecotourism in Costa Rica or in Nepal are good examples.

Economic sustainability refers to the development of economic activities that will last a long time since they do not destroy the world's resource base and compromise the needs of future generations.

Environmental sustainability refers to the long-term sustainable use of environments and resources at present and in the future. A good example is how tropical rainforests or coral reefs can be managed to provide an economic return without destroying the resource base.

Sustainable development (4)

The Earth Summit: Johannesburg, September 2002

	Problems and hopes	Result
Water and sanitation	The main battleground of the summit. Hope for a healthy life for 2 billion people now without access to clean water rested on rich countries having the political will to agree targets and timetables to help install this basic amenity.	Target of halving the number without basic sanitation (about 1.2 billion) by 2015, alongside plans to provide clean water for half those without it. Countries must produce water management and resource efficiency plans by 2005.
Poverty	A third of the world's poorest people looked to the summit to help them escape hunger, poor health, and lack of basic amenities and education.	Recognition that poverty and environmental degradation are linked and that the cycle must be broken. Health and education of women promoted. Aim of halving the 1.2 billion who live on less than $1 a day adopted.
Energy and climate change	How to get electricity to 2 billion people without worsening global warming. Hope of boosting renewable energy technologies.	No targets
Health	Overfishing and the destruction of a main protein source for poor coastal people. Controls on fishing fleets from developed countries needed.	Commitment to restore fish stocks urgently, where possible by 2015, and focus on marine pollution, illegal fishing boats, and the establishment of protected areas by 2012.
Sustainable consumption	A plan to produce the goods and services to make the world a more comfortable place for everyone without destroying the environment.	Agreement to develop an action programme in 10 years, publish indicators to measure progress, give shoppers informative eco-labels.
Biodiversity and natural resources	Concern about the destruction of the earth's life support system.	Aim to reduce loss of biodiversity significantly by 2010 and increase funding and technical resources to developing countries. Attempt to strengthen forest law and reduce illegal logging.
Africa	Hope of new aid after 10 years of the world's worst progress in development and poverty eradication, exacerbated by AIDS and the current drought.	UK government promised to increase aid to £1 billion by 2005. There was agreement on land tenure, women's right to own and inherit land, food security plans, and that Africa needed special attention.
Trade and globalisation	Hope of tackling destruction of natural resources in the name of free trade, unfair competition with local industries, and poor environmental performance. Hope of some control over the World Trade Organisation.	Environment ministers hugged each other when words giving environment treaties equal standing with the WTO were agreed. The WTO will not be able to brush aside development and environment goals.
Human rights	Corruption which leads to the misspending of aid and development money, and lack of human rights and democratic institutions, have hampered progress on sustainable development.	Resistance from the G77 group of developing countries prevented stronger wording, but the relationship between human rights and the environment was recognised.

Applying sustainable development

The UK sustainable development strategy

Themes, issues and objectives	Headline indicators
• Maintain high and stable levels of employment so that everyone can share greater job opportunities	Proportion of people of working age who are in work
• Tackle poverty and social exclusion	Indicators of success in tackling poverty and social exclusion (children in low-income households, adults without qualifications and in workless households, elderly in fuel poverty)
• Reduce both crime and people's fear of crime	Level of crime
• Continue to reduce emissions of greenhouse gases now, and plan for greater reductions in the longer term	Emissions of greenhouse gases
• Reduce air pollution and ensure air quality continues to improve through the longer term	Days when air pollution is moderate or higher
• Improve choice in transport; improve access to education, jobs, leisure activities and services; and reduce the need to travel	Road traffic
• Re-use previously developed land, in order to protect the countryside and encourage urban regeneration	New homes built on previously developed land
• Move away from disposal of waste towards waste minimisation, reuse, recycling, and recovery	Waste management

Question

This question is a typical Unit 4 Global Challenge (6474) cross-unit question. These Section C questions are worth 30 marks and you have 45 minutes to complete them. Allow 10 minutes of this for planning your answers, thinking of the most appropriate examples from your studies to support your arguments.

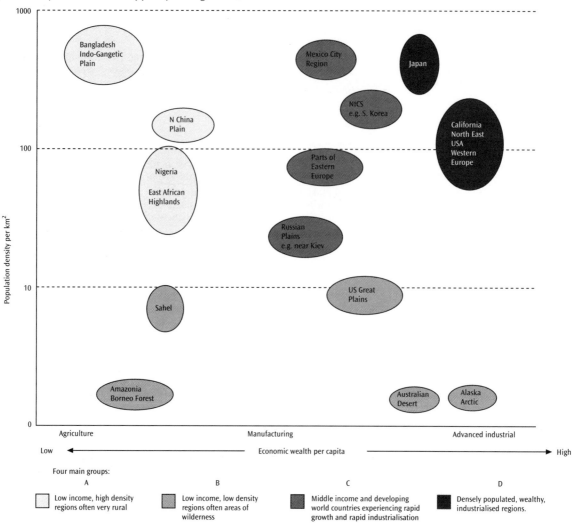

Study the diagram. It attempts to classify a range of world regions on the basis of their population density and relative economic wealth.

(a) For each of the four groups shown, evaluate the likely factors that influence the nature and extent of their environmental degradation. [16]

(b) For named areas within any **two** groups, examine how sustainable development strategies can be used to lessen the rate of environmental degradation. [14]

Total marks 30

Answer guidelines

(a) **Group A:** These areas are intensively farmed (high population densities of largely subsistence farmers) and therefore vulnerable to soil erosion, etc. Where farming has become high-tech (e.g. introduction of Green Revolution) there are issues of environmental degradation from agro-chemicals, etc. These densely populated areas often suffer from water pollution from sewage, etc. as a result of dense rural settlements containing many people living in poverty.

Group B: Whilst environmental degradation is potentially low from indigenous usage because of low densities, much of the subsistence agriculture is non-intensive. There are issues with shifting agriculture (deforestation over a wider area). Also, many environments such as the Sahel are fragile, with potential for environmental degradation from physical causes (climate change and creeping desertification). Environmental degradation such as deforestation is largely a result of exploitation for timber and other resources by MEDC-based TNCs. Some areas are wildernesses. These areas are again less at risk because of the low density of indigenous populations but because of the fragility of the environment can be easily destroyed, e.g. oil exploitation in the Arctic (Brookes Range). Any development leads to loss of aesthetic value of the wilderness itself so has potential to degrade pristine environments.

Group C: Areas of rapid industrial and population growth experience issues associated with the Brown Agenda and are often pollution hotspots. A range of issues would be suitable here – expect examples such as Bangkok, Mexico City, etc. – waste products/disposal, air pollution from factory fumes, water pollution, overuse of water supplies, subsistence, and transport-related issues. Widespread and rapidly increasing pollution will occur unless the capital and technology is available to manage it.

Group D: These regions are advanced economies (largely high-tech/tertiary/quaternary activity) but also highly populated areas. In spite of pollution control measures there will be widespread air pollution and transport-related issues, and localised issues of waste disposal. Inevitably highly urbanised megacities will all have pollution issues.

Suggest a scale as follows. Maximum 5 for any one group.

Marks

5	Sound evaluation of a range of relevant factors looking at nature and extent.
4–3	Some evaluation in a description of some factors. May not consider extent, but usually some ideas on nature.
2–1	One or two basic pollution-related descriptions appropriate to the group.

Maximum 16 marks

(b) **Group A:** Likely to concentrate on sustainable farming strategies such as water conservation schemes in Mali, sustainable rural development schemes to introduce new alternative activities (take pressure off rural areas), e.g. micro enterprises. Sustainable energy, e.g. micro hydro schemes. Development of intensive organic farming strategies and permaculture, pisciculture.

Group B: Likely to concentrate on sustainable forestry management schemes to control deforestation, or ecotourism schemes, to prevent the impact of mass tourism.

Group C: Likely to review the concept of green growth, sustainable use of energy (clean technology), sustainable waste management, possible sustainable water management and development of traffic management strategies, i.e. strategies for managing the Brown Agenda.

Group D: Likely to concentrate on sustainable urban strategies and traffic management. Possibly Agenda 21 strategies of energy, waste, and pollution management.

Note that for groups C and D candidates may legitimately argue that sustainable strategies may not be a great deal of use unless global actions support all the local actions.

Mark up to 9 for each of two groups chosen.

Marks

9–6	A range of clear, relevant, exemplified sustainable strategies underpin a detailed examination.
5–4	Some relevant strategies, with some exemplification, underpin a satisfactory examination.
3–1	One or two sustainable ideas, not well applied to chosen group, likely to be generalised.

Maximum 14 marks

How does Unit 5 work?

This unit provides you with an opportunity to research topics of particular interest to you.

Whilst some unit content could be taught, the emphasis is on independent research. You may already be familiar with some of the definitions and concepts covered in the options as you may have studied them in Unit 4.

There are two parts to the unit:

- **Part 1: Managing natural environments**
  Option 5.1 Environments and resources
  Option 5.2 Living with hazardous environments

Option 5.3 The pollution of natural environments
Option 5.4 Wilderness environments

- **Part 2: Challenges for human environments**
  Option 5.5 Development and disparity
  Option 5.6 Feeding the world's people
  Option 5.7 Health and welfare
  Option 5.8 The geography of sport and leisure

You have to choose *one* option from Part 1 and *one* from Part 2.

What are the Generalisations?

Within each option there is a foundation question and four **Generalisations**. These are the geographical ideas and concepts about which you will gain an understanding by studying the option. You should study each Generalisation in equal depth.

The Generalisations are important because they form the basis for assessment in both parts of Unit 5. Make sure you are familiar with the wording of each Generalisation.

How is this unit assessed?

- **Part 1** is assessed by an examination lasting 1 hour 20 minutes. Two weeks before the examination the **focus** of the essay will be announced. This refers to which of the four Generalisations in each option you will be examined on.

In the actual exam you will be set two essays per option. Both essays will concentrate on the same Generalisation. You only do one of the essays.

- **Part 2** is assessed by an externally-marked coursework report. Each year Edexcel publishes six coursework titles for each option. Your coursework report should be no longer than 1500 words. Again, you do only one question.

In both research essays you will be expected to show a thorough grasp of the **Foundation work**. This refers to the basic definitions, concepts and processes that are fundamental to each option. Before deciding on your research title, make sure you have studied everything in the Foundation for study.

Characteristics of Unit 5

Part 1

In-depth research study of one natural environmental theme integrating study of terrestrial, atmospheric and biotic processes
- assessed by exam essay

Acquisition of research skill from a wide range of sources, e.g. newspapers, journals, CD-ROM and internet

Student-led choice

Part 2

In-depth study of one aspect of the human environment, explaining political, socio-cultural and economic issues
- assessed by coursework report

Opportunities for some primary investigation

Focus on structuring a formal essay and report

- Managing natural environments
- Challenges for human environments

Writing research essays/coursework (1)

What are the examiners looking for?

Both research essays and coursework reports are marked out of 60 and use the following make scheme.

• **Introducing the question, problem or issue** • **Identifying the information needed to answer it**	You could pick up 10 marks in this section. The examiner will want to see a clear definition and description of the question, problem, or issue. You must show that you understand what information is required to answer the question. Remember to refer to a range of scales and/or locations. You will lose marks if you don't define terms completely and accurately.
• **Researching relevant sources, selecting appropriate case study material, and using this knowledge in detail**	15 marks are available if you can show that you have researched your subject properly. Use a wide range of case studies, from a variety of locations and sources. Read around your topic and show that you have done so. Where appropriate, use annotated maps, figures, and diagrams to support your answer.
• **Understanding of general concepts, case studies, attitudes and values, and the application of data and information to the question, problem, or issue**	To be awarded the full 15 marks available you must organise all your data logically, and apply your research material fully to the problem, question, or issue. Show that you appreciate the different values or perspectives concerned.
• **Drawing conclusions on the basis of evidence, and ongoing evaluation**	A balanced, well-supported conclusion could pick up 10 marks. Your conclusion should draw upon evidence given in your essay. It should be built up through the essay progressively.
• **Quality of written communication, including the communication of knowledge, ideas, and conclusion in a clear and logical order, and the use of appropriate geographical vocabulary**	Communicating your ideas with clarity and accuracy is of fundamental importance. 10 marks could be lost if you don't write your essay with clear sense and coherence, and don't ensure that grammar, spelling, and punctuation are correct. Make sure that every paragraph leads to the next in a logical sequence.

Points to consider when planning your essay

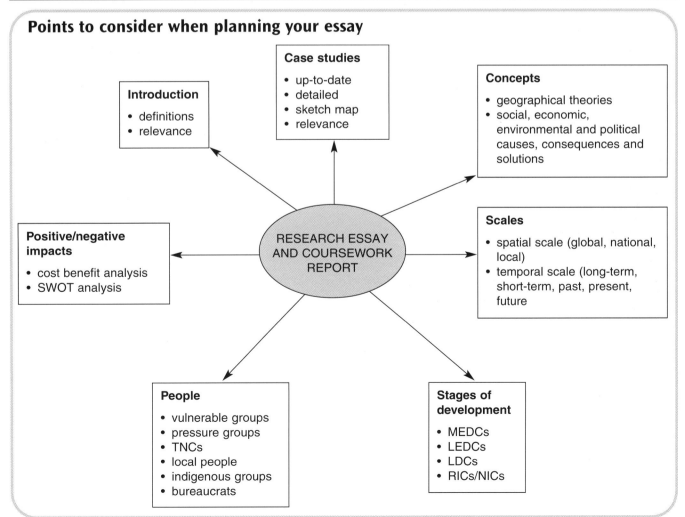

Writing research essays/coursework (2)

Whether you are writing your research essay under examination conditions or as a piece of coursework, many of the principles are the same. Make sure you allow yourself plenty of thinking and planning time before you embark on any research or before you begin writing. In the exam room, time is a key resource, so you will need to work quickly and efficiently.

Choosing a title

The Generalisation allows you to focus on the relevant part of the course. It tells you and the examiner what will happen in the essay. Choose your title carefully, and make sure that you know exactly what you have decided to investigate.

- Look at the **process** or **command words**, e.g. *outline*, *examine*, *assess*. These tell you how to deal with the subject of the essay. Underline the process or command words.

- Underline the **content words**. These will refer to the Generalisations and will tell you what to focus on in the essay. How many case studies will you need? What scale do they need to be?

- Read the **whole title**, making sure that you know exactly what is required and what is relevant.

Planning and organising the research essay

It is best to plan the essay in two stages:

1 Brainstorm all relevant ideas and examples that you could use for the essay. Use a spider diagram to help you put your ideas in order. Make a list of queries that you will need to find out about.

2 Organise the spider diagram/brainstorm it into a **logical order**, so that it answers the question. This will provide you with the basic structure for your essay.

Checklist

- Does your plan include all the ideas and case studies that you brainstormed? ☐
- Does your essay flow? Is it in a logical order? Are the main points and arguments clearly signposted? ☐
- Does your plan appear to answer the question? ☐
- Does your plan follow the mark scheme? ☐

The research

- Collect the material.
- Distinguish between primary and secondary data.
- Note your sources.
- Search the internet. Note that material obtained from the internet must be acknowledged and adapted by the user – plagiarising from the internet is easily detected, as the writing style changes, key words occur in bold, and the essay fails to flow.
- Make references to relevant video notes.

Writing research essays/coursework (3)

Writing in an academic style

The following tips will help you to write in an academic style:

- Make sure that each point (idea or information) has a separate paragraph.
- For the coursework report, write a first draft, and then improve on it (shorten and make it more punchy).
- Material added in an appendix must be relevant to the essay.
- Include a bibliography for the essay.
- Express your ideas clearly. Make the essay flow by having linked sentences and paragraphs – words and phrases such as 'however', 'on the other hand', 'in contrast', and 'in addition' do help.
- Make sure you bring all your arguments and information together in a clear conclusion.
- Do not use abbreviations.

Referencing and bibliography

Good essays and reports will acknowledge sources and include a bibliography. When using quotes you should add the author's name, date of publication, and page number in brackets after the quote, e.g. (Smith, 2001, p.17). Alternatively, you could state *According to Smith (2001)* ..., and give the details in the bibliography.

When writing the bibliography, sort the authors into alphabetical order, and provide date of publication, title of book, and publisher, e.g.

Nagle, G., 2003, *Geography Revision Guide for Edexcel B*, Oxford.

Remember to include website references, too.

Checklist

Does your report include:

- ☐ a clear introduction?
- ☐ a clear aim?
- ☐ models and theories where relevant?
- ☐ relevant case studies?
- ☐ relevant maps and diagrams?
- ☐ a range of techniques?
- ☐ a discussion of any limitations?
- ☐ a clear structure – paragraphs?
- ☐ analysis and explanation?
- ☐ a good conclusion?
- ☐ an evaluation?
- ☐ a bibliography?
- ☐ an appendix where relevant?

Readability – what makes a good report

A **report** is a **factual essay**. Within the report it is acceptable to have headings, numbered sections, bullet points, and so on. On the front page there should be a short abstract or summary outlining the essential nature of the report. This does not have to be very long, as the example on this page shows. It is important that the title at the top of the report is the same as the title set.

The length is 1500 words, with a possible leeway of 10%, so 1650 is the maximum. Above that your report will lose marks.

Words can be lost or saved by using annotated diagrams and photos, maps, and tables but they must each have a figure number and be incorporated into the text. The bibliography should be detailed and extensive, to show the amount of hard work that has gone into the report.

The final product should have all the pages numbered (pagination), a contents page, and if direct quotations are used these should be referenced in a footnote.

Readability

Readability can be achieved in a number of ways:

- A focused introduction
- A logical structure
- Diagrams, maps and photographs that are incorporated into the text, and which add depth and detail to the report (rather than being purely illustrative)
- Sub-headings such as *Introduction*, *Analysis* and *Conclusions*
- A conclusion that is closely linked to the title – and should be sensational
- An appendix that provides transcripts of interviews, details of raw data, statistical analyses, etc.

Relevance

- An abstract or summary of the findings of the report
- Detailed page planning
- A rationale for the choice of case studies

Research

- Select case studies in a logical sequence.
- Try to design original artworks.
- Use footnote quotations from key texts.
- Consider bias in the sources.
- Give full details of references and websites used.
- Produce a contents page and a figures list.
- Include a glossary of technical terms.

Abstract

An abstract is a summary of the whole report, telling the reader something about the data sources and methods used, results, and conclusions. It may even include a list of key words. The following example is an abstract from a report on variations in water quality above and below a sewage outlet.

> The report analysed variations in water temperature, oxygen levels, pH, and other chemical tests at three sites above the sewage outlet (the control site) and at eight sites with increasing distance below the sewage outlet. Measurements were carried out in summer (low flow conditions) and autumn (high flow conditions). The report found significant variations in water quality above and below the outlet during summer but not in autumn. During the summer, water quality had recovered to its original state (i.e. the same as the control site) at a distance of 100 metres below the outlet. During the high flow conditions there were small, but not significant, differences between the control site and the first site immediately below the sewage outlet.
>
> **Key Words:** control site, water quality, indicators of water quality

Part 1: Managing natural environments

Option 5.1: Environments and resources (1)

Sample questions

1 Examine the impact of the uneven distribution of resources on economic activity. (*Generalisation 1*)
2 To what extent do the social and environmental impacts of resource extraction outweigh the economic impacts? (*Generalisation 2*)
3 'The current use of energy and/or mineral resources is unsustainable.' Discuss this statement with reference to a range of examples. (*Generalisation 3*)
4 Using a range of examples, outline the impacts of alternative resource strategies. (*Generalisation 4*)

Sample answer – question 1

Examine the impact of the uneven distribution of resources on economic activity.

The main focus in the specification is mineral and energy resources, although it is possible to use other resources. Answers should examine/explore how the distribution of resources has attracted economic activity (e.g. South Wales, the Ruhr, north-east USA) and how areas without resources have not attracted economic activity. Good candidates will tackle the question and argue that other factors, such as accessibility and wealth, allow some countries to overcome their lack of resources and develop (e.g. Singapore), whereas other areas with resources may export them (e.g. Alaska). Discussion of the changing nature of resources (exploitation, exhaustion) should also be expected.

Introduction (10 marks)

This should define the terms *resources* and *economic activity*. An outline of the relationship between resources and economic activity should be provided (this may be direct and/or indirect), mentioning a range of examples and scales (from the local to the global) to be analysed in detail later. This question refers to uneven distribution, so it is important to give a balanced amount of the haves/have nots.

Researching relevant material (15 marks)

Key aspects include a range of examples at different scales. Details are important. These should be balanced between places with and without resources. Case studies should illustrate places with resources and economic activity (e.g. Lancashire, Ruhr, Damodar Valley), those that export raw materials (Alaska), those without resources but significant economic activity (Singapore, Japan), and those with limited resources/economic activity (Mozambique, Zimbabwe).

Understanding of the Generalisation and application to the question (15 marks)

The key terms are 'the impact (positive/negative) of the uneven distribution (haves/have nots) of resources on economic activity (direct/indirect)'. This impact may change over time.

Drawing conclusions (10 marks)

This will be linked to the main argument – top answers will *examine the impact* of uneven distribution rather than just *describe* the uneven distribution.

Quality of written communication (10 marks)

Use of specialist terminology is essential for high marks. Terms may include *multiplier effect, agglomeration, 'pure' and 'gross' raw materials, footloose industries*.

Key concepts

In your essay, you will need to explore a number of key concepts. The following should be central to your research:

- **conservation:** the protection of natural or man-made resources and landscapes for later use
- **sustainability:** ensuring current rates of resource use don't compromise the ability of future generations to meet their own needs (see pages 136–9)
- **fuel cycle:** the industrial processes that an energy resource has to go through to become an efficient fuel for use in the generation of electricity
- **the 4 Rs:** recycling, repair, re-use, product redesign.

Option 5.1: Environments and resources (2)

Possible case studies

Topics	Examples/Case studies
Fossil fuels National policies	• Coal in China, the UK, the USA, Germany, Australia • Oil in the Middle East, Alaska, Siberia, North Sea • The UK and coal/renewables/nuclear • Hydroelectric power and nuclear power in Japan
Resources and economic development	• Diamonds in Botswana • Tin in the UK, Bolivia, Malaysia • Gold in South Africa, Brazil • Coal in South Wales (19th/20th centuries), Ruhr and Brown Coal Triangle in Germany (20th/21st centuries) • Iron in Australia, Brazil • Uranium in Australia, Namibia • Resource-based industrial regions: Ruhr (Germany), North East (UK), South Wales (UK), Black Country (UK) • Small-scale industrial development: chemicals at Fawley (Southampton), Warrington Science Park (UK)
Environmental impacts of resource exploitation	• Oil in Alaska, Siberia, Nigeria, the UK • Coal in South Wales, China, Germany (Ruhr and Brown Coal Triangle) • Tin in Cornwall, Bolivia, Malaysia • Nuclear power in Japan, the USA (Three Mile Island), Chernobyl (Ukraine), the UK
Future use of resources	• Recycling in the UK, within the EC • Fuelwood in Africa, the Hidden Energy Crisis of the Third World • Industrial development in NICs and LEDCs, e.g. China and India
Strategies for resource use	• Energy crisis in Nepal • Superdams, e.g. The Narmada Dam (India), The Three Gorges Dam (China) • Energy conservation in the UK, the USA, the EC

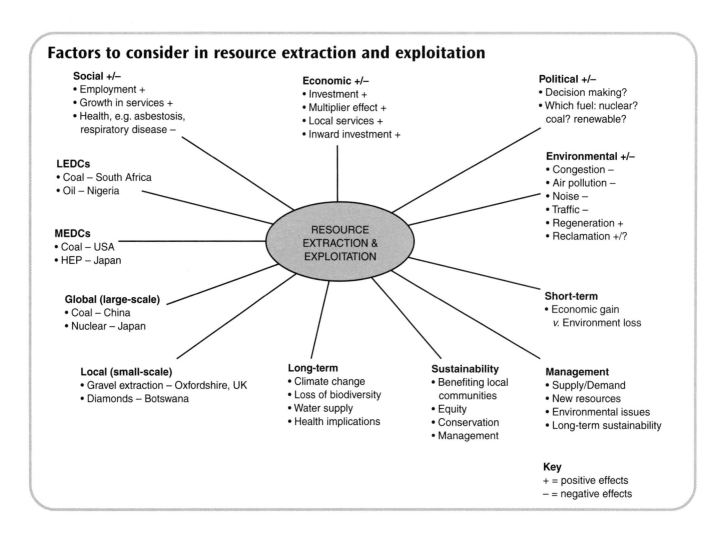

Factors to consider in resource extraction and exploitation

Social +/−
• Employment +
• Growth in services +
• Health, e.g. asbestosis, respiratory disease −

Economic +/−
• Investment +
• Multiplier effect +
• Local services +
• Inward investment +

Political +/−
• Decision making?
• Which fuel: nuclear? coal? renewable?

LEDCs
• Coal – South Africa
• Oil – Nigeria

Environmental +/−
• Congestion −
• Air pollution −
• Noise −
• Traffic −
• Regeneration +
• Reclamation +/?

MEDCs
• Coal – USA
• HEP – Japan

Global (large-scale)
• Coal – China
• Nuclear – Japan

RESOURCE EXTRACTION & EXPLOITATION

Short-term
• Economic gain
  v. Environment loss

Local (small-scale)
• Gravel extraction – Oxfordshire, UK
• Diamonds – Botswana

Long-term
• Climate change
• Loss of biodiversity
• Water supply
• Health implications

Sustainability
• Benefiting local communities
• Equity
• Conservation
• Management

Management
• Supply/Demand
• New resources
• Environmental issues
• Long-term sustainability

Key
+ = positive effects
− = negative effects

Option 5.2: Living with hazardous environments (1)

Sample answer – question 2

'The impact of hazards is socially selective.' Examine this statement with reference to a variety of examples and a variety of scales.

The question focuses on the issue of vulnerability – who is it that is at risk of hazards? The poor are most vulnerable to hazards; at a global scale this refers to LEDCs, at a local scale to disadvantaged groups such as the homeless, or shanty town dwellers. The answer requires a range of examples (most natural hazards would illustrate this) and a variety of geographic scales. The key term is 'socially selective' – the idea that some people are more at risk than others.

Introduction (10 marks)

Candidates should define terms such as 'socially selective' and 'impacts' – the latter include social, economic, and environmental effects. It is important to state why some groups are more at risk (lack of choice, lack of finance, illegal buildings, 'shoddy' buildings, limited planning enforcement, etc.). Case studies at a variety of scales should also be introduced.

Researching relevant material (15 marks)

Details should be given, including facts and figures, location, precise impacts. Case studies need to be selected to show how different social groups are affected, e.g. the impact of Hurricane Mitch on shanty towns, flooding in the UK versus flooding in Mozambique. The key aspect is to illuminate social selectivity.

Understanding of the Generalisation and application to the question (15 marks)

A good essay will identify the factors leading to increased risk – and how certain population groups are affected by these. Other factors such as magnitude and frequency of the hazard, relief measures, communications, will also be important, and may be used in an evaluative sense.

Drawing conclusions (10 marks)

The conclusion may argue for or against the statement, and suggest a hierarchy of scale. Vulnerability in the UK, for example, is not the same as vulnerability in Mozambique. The process is complex, and affected by a range of interacting factors.

Quality of written communication (10 marks)

Specialist terms such as *vulnerability*, *risk*, *marginal populations*, *hazard magnitude*, etc. should be used where appropriate.

Key concepts

Key concepts that should be central to your research for this topic include:

- **hazards:** a natural or man-made event that threatens to adversely affect human life to the extent of causing a disaster. Sometimes hazards are subdivided into
  – natural (earthquakes and volcanoes),
  – climatic (such as hurricanes and drought)
  – geomorphic (such as landslides)
- **vulnerability:** the predisposition to suffer damage due to external events
- **risk:** the probability of a hazard affecting a person, group or even a structure
- **disasters:** when hazards and vulnerability meet

Option 5.2: Living with hazardous environments (2)

Possible case studies

Topics	Examples/Case studies
Tectonic hazards	• North Ridge, Los Angeles, California; Kobe; Mt St Helens; Iceland; Pinatubo, Philippines, Turkey, India
Meteorological hazards	• Hurricane Mitch, Central America (1998) • Mozambique floods (2000), UK floods (2001), European heatwave (2003) • Sahel drought (1970s and 1990s), East Africa drought (2001), China drought (2001)
Geomorphic hazards	• Landslides in Hong Kong (1966); Crickhollow, Wales (2002); Stonebarrow, Black Ven, Dorset
Impacts of natural hazards	• Small scale – Environment Agency website for 'home' location
Multiple hazards	• London, Los Angeles, Mexico City, New Zealand, Japan
Strategies	• Flooding in Mississippi basin (1993) • New Zealand – Integrated Hazard Management • Ganges Delta
Global trends	• Extreme events in the UK – frequency and magnitude

The physical causes and impacts of natural hazards

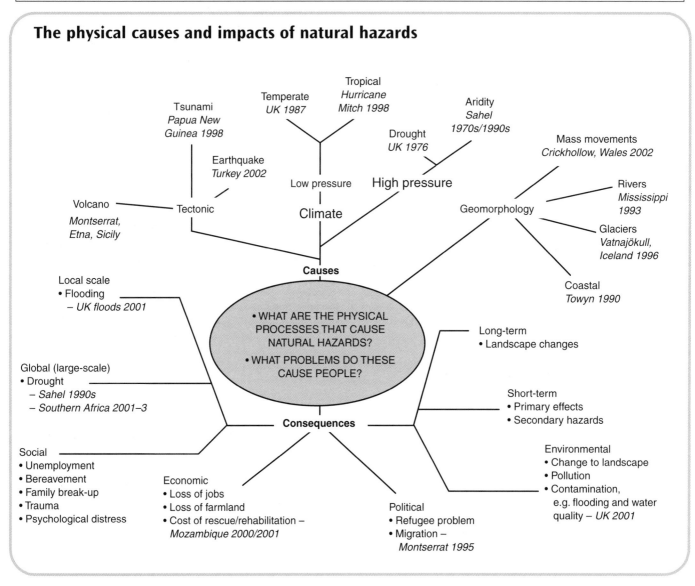

Option 5.3: The pollution of natural environments (1)

Sample answer – question 3

To what extent is it possible to manage the pollution of natural environments? Illustrate your answer with reference to a variety of strategies at different scales.

This question requires an answer that assesses the degree (*to what extent/how far*) it is possible to manage pollution. In some cases it will be possible, in others less so. The range of examples, and their scale, will affect the conclusion reached. Success will depend on how easy it is to trace the source of pollution (point or non-point), and the polluter (individual, company, government), and whether the cause of the pollution is tackled, or whether only the symptoms are treated.

Introduction (10 marks)

The introduction should define terms, and outline different management strategies. Important factors such as source of pollutant, type of pollutant, and polluter, should be included. The range of case studies and scales to be discussed should be included to give a sound plan and basis for the essay.

Researching relevant material (15 marks)

A range of detailed, located case studies at a variety of scales is essential. These should be drawn from LEDCs and MEDCs,

for example traffic pollution in Mexico City, agricultural pollution in the UK, rain in Europe, oil spills in the Galapagos and Alaska, etc. These need to be discussed in relation to management issues. How far is it possible to manage point/non-point pollution? How does it vary with the type of pollutant/polluter? Who pays? What issues are involved in cross-frontier pollution? And so on.

Understanding of the Generalisation and application to the question (15 marks)

The success of management linked to the range of examples is the key focus here. How successful it is will depend on the examples used.

Drawing conclusions (10 marks)

The conclusion will assess how far it is possible to manage pollution. Success is likely to vary with the type of pollution, the nature of the polluter, and the scale of pollution.

Quality of written communication (10 marks)

Geographical terminology such as *source, point, non-point, pathways, cross-frontier, monitoring*, etc. should be used where appropriate.

Key concepts

Key concepts that should be central to your research for this topic include:

- **point sources:** discrete sources of contaminants that can be represented by single points on a map
- **non-point sources:** broad areas where pollutants originate and enter the natural environment
- **pollution:** materials with harmful impacts on the natural environment, or the releasing of such materials
- **waste:** the residual materials and by-products that are generated by human use of the earth's resources and end up unwanted/unused
- **pollutants:** materials that have harmful impacts and degrade the environment.

Option 5.4: Wilderness environments (2)

Possible case studies

Topics	Examples/Case studies
Fragility of wilderness areas	• Antarctica, Nepal, Scottish Highlands • Korup – rainforest • Kalahari Desert, Sahara Desert • Siberia, Alaska
Wilderness area and conflicting demand	• Oil in Alaska • Tourism in Antarctica • Iron ore in Kiruna, Sweden • Tourism at Uluru (Ayers Rock), Nepal, Scottish Highlands • Agriculture in Amazonia
Managing conflict in wilderness areas	• Tourism in Iceland, Nepal, Antarctica, Scottish Highlands • Military operations in Norway • Transport in Alaska • Oil/gas developments in Alaska, Siberia • Tourism in Amazonia • National Parks in the USA, Australia, etc.
Sustainability and wilderness environments	• Management of Antarctica • Galapagos • Management of Arctic areas • Uluru National Park • National Parks in the USA, Australia • Agenda 21 in the UK's National Parks

Conflicts in wilderness areas

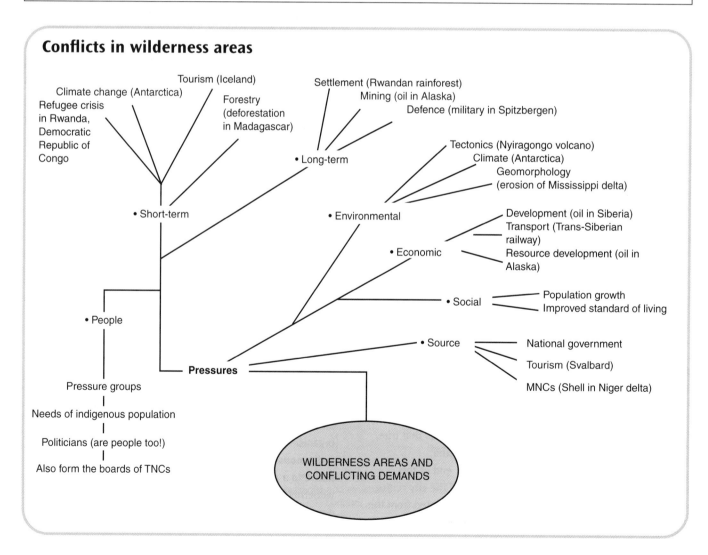

Part 2: Challenges for human environments

Option 5.5: Development and disparity

Option 5.5 examines how development can be defined and measured, how inequalities exist at a number of scales, and looks at strategies for reducing inequality.

Sample questions

1 Outline the factors that lead to geographic variations in development.
2 To what extent do world trade patterns maintain the development gap?
3 Discuss the view that inequalities in development threaten global or national stability.
4 Using examples, assess the effectiveness of strategies to reduce inequalities.
5 How far can local initiatives have an impact on reducing the development gap?
6 'Development inequalities are just as important within urban environments in MEDCs as they are within LEDCs.' Use your research to assess how far this statement is true.

Case studies

Topics	Examples/Case studies
Causes of disparity	• North–South divide • Inequalities within the UK, Italy, China, and South Africa • Trade imbalances, LEDCs and MEDCs • Women/caste in India • Homeless/deprived in London
Inequality and its impacts	• Global – North–South divide • National – South Africa, Indonesia, East Timor • Regional – within UK cities
Investment and aid	• UK aid and Pergau Dam, Malaysia • NGOs – Oxfam in Africa • Operation Hunger in South Africa • World Food Programme
Importance of global action	• Women in Kerala, India • CAMPFIRE in Zimbabwe • Local initiatives in Nepal • Ecotourism in Costa Rica/St Lucia

Impacts of inequality

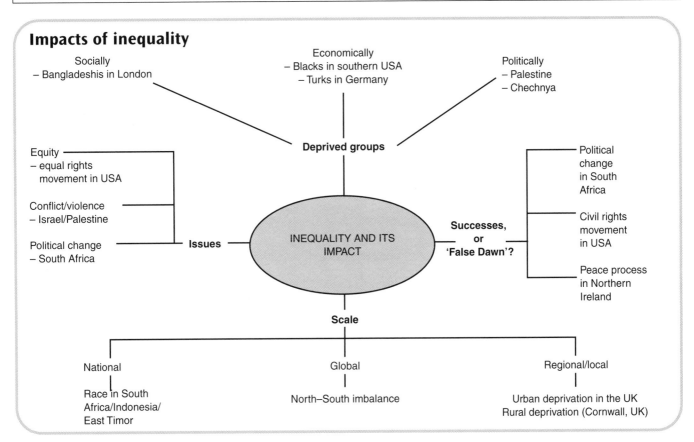

Option 5.6: Feeding the world's people

Option 5.6 examines the relationship between population and growth and food production, and strategies to manage food shortages and excesses.

Sample questions

1 Explain why some parts of the world create food surpluses while other areas endure food shortages.
2 Outline the social, economic, and environmental impacts of intensive farming.
3 Discuss the view that organic farming is morally acceptable but socially and economically disastrous.
4 Comment on the causes and consequences of famine and food shortages.
5 Discuss the issues surrounding GM foods.
6 To what extent do the benefits of the Green Revolution outweigh the disadvantages it caused?

Case studies

Topics	Examples/Case studies
Population pressure and food supply	• Famine: Ireland (1840s), India (1940s), north-east Africa (2000s) • Malnutrition in the UK/South Africa
Inequalities in global food supply	• Drought: Sahel (1970s), north-east Africa (2000s), Afghanistan (2000s) • Civil war: Mozambique (1980–98), Rwanda (1990s), Afghanistan (2001) • Food surplus mountains: EU, USA • Subsidies: EU, USA • Price protection: EU, USA
Responses to the problem of food supply	• Green Revolution: India, Philippines, Indonesia • Intensification of agriculture: EU • GM foods: Monsanto • Farming the oceans: Japan, Norway
Impacts of attempts to increase food supply	• Impact of Green Revolution: India, Philippines, Indonesia • Intensification of farming: BSE, foot and mouth disease, soil erosion • Impact of GM foods: USA, France, the UK
Future strategies	• Technology-dependent: Three Gorges Dam • Low-cost: Oxfam in Burkina Faso • Environmental: organic farming in the UK

Inequalities in food supply

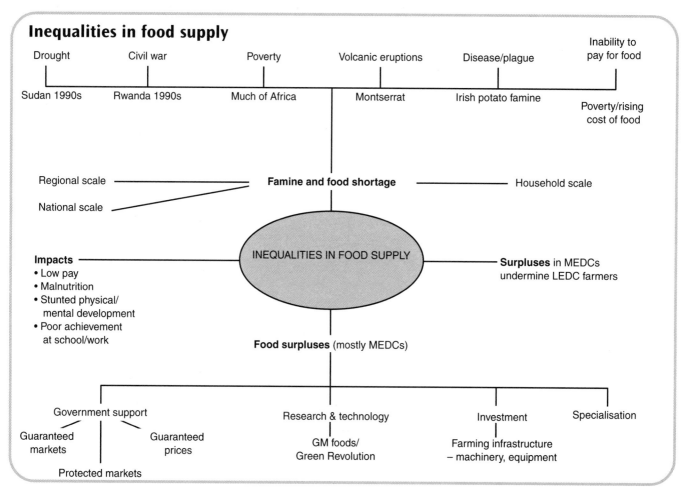

Option 5.7: Health and welfare

Option 5.7 examines how patterns of health and welfare vary at a global, national and local scale. Strategies to combat such inequalities are compared and evaluated.

Sample questions

1 Examine the factors that lead to variations in the level of health and well-being within a population.
2 How and why does access to health care vary?
3 Examine the impact of AIDS on society.
4 Outline the factors that influence geographic variations in either crime or deprivation within an area.
5 Describe and explain how patterns of health, and demand for health care, vary between MEDCs and LEDCs.
6 To what extent does the physical environment contribute to variations in ill-health?

Case studies

Topics	Examples/Case studies
Disease and the environment	• Malaria in Sub-Saharan Africa • Bilharzia in Sub-Saharan Africa • Bronchitis and air pollution • Transport and the spread of disease, e.g. AIDS in Africa • Variations in health: the UK, the USA • Variations in health care: the UK, the USA
Social welfare	• Crime in Oxford • Income support/benefit payments in London
Spatial variations (causes)	• Welfare provision in the UK • Variations in welfare provision in South Africa
Impacts of disease on society	• AIDS: Uganda, the UK, Australia • Ebola in the Congo, SARS in China
Challenges	• BSE in the UK • Variant CJD in the UK • Homeless in the UK, e.g. Oxford • Ageing populations in Japan

Impacts of disease

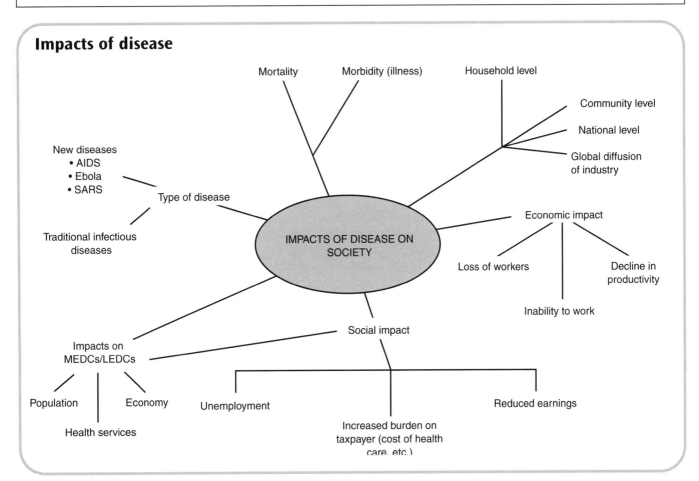

Option 5.8: The geography of sport and leisure

Option 5.8 examines the growth and impact of the sports and leisure industry.

Sample questions

1 Assess the impact of sport or leisure on economic development at a local or national scale.
2 'New sporting developments are economically vital but environmentally disastrous.' Discuss this statement with reference to examples.
3 Outline the factors that have led to spatial variations in sport or leisure at a national or global scale.
4 Outline the role of TNCs in sports-related developments.
5 To what extent do major sporting events, such as the Olympic Games, allow for sustainable development?
6 For a country you have studied, outline the environmental impacts of recreation.

Case studies

Topics	Examples/Case studies
Concentration of sports	• Gaelic football and hurling in Ireland • Australian rules football • Baseball and American football in the USA • Cricket in ex-British colonies
Evolution of key sports locations	• Manchester • Olympic Games hosts • Wembley, London • Milton Keynes Superbowl
Impacts of sporting developments	• Olympic Games and Atlanta, USA • Sydney Olympic Games • Golf courses • Mountain biking
Sport, leisure, and economic benefit	• North–South divide • Migration of football players in England's Premiership
Alternative models of sport	• Globalisation of football • The media and football • Sport as big business rather than local community-based participation

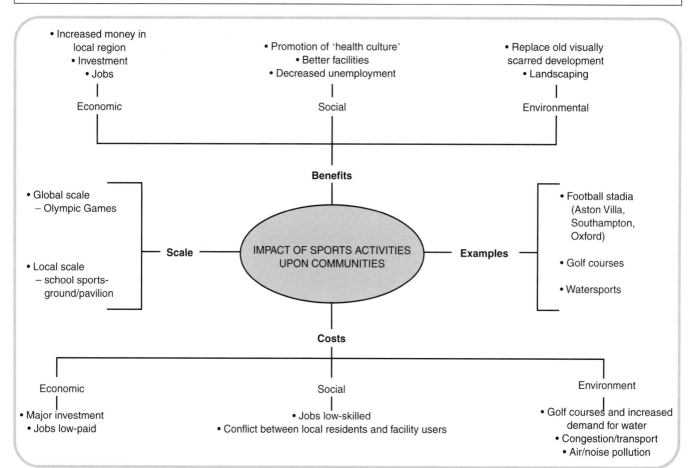

Issues analysis

This unit draws together understanding from physical, human, and environmental geography. The knowledge-based content is taken from Units 1, 2, and 4:

1 **Changing landforms and their management** – *River and coastal environments*

2 **Managing change in human environments** – *Rural and urban environments*

4 **Global challenge** – *The natural environment*, and *Population and the economy*

It also includes common elements from the **5 Researching global futures** options and from the **Environmental investigation** enquiry.

How is the synoptic unit assessed?

Assessment is generally by the analysis of an issue or issues in a particular location. A variety of scales from the local to the global may be used, and over time the places will include the UK, other MEDCs, and LEDCs.

You will be expected to apply your knowledge and understanding to unfamiliar contexts. Examiners will be looking to see how you have made connections and linkages.

The synoptic paper tests ability to:

- use a structured route to enquiry
- interpret and analyse a range of data and resources
- select and use an evidence base analysed from a wide range of sources
- make linkages between a wide range of topics
- use decision-making skills to evaluate a number of options and, where appropriate, recommend a decision and explain the result
- evaluate a range of opinions concerning an issue, using geographical experience to identify and analyse potential conflicts
- offer advice on various techniques of investigation used by decision makers, and on implementation to suggest ways of monitoring the impacts of decisions.

Framework for developing issues analysis and decision-making skills

1 **What is the process of decision making?**
Problem identification→evaluation of evidence→weighing-up of alternatives→decision making→justification and explanation of results

2 **A study of the players in decision making and their likely values position in a variety of scenarios**
a Global agencies
b International agencies
c National and local government (including government agencies such as the Environment Agency and the National Parks Authorities)
d Multinational and other business enterprises
e Non-government organisations (NGOs)
f Pressure groups
g Interested individuals

3 **The psychology of decision making**
Understanding of the behavioural approach (optimisers and satisfiers). Pred's behavioural matrix (illustrate). Role of personal preference and perception.

4 **The politics and economics of decision making in local, regional, national, and international scenarios**
a The importance of economics in determining outcomes (e.g. in coastal management).
b The role of politics (including party politics) in influencing outcomes (e.g. in bypass routes or industrial location).
c The role of informal green groups (e.g. ecowarriors).

5 **Decision making in an environmental context**
a The major standpoints – conservation *v.* exploitation, sustainability *v.* growth, business as usual *v.* sustainable options. Exploration of significance, feasibility, etc. of options.
b Environmental impact analysis – assessment of likely improvement, or maintenance or deterioration with relation to existing situation of possible actions.
c Role of environmental legislation at local, regional, national, and global scales.
d Establishment of sustainability targets (conservation of resources, enhancing environmental quality, balanced development, social equity, community participation goals).

6 **Decision-making and problem-solving skills and techniques**
a Developing and using techniques of decision making. Use of tabulation, scaling, weighting, matrices, ranking, charting, sieve mapping, critical path analysis, cost benefit analysis, monitoring techniques.
b Using literary, graphical, numerical, and IT skills to analyse resources, evaluate options, and assess opinions.

The Millennium Dome – what should be done with it? (1)

Thames Gateway London Partnership

Large areas to the east of London have, in the past, missed out on the economic development, investment, and employment growth that can be seen in many parts of West London. The Thames Gateway London Partnership is working for more balanced development in London by strengthening the Thames Gateway's role as:

• a centre of excellence for manufacturing, research, and development
• an international transport interchange
• a prime location for business and financial services for academic and research institutions and for international tourism.

It is the Partnership's vision that by 2006 the Thames Gateway will be:

• a thriving, prominent sub-region for London and the South East, able to reach directly into the global economy
• a manufacturing centre of excellence and a key focus for technology futures backed by strong research and development

• an international tourism, cultural industries, and heritage venue, and focal point for international travel to London and the UK
• an internationally renowned centre of academic excellence
• a critical satellite area for business and financial services
• an area in which ethnicity and diversity is valued, and its economic benefits realised, to provide access to new markets and product development at home and abroad
• an area known in Europe for its leading edge and innovative skills
• an area offering access to economic opportunities to all its residents
• an area of environmental excellence as the key to inward investment and sustainable regeneration
• an effective sub-region with strong and committed public/private/community and voluntary sector partnership, including that with the black and ethnic minority community.

The Millennium Dome – what should be done with it? (2)

Land use in the 1970s

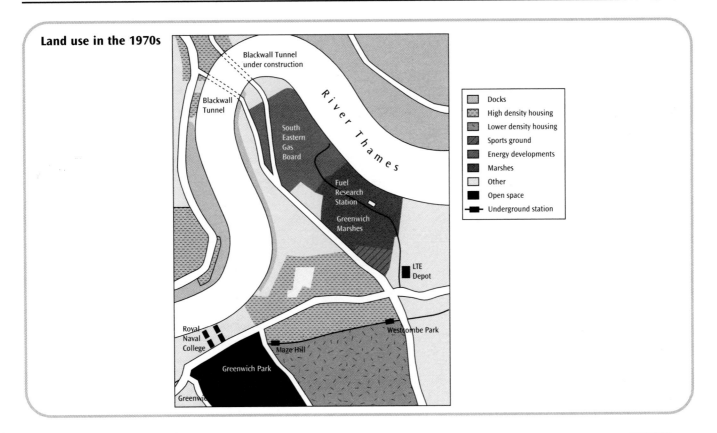

Need and deprivation

The Thames Gateway has:

- the largest concentration of unemployment in the UK (including particularly high unemployment in the 25–34 age group and amongst ethnic minority communities) – on this basis alone it should have full Development Area Status
- some of the poorest urban areas in northern Europe, with Newham 1st, Tower Hamlets 7th, Lewisham 11th and Greenwich 14th in 1997 deprivation score tables; the eight most deprived wards in Newham are amongst the 70 most deprived wards in the UK
- GDP per person is only half that of the Greater London Area.

The Thames Gateway has:

- indigenous manufacturing enterprises under pressure, and is a region facing serious business retention problems in certain sectors
- lost 13 300 manufacturing jobs between 1991 and 1996
- a problem in some areas of crime and a fear of crime which has inhibited economic and community development
- a legacy of a major derelict and contaminated land problem
- a legacy of skills mismatch between those possessed by communities and the needs of modern industry
- a shortage in some areas of premises suitable for the needs of modern industry
- in parts, a poor and unattractive environment which has held back development.

The combined efforts of central and local government, the private and public sectors are beginning to realise the potential of the Thames Gateway. Major infrastructural developments are either in place or in the pipeline: transport linkages include:

- Stansted
- City Airport
- Channel Tunnel Rail Link
- M25
- A13
- M11
- the South Thames Development Route
- the Jubilee Line
- Docklands Light Railway
- East London line extensions
- world-class port and river facilities
- proposed Thames river crossings.

The area includes a large number of major sites with excellent modern development potential. Such development will afford the opportunity for housing and employment to be linked via integrated transport linkages in new sustainable communities.

Together, the Thames Gateway London Partnership and the Lee Valley Partnership may suffer major disadvantage and deprivation but they are also areas where increasingly the essential needs of inward investors and leading-edge indigenous enterprises can be met.

The Millennium Dome – what should be done with it? (3)

Proposed development for the Greenwich Peninsula

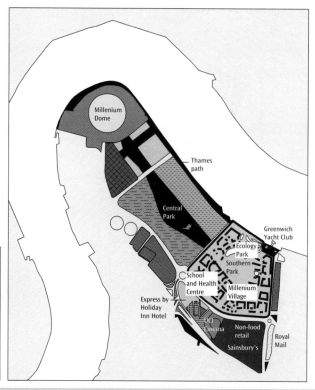

Key:
- Mixed use (CBD, residential, retail, leisure)
- Residential (high density)
- Residential (low density)
- Leisure
- Employment
- Royal Mail Distribution Centre
- North Greenwich Bus and Underground interchange
- Retail (food and non-food)
- Existing use
- Open spaces

Dereliction in the Thames Gateway

The Thames Gateway (or East Thames Corridor) is often associated with dereliction and contamination. It is certainly true that the Thames Gateway has a long history of industrial activity, including a wide range of potentially contaminating land uses. Housing is the most sensitive to contamination in the ground. About 10% of land in the Thames Gateway with housing potential is contaminated.

Nevertheless, the presence of contamination does not rule out development, as there is now a range of treatments available to restore contaminated land. The Millennium Dome, for example, is built on the Greenwich peninsula, on which there was once a gasworks. In the UK the most common form of remedial measure is excavation and off-site disposal. There are, however, significant cost implications.

What to do with the Dome
Dome factfile

The Millennium Dome cost £850 million to create, and is said to be costing almost £1 million a month to keep empty, in maintenance and security costs. A string of proposals for its after-use, including theme parks, media, new technology centres and an office city, have all collapsed.

Millennial dreams

- Tussaud's Group and the BBC planned a TV-based theme park with replica sets and life-size characters.
- Dome Europe, backed by Nomura and Sony, planned to expand the zones, open an outdoor market and keep the millennium experience.
- Legacy plc, with Robert Bourne, hoped to create a 24-hour city and business park based on Silicon Valley.
- Former Dome boss Pierre-Yves Gerbeau, with Ministry of Sound's James Palumbo, wanted a visitor attraction in the day, and concerts, parties, and sports events at night.
- Less serious ideas included a fat farm for obese people, and an indoor beach based on an attraction in Japan.
- The empty shell costs taxpayers nearly £40 000 a day to maintain.
- Two other attempts to sell the Dome have failed.

The Millennium Dome – what should be done with it? (4)

Extract 1
US sports tycoon wades into Dome contest

An American billionaire is behind a plan to turn the Millennium Dome into an indoor sports and entertainment complex. The Anglo-Australian Meridian Delta consortium has had talks with English Partnerships, the government agency handling bids for the site in Greenwich. A spokesperson for Meridian Delta said: 'We have plans to develop a world-class Olympic-standard 20 000 seat sports and entertainment arena, filling a key gap in London's venue market.'

As well as the LA Lakers, the billionaire Philip Anschutz owns hockey and soccer franchises in the USA, and has a stake in the ownership of London's Docklands Arena entertainment complex. Meridian Delta is likely to face stiff competition for the Dome, however. Property developer Tops Estates yesterday announced its plan to convert the Dome into a world-class sporting academy.

The company, which is in talks with the Lawn Tennis Association and an indoor ski specialist about co-operation, also intends to build an entertainment and retail park on the site.

Adapted from *The Guardian*, 8 December 2001

Extract 2

The Greenwich peninsula was once a neglected, rundown area with poor transport links. Then the government's big millennium project – along with a huge bus and tube station – came along to regenerate the area.

North Greenwich is a combined underground and bus station of prize-winning design and unprecedented scale. All around it is an area of London that, until the station opened, had never had sufficient public transport. Bus routes and tube tunnels, at great expense, have been bent towards the new interchange. The Jubilee line extension was hurriedly finished during 1999 so that North Greenwich could open on time.

Extract 3

In Greenwich, away from the Dome and the station, the rest of the peninsula seemed even more adrift from London. Millennium Way, the new dual-carriageway, is quiet enough to lie down on. The great expanses of car and coach park, for the crowds who never quite came, have become a park-and-ride scheme.

More than 10 minutes' walk from the tube, beyond a fragile-looking strip of new park, the outline of the Millennium Village promised long and loud by ministers is emerging. There are smart riverside flats, a health centre and school, and a commercial strip that is pure American suburbia – as if the Dome's corporate sponsors have been given the run of the rest of the area as well. There is one street of occupied houses.

Extract 4

5 June 2001

Quintain Estates & Development is now working with English Partnerships and Greenwich council on devising a development plan for the Greenwich peninsula. The Duke of Westminster's Grosvenor Estates company is part of a group of property developers working with BBC Worldwide, the commercial arm of the corporation, to keep the Dome open as a visitor attraction.

Quintain has requested planning permission from Greenwich council for mixed use, including housing, on the 10 hectares it owns next to the Dome while the wider development of the peninsula is considered.

Extract 5
An Eden Project

The Millennium Dome, a blot on the London skyline and a mortal embarrassment to the government, could become another Eden, a demi-paradise of tropical flowers, fruit, and vines blooming in rich Cornish soil. The proposal has been put forward by the creators of two of the most successful millennium projects, the Eden Project in Cornwall and the London Eye. The blighted Greenwich peninsula could become a model of green regeneration. The plan also envisages thousands of new homes in 50-storey residential towers, and green landscaping across the 120 hectare former gasworks site in south London.

One of the problems with the site was heavy pollution from a century of industrial use. The surface was cleared, and the lower layers capped, but the entrepreneur behind the Eden Project proposed that topsoil could be shipped around the coast from Cornwall, thus keeping a link with the Eden Project.

The Millennium Dome – what should be done with it? (5)

Extract 6

The Wellcome Trust, one of the world's foremost medical charities, is negotiating with the government to turn the Millennium Dome into a £300 million biomedical research centre. It proposes to convert the former London attraction into laboratories. The British charity – which has promised to spend £3 billion on biomedical research – proposes to convert the former London attraction into laboratories. It refuses to discuss whether it has bid for the building.

The government is increasingly anxious to sell the Dome and its 52 hectare site in Greenwich, which ended up costing more than £850 million and still costs nearly £1 million a month to maintain, despite closing at the end of December.

Extract 7
A new town

Lord Falconer, the minister for housing, planning, and regeneration, has begun discussions about keeping the Dome in public hands and leasing it to a private company as an entertainment venue or retail park. This would allow the government to sell separately the land around the Dome, which property developers regard as far more financially viable. It is understood that discussions have begun with two companies interested in taking out 10- to 20-year leases on the Dome. One, from a US entertainment company, would involve major sporting events and spectacular concerts. Other talks are thought to be taking place with a UK-based property consortium with plans for a retail park.

Housing supply and demand in London

London is no longer the only British city where public services are threatened by a serious shortage of affordable houses for essential workers. Yet nowhere is the problem as acute as in the capital. Property prices have risen faster there than in any other part of the country – tripling in 10 years. London has the highest housing demand in the UK, but it produced the lowest housing increase of any region in the 1990s.

A succession of reports has pointed to the need for more affordable houses to stem the outflow of key workers, such as police officers, teachers, and nursing staff, unable to meet London's spiralling housing costs. Less than half the accommodation target has been achieved. The shortage of support staff – cleaners, porters, clerics – is just as grave. The mayor of London's housing commission recently estimated that London needs 28 000 extra 'affordable' houses a year.

Something bold and dramatic is therefore needed, an initiative that will grab the headlines and generate its own momentum. New towns go back a century, but until now have always involved the export of workers from existing cities. What about a series of linked communities, complete with supporting services, with some 5000 homes for low and moderately-paid key workers? It would need a large site, but English Partnership, the public development agency, already owns one. It is a 120 hectare site, on which £185 million has already been spent to decontaminate the ground. There would be a further benefit: it would resolve a deeply embarrassing political problem, for the Millennium Dome sits in the middle of this site and, with its adjoining car parks, accounts for one-third of the site. Demolish it. In its place, we should erect homes fit for public-service heroes.

This is a good time for a new direction. With its £3.5 billion Jubilee line link, the Dome site is ideally placed to regenerate public services across London. Belatedly, taxpayers would get a return for that investment. And there is already a prototype on which the new London town could be based: the new Millennium Village of 1377 homes being built on 13 hectares of the existing site. Units are being constructed around people-friendly squares to foster a sense of community. High-energy-saving construction is expected to reduce gas and electricity bills by 80%. All homes are wired for the internet and for a village intranet service. The emphasis is on innovative architecture and design. Now a new competition should be held, open to all architects, to develop the new neighbourhoods.

The 120 hectare peninsular site could make a 'significant contribution' to London's housing problem. It could take 5000 more houses in addition to the 1377 being built in the Millennium Village. The views of the commission add new urgency to the debate about the future of the peninsula and the dilemma of finding a use for the empty £850 million Dome, which is now costing £1 million a month in running costs. English Partnerships, the government regeneration agency which spent £185 million reclaiming the former gasworks site on the peninsula for millennium attractions, has now employed three firms of consultants to 'market test' the Dome and its surroundings with potential developers – adding yet more to the bill. This is seen by some as a final attempt to find a use for the structure.

London's property prices have tripled in 10 years, putting even the cheapest one-bedroom £80 000 flats out of reach of young public-sector professionals, let alone the average worker on little more than £20 000. Housing experts in the capital say that anything between 20 000 and 30 000 affordable homes are needed to meet growing demand. However, new figures from the Office of National Statistics show that only 2900 social

The Millennium Dome – what should be done with it? (6)

Housing supply and demand in London (continued)

homes for renting were built in the last recorded year, more than 1000 fewer than eight years ago. As a result, the shortage of workers in essential services is growing. Last week an official appointed as NHS 'housing tsar' said he would be unable to meet a commitment to find 2000 affordable homes for nurses by the end of this year. Instead, he will be lucky to find 800. The mayor of London's housing commission has called for an extra 28 000 affordable homes annually, while the National Housing Federation – representing the main social providers – has put the figure more modestly at under 20 000.

Problems have been compounded by London's growing population, rising by some 40 000 annually according to the latest figures. While around 320 000 are leaving the capital each year – often for relatively cheaper housing in the surrounding South East region and beyond – 360 000 are coming in, with the largest proportion (almost 200 000) from overseas. Partly as a result, demand for council housing, and homes administered by government-funded housing associations, is also going through the roof: 209 600 families are now on council waiting lists, according to the association of London government. But there is precious little land for new homes.

Housing needs and suburban decline

Housing needs

The government has estimated that some 5 million new homes will be needed in the UK by 2016, despite the lack of population growth. The main reason for the increased demand for housing is changes in family structure. The traditional nuclear family (the stereotypical three generations of family living in one household) has declined, while there has been an increase in the number of single people living away from home, divorced couples, the elderly, and unmarried.

This makes the 120 hectare Greenwich peninsula significant, because it is the largest 'brownfield' site in the capital. The Dome and surrounding land occupies 19 hectares, with adjoining car parks taking another 25 hectares – sites more than three times the size of the 13 hectare Millennium Village, where 150 homes have now been occupied and 1227 more are planned by 2005. Only 20% of them are being offered for rent by a housing association, with the remainder priced from £112 000 for a one-bedroom flat to £505 000 for a three-bed penthouse. But aside from the Dome, the car parks, and the Village, 64 hectares are still available for development.

'This is an ideal site for a high-density, mixed use development in a series of contiguous neighbourhoods, each with its own identity, to create a new urban district for London – the first one for 150 years,' enthused a local government official. 'The opportunity is immense ... a new town in a city.'

Fewer homes but ever more buyers

- Seventy years ago a typical three-bedroom semi in Greater London cost between £600 and £800, the equivalent of £18 000–£24 000 today.

- Government plans for a £250 million starter homes scheme – aimed at helping key public sector workers to buy homes over the next three years – have been criticised as inadequate. To be effective, the National Housing Federation says, the scheme needs to be twice as large.

- Twenty years ago, with a smaller population, London had 171 000 more houses available to rent. Many were sold off under the last government.

- More than 209 000 London families are on council house waiting lists. No council houses are now being built.

- In 28 London boroughs incomes of more than £40 000 are needed to buy a house with a 95% mortgage, according to the National Housing Federation. They say that in only one borough, Barking and Dagenham, would a £30 000 income be enough for a loan.

- In the last recorded year some 12 300 homes were built in London – 3000 of them for rent as social housing. This compares with 17 200 nine years ago (4000 of them social housing).

- With the greatest national demand for new homes, London has the lowest percentage increase. From 1991 to 2000 the capital's housing stock rose by only 4.8%, against a UK average of 7.1%.

Flood maps

Much of central London, including the Houses of Parliament and Docklands (on the Isle of Dogs) are at risk of flooding as they are located in a floodplain There is a greater than 1% chance that these areas could be flooded in any particular year.

The Floodline number is 0845 9881188.

www.environment-agency.gov.uk will give you access to the Floodline website.

How to write a good answer (1)

1 Outline the physical and human features that have hindered the development of the Thames Gateway in the past.

The answer looks for both physical **and** human features, and better answers will look for the links between them.

Physical factors include:

- inaccessibility
- low-lying, prone to flooding
- poor-quality marshland
- the River Thames – hindered north–south movement of people and goods.

Human factors include:

- poor transport network
- an outdated manufacturing base
- widespread dereliction and contamination
- a history of use as London's dumping ground
- high levels of deprivation
- a lack of investment.

Note: Look for synoptic links between physical and human factors, and within physical factors and within human factors.

The question focuses on the Thames Gateway – the area from London's East End to the Medway cities of Gillingham and Chatham. Examples from this whole area are relevant. Top answers will link factors, e.g. the eastward-flowing river making north–south routes difficult and costly. The historic legacy of docks and dock-related industries, and the decline of Docklands owing to the shallow depth of the Thames (larger vessels could not negotiate the tortuous meanders of the river) led to the removal of London's Docks downstream to Tilbury.

2 Write a report on the current pressures, both local and national, to develop the Thames Gateway, and show how these could be addressed by developments in the area.

There is a wide range of pressures, such as:

- housing – there is a shortage of houses in the South East
- recreation – there is a lack of a national state-of-the-art sports venues in the UK
- employment – there are pockets of very high unemployment in areas of former manufacturing
- energy – London generates huge amounts of waste, and this could be used to generate electricity by expanding WFE (Waste for Electricity) generators in a new power station
- environmental – much of the Thames Gateway/Greenwich is derelict and/or contaminated; in addition, air and water quality need improving.

You should talk about a range of pressures, and use supporting evidence to illustrate the point. Any developments are therefore likely to be **multiple** in nature, i.e. they will tackle a range of these issues rather than focusing on just one. Developments need to offer **long-term** solutions rather than just **short-term** ones. You should also note that the local/regional scale of this example fits into the larger **national** context. However, by tackling one pressure – such as unemployment – other pressures may be adversely affected, e.g. traffic congestion, air quality, etc.

Your answer should be realistic, and make links to the pressures and the potential solutions.

How to write a good answer (2)

3 Summarise the costs and benefits of using the Greenwich peninsula for:
   a an indoor sports and entertainment arena
   b a 24-hour city and high-tech business park
   c an Eden-type project
   d a new town.

The answer could be in continuous prose (essay type) or might be in the form of a table. Be careful with tables – they often lead to abbreviated answers. Make sure that all points are developed and appropriate examples are used where required. Costs and benefits **might** include the following:

a An indoor sports and entertainment arena

Costs	Benefits
• expensive development • non-essential • does not tackle urgent problems such as poverty, deprivation, etc. • high opportunity cost, i.e. land could be used for more worthwhile projects	• prestige development – possibly of international status • part of growth industry • generates much local employment in services • will attract money from other boroughs as people use the facilities

b A 24-hour city and high-tech business park

Costs	Benefits
• very expensive, especially the business park • limited number of high-paying jobs • much government money to be spent on infrastructure in order to attract foreign investment • not really appropriate to the needs of the local community	• employment in service sector • multiplier effect in local economy • '24-hour' means more jobs – at least three shifts • inward investment in high-tech businesses • diverse employment

c An Eden-type project

Costs	Benefits
• doesn't create many jobs • does not generate as much export earnings (though some will be earned) • if successful will lead to traffic congestion, pollution, etc. • limited multiplier effect – too narrowly based	• sustainable • environmentally-sound – best option • produces 'green space'/fresh air for local population • educational benefits – school trips • will help improve local infrastructure/traffic, etc.

d A new town

Costs	Benefits
• limited long-term job creation • not attractive for inward investment • housing might not be low cost – limited multiplier effect here • doesn't tackle problem of poverty or deprivation	• addresses the housing shortage – locally and regionally • excellent short-term job gains • increased demand for services • increases local purchasing power

Top answers will be balanced and detailed, and examine the four options equally.

How to write a good answer (3)

4 Using examples you have studied, write a report on the possible management strategies for the environmental problems of brownfield sites.

You need to show a critical understanding of the nature of problems and their solutions. Problems include:

a derelict/contaminated land

b air and water pollution

c visual pollution such as graffiti

d congestion and traffic

e overcrowding of buildings/lack of biodiversity

f poor accessibility

g lack of space

h outdated buildings and a poor infrastructure (old cables, pipes, sewers, etc.).

None of these problems is unique to brownfield sites, although the concentration of them in small areas is a problem in itself.

Management strategies are diverse and need to take into account the complex interactions between processes/features. Possible solutions include:

- cleansing of topsoil and bedload – especially in areas of former industrial/energy developments
- monitoring air/water quality and implementing schemes to improve them, e.g. restricting traffic/promoting public transport, restoring rivers
- removing graffiti, using high-quality materials for building works, more police officers on the beat
- improving rail access, bus lanes, pricing policies, for private cars/lorries
- designating open space and park land, tree planting.

Credit will be given for answers that attempt to integrate the multi-causal, multi-factorial nature of inner city problems, and answers that discuss the need for sustainable strategies, which include local participation. Agenda 21 may feature heavily in some answers.

Answers should be well-structured, balanced, realistic, and should show a clear understanding of the complexity of the issues.

Writing frames (1)

There are a number of writing frames for answering an essay or a report. In general, the essay title and the material to be included will suggest what type of structure should be used. However, for all questions you need to:

- examine closely the wording of the question and
- plan your answer.

It is better to spend time thinking and planning, so that you do not waste time writing about irrelevant material. Writing for 35 minutes on relevant material is better than 45 minutes on irrelevant material.

Reading the question

Read the question carefully and underline the command words and the topic to be discussed. There may be some technical words such as 'and', 'either . . . or'. Questions with 'and' in them generally ask for some factual comment and then require some interpretation. Often the interpretation is more important than the recall of fact. Questions stating 'with the use of examples. . .' may allocate one-third or half of the marks for the examples used. If you do not answer the question you cannot get the marks.

Command words

These tell you what to do in the essay or how to use the material. There are a number of such command words:

- **analyse**   examine carefully the details of a theory, pattern, distribution
- **assess**   estimate the importance of
- **compare**   look for similarities and differences between features
- **contrast**   bring out the differences
- **criticise**   give a critical account of (discuss rather than blame)
- **describe**   show the details and characteristics of
- **discuss**   examine by argument, giving the pros and cons
- **distinguish** show the differences between
- **evaluate**   show the relative importance
- **examine**   investigate in detail
- **explain**   show in detail how something works
- **illustrate**   show with the use of case studies and examples
- **justify**   present an argument for
- **outline**   show the general principles or main features rather than minute details.

Types of essay

There are three main generic types of essay: description, explanation, and evaluation, although not all essays fit into this classification. **Descriptive** essays are the easiest and require factual recall. Very few, if any, A2 essays will be purely descriptive. By contrast, **explanation** requires you to give reasons and account for why a particular object is the way it is. Lastly, **evaluation** expects an opinion based on the evidence presented throughout the essay. Alternatively, you may be given a ready-made evaluation and asked to say how far you agree.

From case study to concept

A case study is a detailed real example of a geographical feature, process, or environment. Using case studies is essential for good grades. However, they are not always used to the best effect. Most examiners' reports mention the fact that too few case studies are used but some also mention that case studies are used but not related to the question. The key is to link case studies to the underlying concepts.

Finding case studies

Source of case study	Advantages	Disadvantages
Textbooks	• Easy to access • Not too detailed • Someone has chosen the case studies for you	• Dated • The case studies might not suit your chosen area of study • Insufficient detail?
Articles and journals	• More detailed and usually written by experts (depending on the journal)	• May be biased • Too academic • Might lack popular appeal
Web	• Easily available • Large number of sources	• Bias is a major issue • Information posted is determined by the outlook and aims of the website owner
Media (press and TV)	• Up to date • Relevant	• Lack of hard data • Bias in the media
Specialist reports and surveys	• Detailed, thorough	• Difficult to get • Few and far between • Expensive to undertake in terms of time and money
Interviews	• Good source of primary data	• Expensive to undertake in terms of time and money

It is important to use a range of data sources to amass case studies: national press, TV, the internet, books and articles for example – but being aware that each source has its strengths and weaknesses. For particular topics, such as 'Hazards', develop a **Hazards diary** – a diary of events that happen – so that some of the immediacy of a hazard can be brought into essays. Similarly, a **dossier of development and disparity** can be developed, so as to collect and organise case studies, examples, facts and figures that could be used in a report on development and disparity.

Case studies and concepts

Having developed and collected a range of case studies, it is important to use them well in exams. **Planning** how to use each case study in an answer is key.

For example, the case study on coastal features in Norfolk can be used in a number of ways. It is very unlikely that a question will be set which states 'Describe and account for coastal features in Norfolk'. Instead there will be questions on deposition, coastal ecosystems, refraction, longshore drift, and so on. Looking back at that case study, it is possible to see a number of geographical concepts such as rock type and structure, mass movements (rock falls), coastal erosion, cliffs, barrier beaches, longshore drift, wave refraction, low-energy coastlines, and storm events.

Similarly, there is unlikely to be a question asking specifically about urban growth in Ireland, in particular that of Dublin. However, the case study of urban growth in Dublin can be used to help answer questions on urbanisation, urban growth, market towns, rural hinterlands, rural-to-urban migration, international migration, population change, inner city issues, slums/estates, deprivation, pollution, dereliction, social problems, suburbanisation, greenfield sites, industrial decline (deindustrialisation), service sector, decision making, out-of-town retailing, office location, and centralisation!

It is a good idea to list at the end of each case study all the concepts that are covered by that case study. It can then be used as illustrative material for a question on each of those concepts. Alternatively, it may be possible to slant the angle of the case study, for example from urban growth to population migration or population change, and make much more use of the case study than just as a named example.

Revision tips

Revision involves pulling all the elements of the course together. To be successful, revision work needs to be planned, and it needs to be geared towards the needs of the exam.

Planning your revision

1 You must know what the exam consists of. If you do not have any recent exam papers, you can order some from Edexcel (use the contact details below). For this you'll find it useful to know your syllabus number.

2 Familiarise yourself with the layout of the exam paper.

3 Revise in short manageable chunks; do not attempt to do the whole subject in one go, but take each topic in turn. Create a revision checklist to make sure you cover all material adequately.

4 When you revise, use whichever method, or methods, you feel most comfortable with. These could include:
   • using highlighter pens
   • creating lists and rhymes
   • making note cards
   • making up mnemonics (the first letter of words, e.g. CASH standing for **c**orrosion, **a**brasion, **s**olution, and **h**ydraulic impact, i.e. the types of erosion in a river or at the coast).

5 Take regular, varied breaks; it is difficult to concentrate for more than 40 minutes at a time. Have a 15-minute break first of all. After the next 40 minutes take a longer break. Then after the next 40 minutes take a shorter break, and so on.

6 Test yourself. This could involve writing answers to past questions, drawing sketch maps, learning facts and figures, identifying symbols on an Ordnance Survey map, etc. Ask a teacher, parent, or friend to assess you. If you ask a friend, then two of you are revising and helping each other's work.

7 Reward yourself with a treat.

8 Do not work too late; it is important to get plenty of sleep.

9 Create a revision timetable and stick to it! Your timetable should take into account when your exams are in all other subjects.

10 Make sure you revise a topic more than once. Two or three revisions of a topic improve memory and recall considerably (see 'The forgetting curve' below).

The forgetting curve

Most pupils' memory is good over a short time. However, to be able to recall information a day later, or a week later, generally requires one or two revisions of the material. To recall information a month later may require an extra revision period.

Essentially, the more often you revise a topic the more information you can recall.

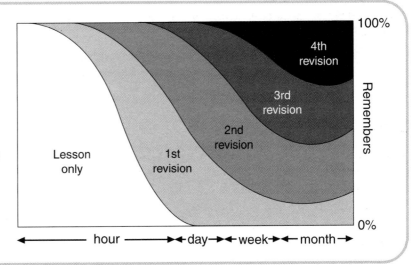

Contacting Edexcel

For advice, information, and help you can contact Edexcel.

Address

Edexcel Customer Service
Stewart House
32 Russell Square
London WC1B 5DN

Telephone

0870 240 9800 (Monday to Friday, 8 am to 6 pm)

Email

enquiries@edexcel.org.uk
(you should include your centre number in the 'Subject' field)

Website

www.edexcel.org.uk/

Index